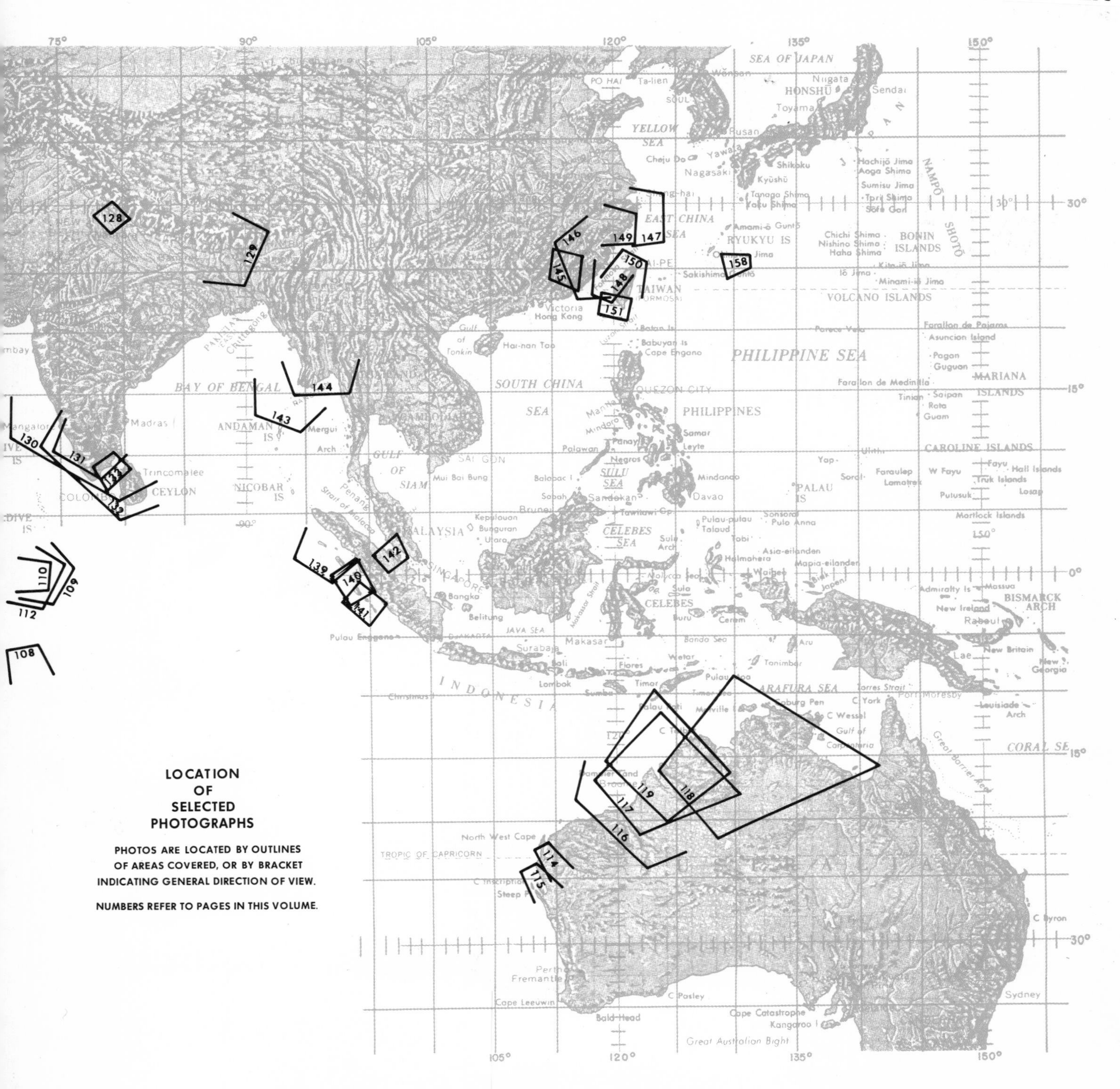


## LOCATION OF SELECTED PHOTOGRAPHS

PHOTOS ARE LOCATED BY OUTLINES OF AREAS COVERED, OR BY BRACKET INDICATING GENERAL DIRECTION OF VIEW.

NUMBERS REFER TO PAGES IN THIS VOLUME.

# EARTH PHOTOGRAPHS from Gemini VI through XII

*Scientific and Technical Information Division*
OFFICE OF TECHNOLOGY UTILIZATION 1968
NATIONAL AERONAUTICS AND SPACE ADMINISTRATION
*Washington, D.C.*

1

2

5

6

1 Gemini spacecraft were built at the McDonnell Aircraft Corp. plant in St. Louis, Mo. Two are shown here undergoing tests in the plant's "white room."

2 The Gemini V crew, Gordon Cooper and Pete Conrad, acknowledged the good wishes of the pad crew as they walked toward the gantry for their flight.

3 The Gemini spacecraft were launched from the Kennedy Space Center on the east coast of Florida. The countdowns were heard throughout the world.

4 Gemini VI and Gemini VII were the first two to rendezvous in space. Gemini VII also set an endurance record of 14 days during its mission.

5 An Agena target was photographed from Gemini XII while connected to it by a Dacron tether. This permitted stabilization by the gravity gradient.

6 The first two-man crew in space, John Young and Gus Grissom, were photographed inside the cabin of Gemini III just before their flight in March 1965.

7 Astronaut Ed White's "walk in space" was the first extravehicular activity by U.S. astronauts. Some photos were taken with the hatch open.

8 Gemini astronauts landed on the sea. A recovery carrier and rescue swimmers are seen here attaching a flotation collar before opening the hatch.

3

4

7

8



# EARTH PHOTOGRAPHS from Gemini VI through XII

*Scientific and Technical Information Division*
OFFICE OF TECHNOLOGY UTILIZATION 1968
NATIONAL AERONAUTICS AND SPACE ADMINISTRATION
*Washington, D.C.*

For Sale by the Superintendent of Documents, U.S. Government Printing Office, Washington, D.C. 20402 - Price $8.00
*Library of Congress Catalog Card Number 68-61301*

# FOREWORD

PHOTOGRAPHS of terrain and weather taken during Gemini flights showed that both geological and manmade landmarks and storms in the Earth's atmosphere could be viewed advantageously from orbital altitudes. The many spectacular color photographs of the Earth brought back by the astronauts have both heightened men's appreciation of their environment and increased scientists' knowledge of it. This Special Publication contains a mere sampling of the photographs available.

The Gemini program was approved in November 1961 to develop long-duration manned flight and rendezvous capabilities. In 1963 the program goals were broadened to encompass four more objectives: precise reentry control, attainment of flight and ground crew proficiency, extravehicular capability, and scientific experiments. When this program was completed in November 1966, the astronauts had acquired nearly 2000 man-hours of space-flight experience and all six objectives had been achieved.

The two-week flight of Gemini VII in December 1965 was the culmination of a series of progressively longer missions, and demonstrated that men could survive and work in space effectively for longer periods than a lunar voyage would require. A further requirement for the journey to the Moon is rendezvous and docking, and this was accomplished repeatedly by a variety of techniques. In postdocking maneuvers the Gemini astronauts used the thrust of the Agena target vehicle to set new altitude and speed records, thus increasing confidence that their successors will be able to proceed farther into space.

When the Apollo spacecraft returns from the Moon, its high velocity requires that its flight path into the Earth's atmosphere be controlled with great precision. The Gemini astronauts used aerodynamic lift generated by their spacecraft and an onboard computer to guide their vehicles to preselected landing areas. Their successes, and early Apollo flights, provided increased assurance that the men going to the Moon could return safely.

Both flight and ground crews demonstrated great proficiency during the Gemini program. On rendezvous missions, the Gemini spacecraft had to be launched after the target vehicle with precision measured in seconds. This was done with complete success. Dual launching made a rendezvous possible in less than one orbit after the liftoff of the Gemini spacecraft on the 11th mission. The Mission Control Center in Houston, Tex., repeatedly controlled missions involving more than one space vehicle, and controlled a dual mission in which both vehicles were manned during the Gemini VII/VI mission.

Extravehicular activity by Gemini astronauts showed the need for body restraints, and on the final mission numerous planned work tasks outside the vehicle were performed without difficulty. The technological experiments also included tethering a target vehicle to a spacecraft, as an aid to station keeping and a means of inducing a small artificial gravity field by rotation.

The scientific experiments undertaken at the same time as these unprecedented demonstrations of what men can do in space yielded information that was hitherto beyond the reach of scientists. A total eclipse of the Sun was observed from space for the first time and the airglow and zodiacal light were photographed.

The personnel, equipment, and facilities employed in the Gemini program have since been integrated into other NASA and Department of Defense manned space flight programs. The technological legacy of the Gemini flights lives on. It is a harbinger of greater achievements both in space and on Earth, achievements with more beneficial results than our generation can now foresee.

GEORGE E. MUELLER
*Associate Administrator for Manned Space Flight, NASA*

# PREFACE

THE photographs in this volume resulted from two of 22 scientific experiments that were part of the Gemini program. These were the experiments in Synoptic Terrain Photography (S-005) and Synoptic Weather Photography (S-006). Many of the pictures obtained in these experiments already have been put to geologic, meteorologic, and oceanographic use. Historians and directors of human affairs, as well as students of physical phenomena, have found the perspectives afforded stimulating, and the value of such portraits of the Earth in agricultural, urban, and other kinds of research is becoming increasingly evident.

The Gemini science experiments were a continuation and expansion of work begun during the Mercury series of flights. These experiments were designed to take advantage of man's presence in space. The astronauts acted as the sensors, manipulators, and operators of the equipment, and exercised judgment based on their understanding of the objectives. Their interest, imagination, and ingenuity contributed greatly to the success of the program.

JOHN E. NAUGLE
*Associate Administrator,*
*Office of Space Science and Applications, NASA*

The first rendezvous of two space vehicles is shown here in fine detail as photographed by Tom Stafford in Gemini VI. Gemini VII's thruster ports appear as dark, round spots from 40 feet away. The yellowish covering on the right end is a thermal shield that protected various subsystems mounted in the adapter section. The trailing straps covered an explosive cord that severed all connections between the spacecraft and its launch vehicle when they separated. Gemini VI was starting its sixth orbit when this picture was taken.

GEMINI VI DECEMBER 15, 1965 S65-63204

Gemini VII appears balanced on the horizon as the two spacecraft orbit the earth. Its rendezvous and the recovery section in the spacecraft nose, which housed the parachute and other recovery aids, is shown in this picture. The small white objects to the left of the words "United States" are horizon scanners that measure spacecraft attitude. The command pilot's window is directly above. The two protrusions from the white, adapter section are cryogenically cooled radiometers, part of the Gemini inflight experiments program. Cloud formations seen below the spacecraft result from convective clouds pushing up through broad areas of cirriform clouds.

GEMINI VI DECEMBER 15, 1965 S65-63188

The rendezvous target for the Gemini XII mission was the Agena space vehicle, shown (on the next page) before docking over the Pacific Ocean near the end of the third orbit. The naillike object in the foreground is a heavy metal bar that is attached to the nose section of the Gemini spacecraft to facilitate docking. When docked, the Agena was able to propel the two spacecraft to the highest altitudes achieved by man up to that time. This was done during the Gemini XI mission when Astronauts Pete Conrad and Dick Gordon looked down at the Earth from 741.5 nautical miles.

GEMINI XII NOVEMBER 15, 1966 S66-62756

Gemini IX rendezvoused with an augmented target docking adapter (shown at the far right) that was launched as a replacement for an Agena target which had failed to achieve orbit on an earlier attempt. Docking with this spacecraft was not possible because its plastic nose fairing did not separate and it was quickly named the "angry alligator." "Early in the first daylight after rendezvous," Astronaut Thomas P. Stafford wrote of this picture, "our suspicion that something was amiss was photographically confirmed. The 'angry alligator' appeared to be nibbling at Roques atoll." This happened over the Caribbean, north of Caracas, and the Isla Orchila can be seen. Clouds in the upper right hide the coast of Venezuela.

GEMINI IX JUNE 3, 1966 S66-37923

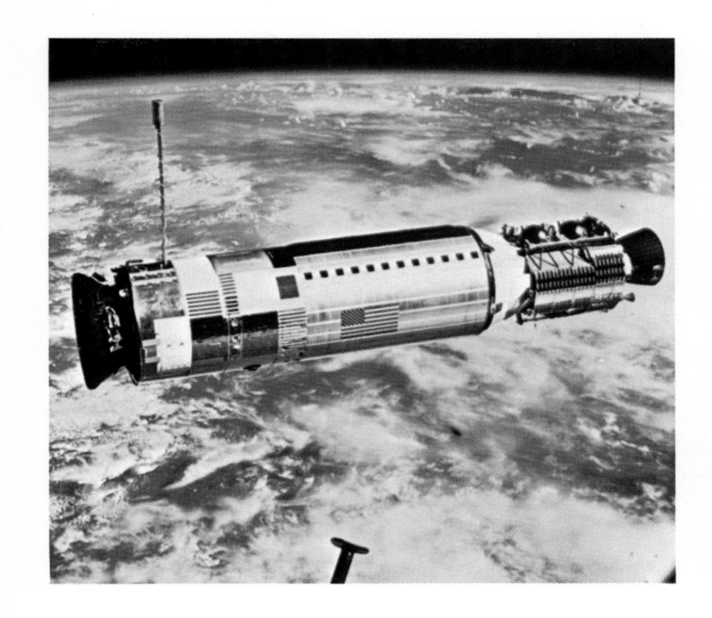

# CONTENTS

# ACKNOWLEDGEMENTS

THE photographs in this book were chosen from among hundreds that the Gemini astronauts took in the course of scientific experiments that included synoptic terrain and weather photography. In these particular experiments, Paul D. Lowman, Jr., of the Goddard Space Flight Center, and Kenneth M. Nagler and Stanley D. Soules, of the Environmental Science Services Administration, were the principal investigators. Robert E. Stevenson, of the Bureau of Commercial Fisheries at Galveston, Tex., joined them as a representative of oceanographic interests.

Since NASA's charter requires disclosure of scientific information likely to be generally useful, Robert E. Gilruth, Director of the Manned Spacecraft Center, proposed that a representative group of the pictures now available be published for the use of the many scientists who are concerned with features of the Earth's surface. Jocelyn R. Gill, Gemini Science Manager, was responsible for the organization of the book and headed the technical panel that recommended publication of these photographs.

Richard W. Underwood and Herbert Tiedemann, of the Manned Spacecraft Center, identified the areas shown in the photographs. The principal investigators provided information for the captions with the help of Dr. Stevenson, Mr. Tiedemann, Herbert Blodget of the Goddard Space Flight Center, James Williams of the Environmental Science Services Administration, James Bailey of the Bureau of Commercial Fisheries, Lawrence Dunkelman of Goddard Space Flight Center, and Samuel H. Hubbard of the Office of Manned Space Flight. The U.S. Geological Survey library staff was especially helpful to them.

Senor Ing. Guillermo Salas contributed geological information regarding pictures taken over Mexico. A. L. Grabham and L. Moskowitz of the U.S. Navy Oceanographic Office and other representatives of Government agencies and contractors served with NASA personnel on the technical panel, and a roster of the individuals who assisted its members would be extremely long. Among those who contributed especially valuable help and advice were John Bridgewater, Le Forrest Miller, Jose Toro, Ronald Dalrymple, Robert Dubinsky, and William Vest.

# Part I. Introduction

This is a companion volume to *Earth Photographs from Gemini III, IV, and V,* which was issued in 1967 as Special Publication 129. This one presents photographs taken on seven later flights, those of Gemini VI-A, VII, VIII, IX, X, XI, and XII. The crews, the dates, durations, and altitudes of these flights are listed in table 1, which also shows the cameras and films that were used on each flight.

In these seven flights, Gemini spacecraft orbited the Earth 421 times and the astronauts took nearly 1900 high-quality color photographs of its surface from above the atmosphere. Those reproduced here are a representative sampling of them, chosen with the current interests of earth scientists in mind.

In the previous volume, SP-129, the pictures taken on each flight were separated and presented sequentially. In this one they are juxtaposed, to group them geographically. This was done for two reasons: To enable a person interested in a particular geographic area to turn quickly to the photographs of that area, and to enable the reader to imagine himself circling the world and seeing it in somewhat the same way that it appeared to the astronauts.

The pictorial journey in the pages that follow begins at the launching site of the Gemini spacecraft, the Kennedy Space Center in Florida. It proceeds eastward between the latitudes of approximately 30° North and 30° South. Photographs taken on different flights and different revolutions, at different altitudes and times of day, and in different seasons of the year are intermingled in this presentation. The first and the last pictures in the book are both of Florida, but they are separated here by pictures taken at various times between December 15, 1965, and November 16, 1966, on many journeys around the world. The dates given below the photos are in Greenwich mean time.

The nine groups into which the pictures are divided in this volume correspond approximately with ways in which the Earth is often divided in an atlas of the type readily available in many homes and in most libraries. This facilitates use of common maps while examining these photographs. Attention is called in many of the captions both to geological divisions of the Earth and to national boundaries.

The explanatory notes beneath the pictures suggest some, but by no means all, of the ways in which scientists concerned with features of the Earth are finding high-altitude photography helpful. The objectives of the Gemini flights included a variety of scientific experiments for investigators representing numerous distinct scientific disciplines. These are listed in table II.

A Hasselblad 500C camera and a Hasselblad super-wide-angle camera, modified by NASA, were used on the Gemini flights. On the last four flights a specially designed 70-millimeter camera built by the J. A. Maurer Co. also was used. The pictures chosen for this book are presented in the square format of the original film.

Overlapping photographs were taken of many areas and can be used to obtain stereoscopic views. NASA can provide either transparencies or photographic prints of these pictures to members of the academic and scientific community who have specific professional uses for them in mind. Researchers should address specific inquiries, indicating their requirements, either to the National Aeronautics and Space Administration, Manned Spacecraft Center, Science and Applications Directorate, Houston, Tex. 77058, or to the National Space Science Data Center, Code 601, Goddard Space Flight Center, Greenbelt, Md. 20771.

Persons having commercial or industrial applications in mind should address their requests for such photographic materials to Technology Applications Center, University of New Mexico, Post Office Box 181, Albuquerque, N. Mex. 81706.

TABLE I.

*Gemini Flights VI–A Through XII*

| Flight | Crew | Date | GMT | Duration | Orbit (approx) | Camera | Film [2] |
|---|---|---|---|---|---|---|---|
| VI–A[1] | Capt. W. M. Schirra, Jr.<br>Maj. T. P. Stafford, Jr. | Dec. 15, 1965<br>Dec. 16, 1965 | 13:37<br>15:28 | 25 hr 51 min,<br>16 revolutions | 100 by 161 miles (statute) | Modified Hasselblad 500C, 80-mm Zeiss planar lens, *f*/2.8 | Eastman Kodak Ektachrome MS (S.O. 217) |
| VII. . . | Lt. Col. Frank Borman<br>Comdr. J. A. Lovell, Jr. | Dec. 4, 1965<br>Dec. 18, 1965 | 19:30<br>14:05 | 330 hr 35 min,<br>206 revolutions | 100 by 204 miles | Hasselblad 500C w/80-mm Zeiss planar lens *f*/2.8 and 250-mm Zeiss sonnar lens, *f*/4.5 | S.O. 217<br>8443 (infrared)<br>3400<br>2475 |
| VIII. . | N. A. Armstrong<br>Maj. D. R. Scott | Mar. 16, 1966<br>Mar. 17, 1966 | 16:41<br>3:22 | 10 hr 42 min,<br>7 revolutions | 100 by 161 miles | Hasselblad 500C w/80-mm planar lens, *f*/2.8 | S.O. 217 |
| IX. . . . | Lt. Col. T. P. Stafford<br>Lt. Comdr. Eugene A. Cernan | June 3, 1966<br>June 6, 1966 | 13:39<br>14:00 | 72 hr 21 min,<br>45 revolutions | 99 by 166 miles | Hasselblad 500C w/80-mm planar; Hasselblad super-wide-angle-C w/38-mm Zeiss Biogon, *f*/4.5; J. A. Maurer 70-mm space camera w/Schneider 80-mm lens, *f*/2.8 | S.O. 217 |

Persons wishing such pictures for other purposes should address their inquiries to the Audio-Visual Branch, Public Information Division, Code FP, NASA, Washington, D.C. 20546 (telephone: Area code 202, 96-21721).

Additional information regarding the Gemini program will be found in NASA SP-138, *Gemini Summary Conference,* priced at $2.75 and for sale by the Superintendent of Documents, U.S. Government Printing Office, Washington, D.C. 20402. NASA SP-129, *Earth Photographs from Gemini III, IV, and V,* may be purchased for $7 from the Superintendent of Documents.

TABLE I (Continued)

*Gemini Flights VI–A Through XII*

| Flight | Crew | Date | GMT | Duration | Orbit (approx) | Camera | Film [2] |
|---|---|---|---|---|---|---|---|
| X..... | Comdr. John W. Young<br>Maj. Michael Collins | July 18, 1966<br>July 21, 1966 | 22:20<br>21:07 | 70 hr 46 min, 44 revolutions | 100 by 167 miles and excursion to 475 miles | Hasselblad super-wide-angle-C, Zeiss Biogon 38-mm lens, *f*/4.5; J. A. Maurer 70-mm w/Schneider 80-mm lens, *f*/2.8 | S.O. 217 |
| XI.... | Comdr. Charles Conrad, Jr.<br>Lt. Comdr. Richard Gordon, Jr. | Sept. 12, 1966<br>Sept. 15, 1966 | 14:42<br>13:58 | 71 hr 17 min, 44 revolutions | 100 by 177 miles and excursion to 850 miles | J. A. Maurer 70-mm space camera w/80-mm Schneider lens, *f*/2.8; Hasselblad super-wide-angle w/38-mm Biogon lens, *f*/4.5 | S.O. 368 |
| XII... | Capt. J. A. Lovell, Jr.<br>Maj. E. A. Aldrin, Jr. | Nov. 11, 1966<br>Nov. 15, 1966 | 20:46<br>19:21 | 94 hr 34 min, 59 revolutions | 100 by 175 miles | J. A. Maurer 70-mm space camera w/80-mm Schneider lens, *f*/2.8; Hasselblad superwide-angle w/38-mm Zeiss Biogon lens, *f*/4.5 | S.O. 368 |

[1] Gemini VI was rescheduled to follow Gemini VII and was renumbered "Gemini VI–A."

[2] Films used for synoptic terrain and synoptic weather photography experinents were:

| *Name* | *Type* | *Size mm* |
|---|---|---|
| S.O. 217 | Eastman Kodak Etkachrome transparency | 70 |
| S.O. 368 | Eastman Kodak Ektachrome transparency (improved) | 70 |
| 8443 | Eastman Kodak Ektachrome, infrared | 70 |
| 3400 | Eastman Kodak Panatomic X (ASA–80) | 70 |
| 2475 | High Speed (ASA–1200) | 70 |

Table II

*Gemini Science Experiments*

+, experiment successful; —, experiment incomplete

| No. | Title of investigation | Principal investigator | Flights | | | | | | | | | |
|---|---|---|---|---|---|---|---|---|---|---|---|---|
| | | | III | IV | V | VI | VII | VIII | IX | X | XI | XII |
| S001 | Zodiacal Light and Airglow Photography | E. P. Ney, University of Minnesota | | | + | | | − | + | + | | |
| S002 | Sea Urchin Egg Growth —Zero-G | R. S. Young, Ames Research Center | − | | | | | | | | | |
| S003 | Frog Egg Growth— Zero-G | R. S. Young, Ames Research Center | | | | | | − | | | + | |
| S004 | Effect of Zero-G and Radiation on Blood | M. A. Bender, Oak Ridge National Laboratory | + | | | | | | | | + | |
| S005 | Synoptic Terrain Photography | P. D. Lowman, Jr., Goddard Space Flight Center | | + | + | + | + | | | + | + | + |
| S006 | Synoptic Weather Photography | K. Nagler and S. D. Soules, Environmental Science Services Administration | | + | + | + | + | | | + | + | + |
| S007 | Spectrophotography of Clouds | F. Saiedy, Environmental Science Services Administration | | | + | | | − | | | | |
| S008 | Visual Acuity in Space | S. Q. Duntley, Scripps Institute | | | + | | + | | | | | |
| S009 | Nuclear Emulsion | M. M. Shapiro, Naval Research Laboratory, and C. D. Fichtel, Goddard Space Flight Center | | | | | | − | | | + | |
| S010 | Agena Micrometeorite Collection | C. L. Hemenway, Dudley Observatory | | | | | | + | + | − | | − |
| S011 | Airglow Horizon Photography | M. J. Koomen, Naval Research Laboratory | | | | | | | + | | + | + |
| S012 | Gemini Micrometeorite Collection | C. L. Hemenway, Dudley Observatory | | | | | | | + | − | | + |
| S013 | Ultraviolet Astronomical Photography | K. G. Henize, Dearborn Observatory | | | | | | | | + | + | + |
| S026 | Gemini Ion Wake Measurement | D. Medved, Electro-Optical Systems | | | | | | | | + | + | |
| S029 | Libration Regions Photography | E. C. Morris, U.S. Geological Survey | | | | | | | | | | − |
| S030 | Dim Sky Photography/-Image Orthicon | E. P. Ney, University of Minnesota and C. Hemenway, Dudley Observatory | | | | | | | | | + | |
| S051 | Sodium Vapor Cloud Photography | J. Blamont, University of Paris | | | | | | | | | | − |
| S064 | Ultraviolet Dust Photography | C. L. Hemenway, Dudley Observatory | | | | | | | | | | − |

# Part II. Across the Atlantic

I'LL put a girdle round about the world in forty minutes," said Puck in *A Midsummer-Night's Dream.* The pages that follow show the Earth as one might see it from such a girdle.

This imaginary tour begins and ends at Cape Kennedy, from which the Gemini spacecraft were launched. The astronauts turned their cameras in numerous directions while going around the world and photographed some sights from several sides and angles. Pictures that they took are not shown here in the order in which they were taken, but the date of each one is given below it.

Cape Kennedy is on Florida's east coast, near St. Augustine, the oldest city in the United States. The astronauts sped east from Florida, over steppingstones of history that are still called the West Indies. On some of their many crossings of the Atlantic, their first glimpses of the Old World were of the Canary Islands, from which 15th-century explorers sailed south and west to discover a relatively small planet's immensity. Several of their photographs of the West Indies and the Canary Islands have been included here because contemporary oceanographers and meteorologists are finding them highly informative.

Gemini photographs already have been used to check interpretations of pictures transmitted to Earth from unmanned weather satellites, and there is no longer any doubt that a multitude of constructive uses will be found for photographs taken from high altitudes. "Our unearthly satellites," Edgar M. Cortright, Director of the Langley Research Center, has written confidently, "will help us solve a host of earthly problems."

The Sun's glitter pattern had shifted eastward when this picture was taken, a minute after the preceding one. Oceanographers can obtain information about the changes in the sea's surface from pairs of pictures such as these. Cuba extends nearly all the way across the top of this one. Near the center, to the left of Grand Bahama Island, is Great Abaco Island. The islands of Andros, New Providence, and Eleuthera also can be seen despite the scattered clouds. A dark irregular spot in the sea near the center, left of an intense reflection of sunlight, indicates the location of the Little Bahama Bank.

GEMINI XII NOVEMBER 12, 1966 S66-63423

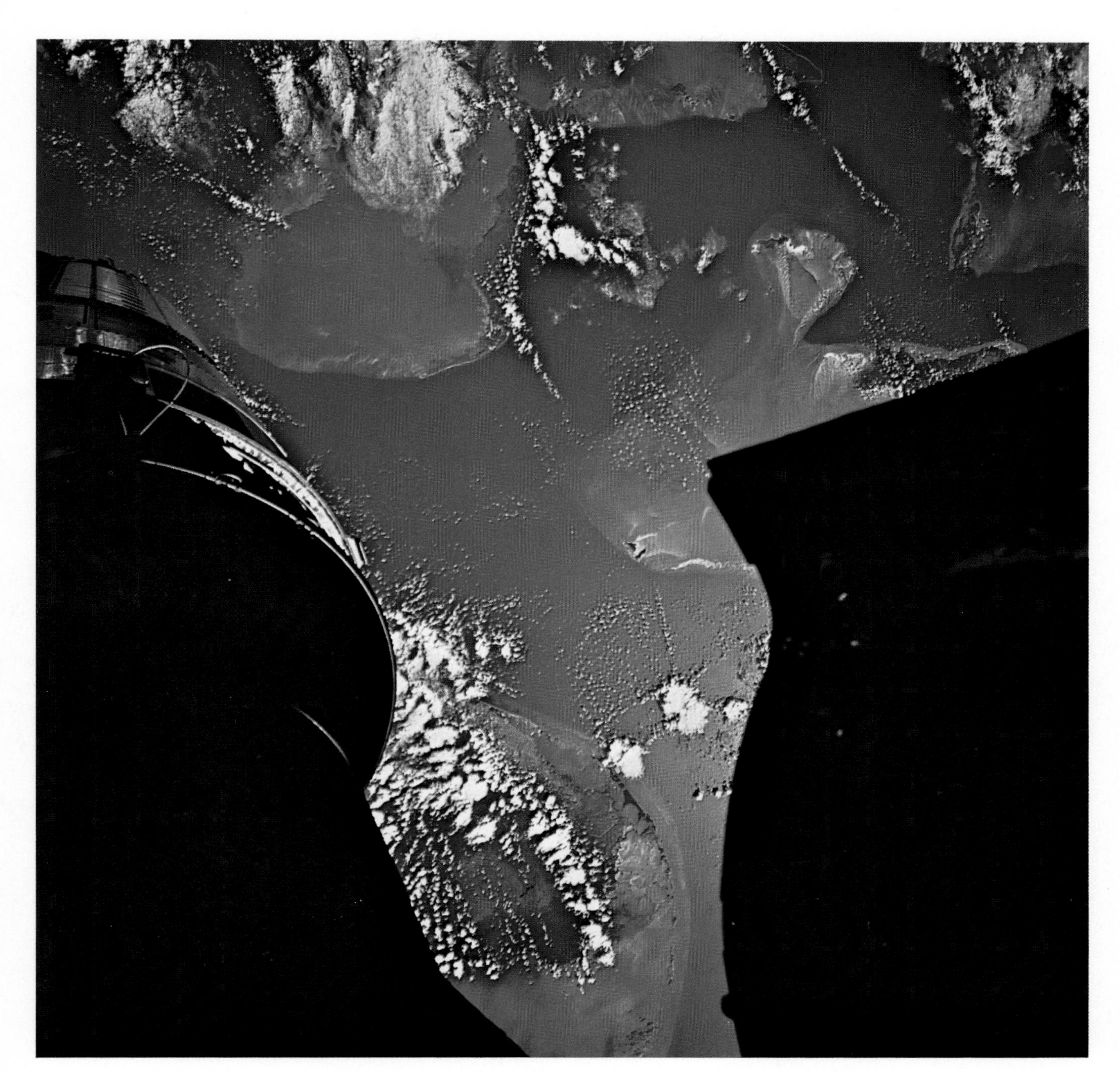

Bimini Island is in the center of this eastward view from over the Florida Keys in the foreground. South of Bimini, **U**-shaped bars indicate the spillover of water onto the shallow surface of the Great Bahama Bank. Similar bars can be seen around the Berry Island group and the northern end of Andros Island in upper center. In each case the water spills toward a central portion of the Great Bahama Bank during storm surges. A long sandbar is formed where flooding waters meet. On the ebb, water flows into a channel between the Great Bahama Bank and Grand Bahama Island to follow the Gulf Stream northward.

GEMINI XII NOVEMBER 12, 1966 S66-62908

The large mass of cirrus and cirrostratus clouds in this northwesterly view of the sky over the Atlantic Ocean is the western edge of tropical depression Celia, which rapidly intensified and became a hurricane the following day. Cuba is at the left edge of this photo, and the coast of Florida, Georgia, and South Carolina can be seen near the horizon. The cumulus-cloud streets at the left edge of the cloud mass are alined with the low-level wind, which spirals around and inward toward the storm's center. Pictures from operational meteorological satellites, less detailed but covering larger areas than the Gemini views, are used to track tropical storms.

GEMINI X JULY 19, 1966 S66-45692

From left to right above the spacecraft's nose here are parts of Abaco Island, shoals and flats around the Berry Islands, and the tip of Andros Island. New Providence Island, the site of Nassau, is in the upper center. Sand flats and the elongation of spillover bars show the direction of the currents. The net flow between the Berry Islands and Andros Island is from east to west. Layers of stratocumulus in the upper right are spread across the deep waters of the Tongue of the Ocean. In those clouds one can clearly see an unusual break. This kind of pattern has been noted in other pictures of stratocumulus over the sea.

GEMINI VII DECEMBER 11, 1965 S65-63753

Above the northern tip of Andros Island, in the center, the sea off the Florida coast is light blue where it is shallow and darker blue where the Northeast Providence Channel leads into the Tongue of the Ocean to the south. Dunelike depositions of sand can be seen in the shallows. The Berry Islands are in the foreground, and New Providence Island at the upper left. Patches of cumulus and stratocumulus cover some of the view, and a band of cirrus crosses the upper part. Although the Great Bahama Bank began to form in the Cretaceous period, coral built up the present islands after the sea-level rise that followed the last glaciation.

GEMINI VII DECEMBER 5, 1965 S65-63825

Tropical clouds camouflaged the islands bordering the Caribbean Sea when this photo was taken. The Agena target vehicle was tethered to Gemini XI, and Jamaica lay directly above it in this northeasterly view. In the upper left, cirrostratus covered a disturbed area containing thunderstorms, and elsewhere cumulus and cumulus congestus covered the region under a sparse veil of cirrus clouds. Eastern and central Cuba were in the top center and beyond them the Great Bahama Bank was visible. Serraña Bank was left of center at the lower edge, and reefs and cays of Bajo Nuevo were to the right of the Agena.

GEMINI XI SEPEMBER 14, 1966 S66-54571

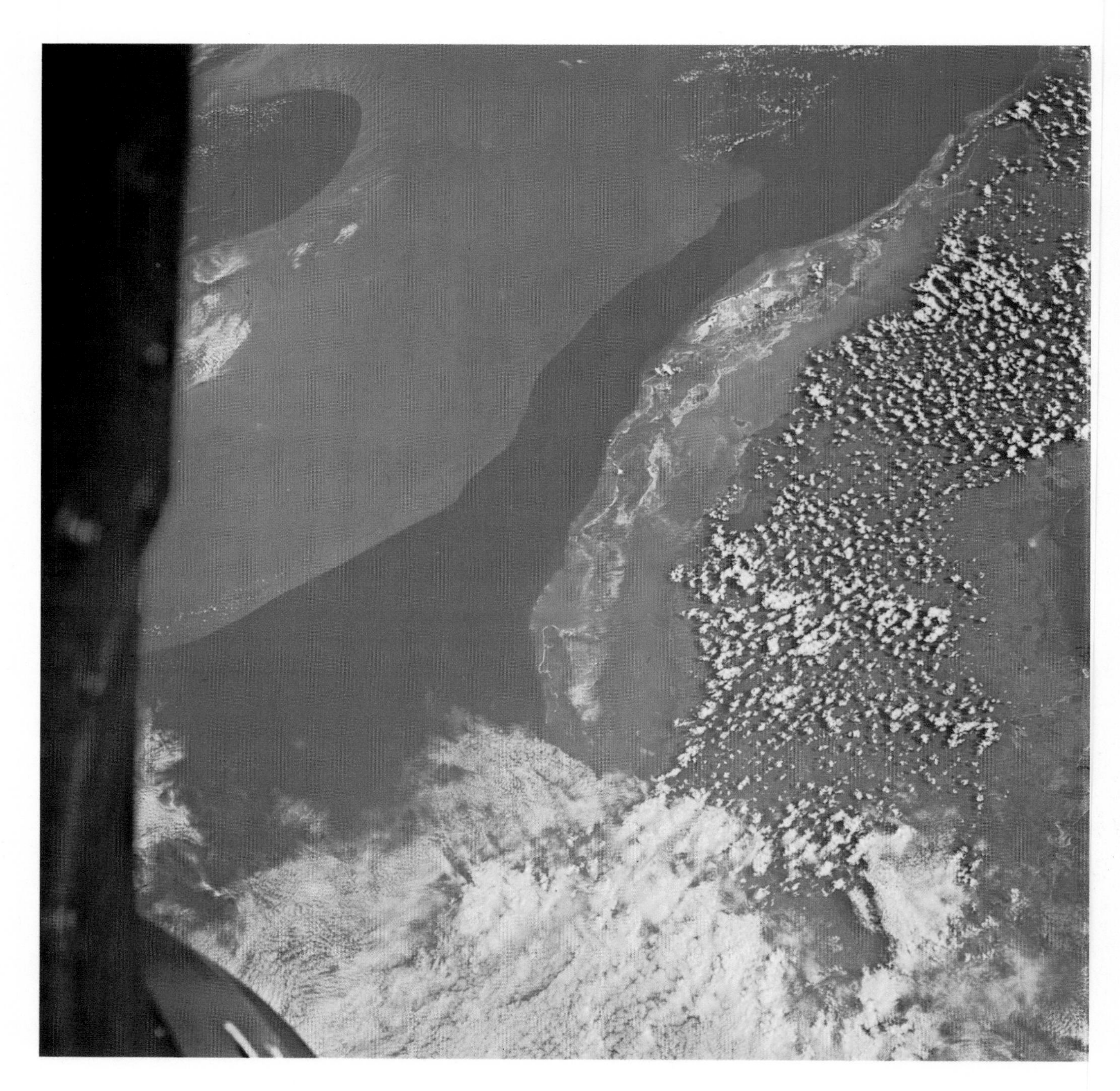

The roughly diagonal line here is Cuba's north coast. Cumulus and cirrocumulus clouds hover over its farms. Caibarién is under the clouds at the lower left, and the pouch-shaped harbor of Nuevitas is in the upper right corner. Slight submergence of the land in recent geological time has notched this shoreline, and left many islands, reefs, and bays. The light-blue area offshore is the Great Bahama Bank, where the sea is only about 30 feet deep. The darker, circular area at the upper left edge is the Tongue of the Ocean, where it is about a mile deep. One can see how submarine erosion has notched the sea floor around this deep area.

GEMINI VII DECEMBER 13, 1965 S65-64025

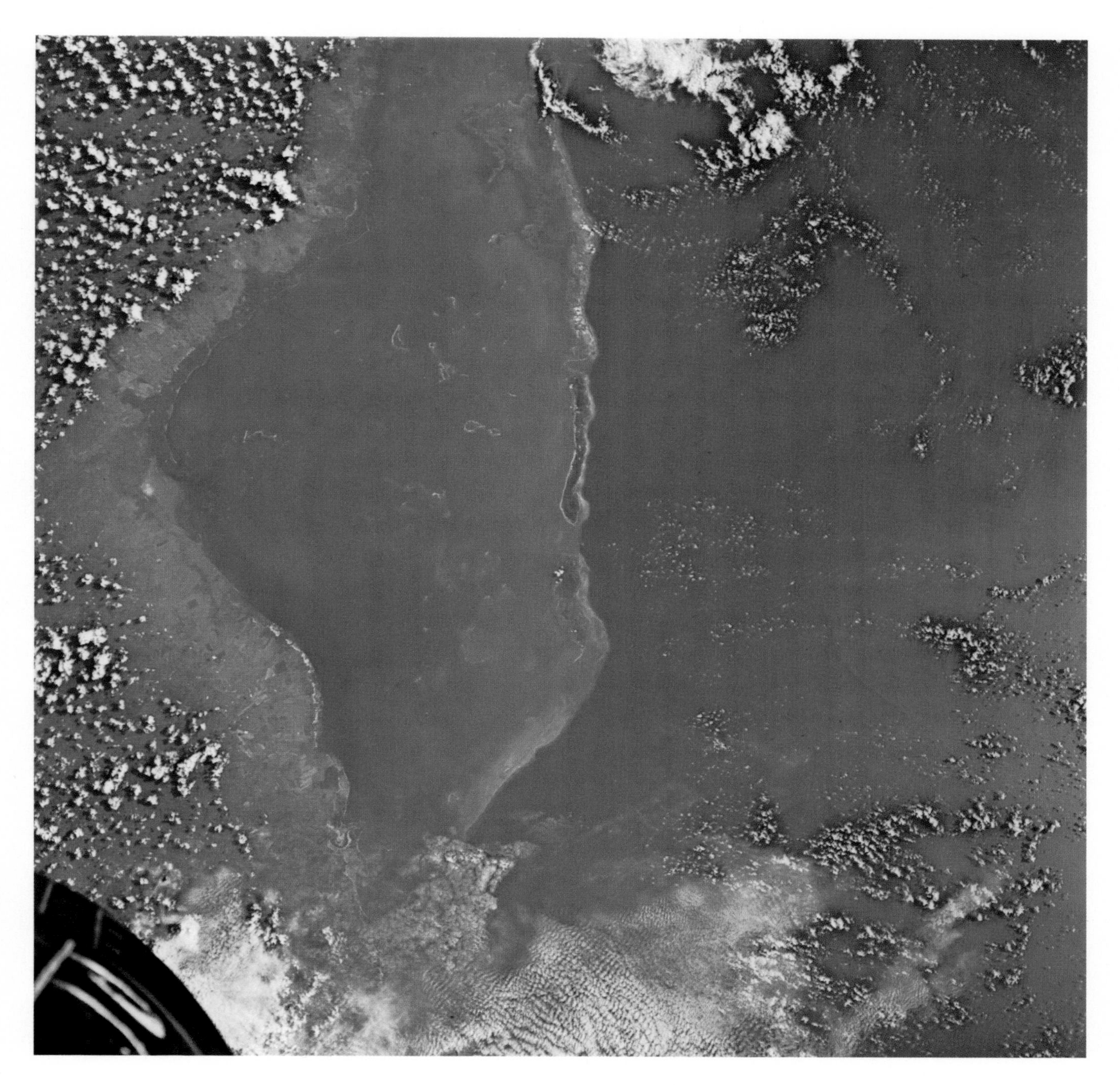

At the left here is Cuba's southern coast. The keys of Jardines de la Reina, south of Camagüey province, are in the center. Santa Cruz del Sur is a short distance beyond the upper end of this strip of the coast, and Trinidad is below it. The keys shown are on the outer edge of large shoal banks and are heavily ringed with coral reefs. Submarine features of the area between the keys and the mainland can be seen clearly enough to be charted from this photograph. The geology is mostly Tertiary sediments overlying folded Cretaceous and Jurassic strata. Marine sediments are confined to the coast and offshore areas.

GEMINI VII DECEMBER 13 ,1965 S65-64026

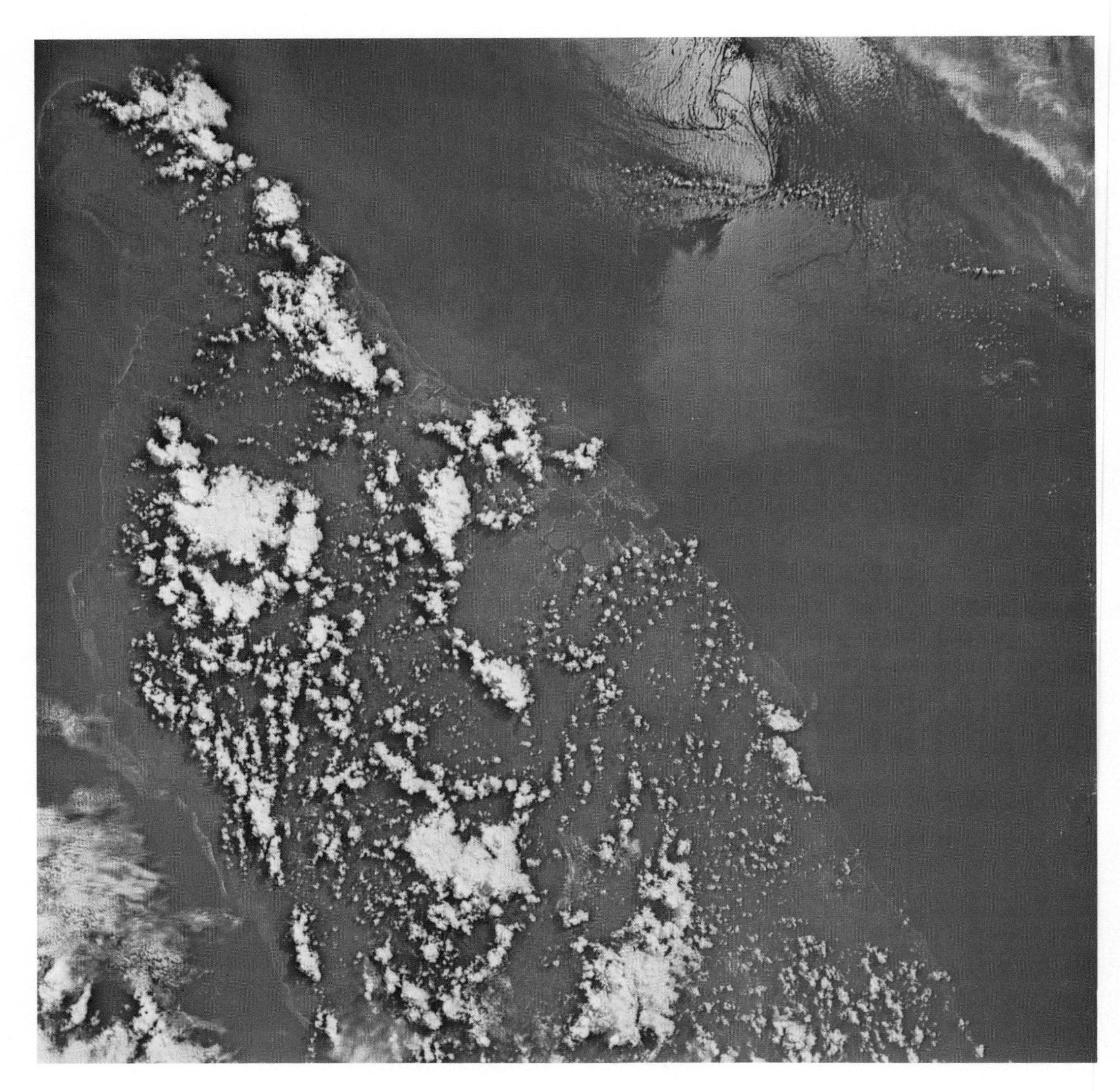

The eastern tip of Cuba is at the upper left here, the U.S. naval base at Bahía de Guantánamo in the center, and Santiago de Cuba farther down the south coast. Daytime heating of the land had caused typical cumulus activity over Oriente Province. Above Guantánamo Bay you see the edge of the Sun's reflection in the Windward Passage. Wave trains and slicks in the glitter pattern indicate the general water motion. A shear in the cloud line indicates low-level convergence over a shear in the water. Water motion and waves often can be seen best when a photo includes the Sun's reflection from the sea.

GEMINI VII DECEMBER 5, 1965 S65-63826

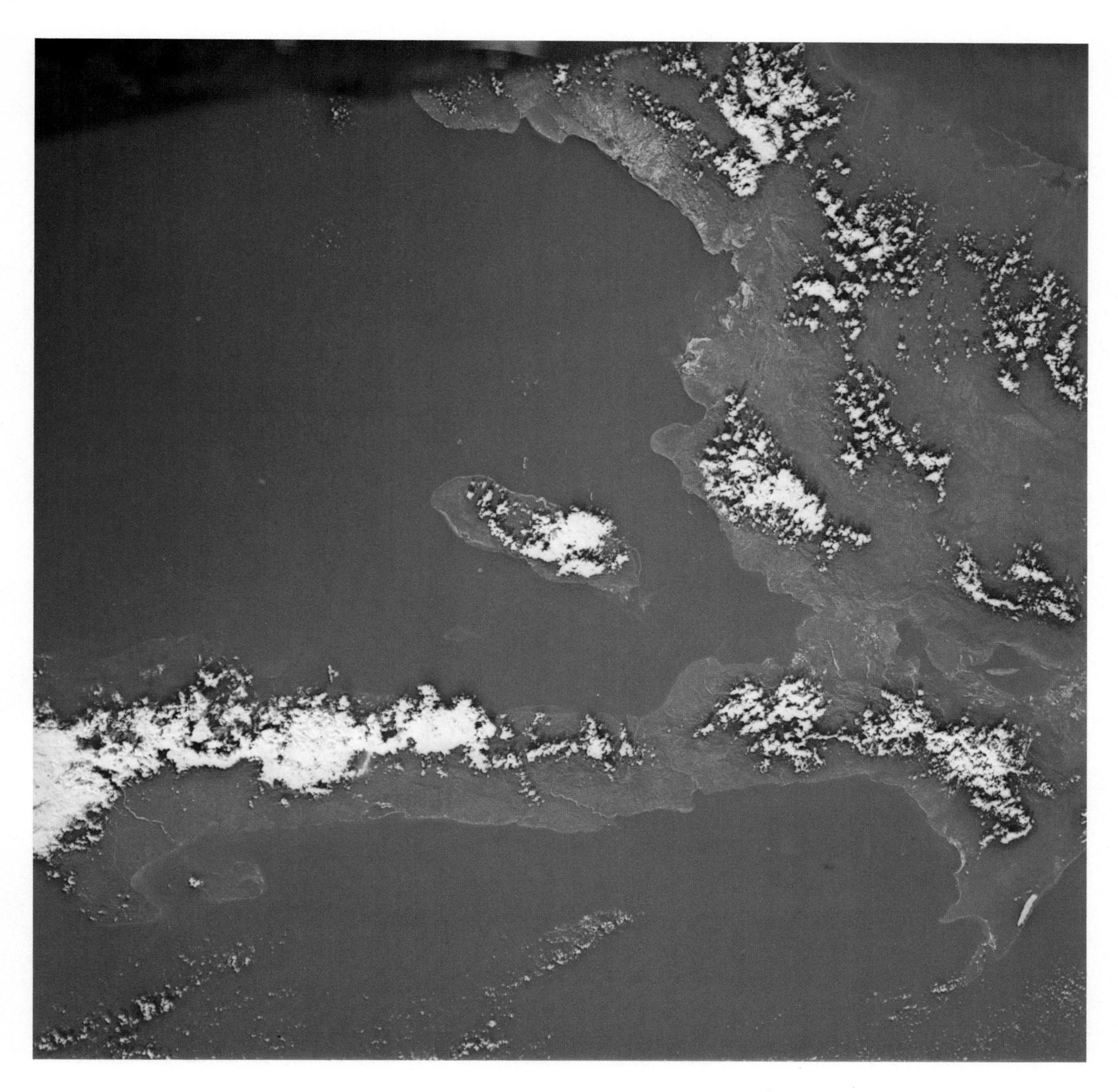

Most of Haiti is shown here with cumulus clouds piled over the highlands. The large island in the center is the Île de la Gonâve. East of it, at the lower right end of a nearly rectangular harbor, is Port au Prince. Near it are two large lakes, between which the common boundary of Haiti and the Dominican Republic runs; it ends left of the prominent capes in the lower right corner. Coral reefs border much of the coastline. The upper peninsula is an extension of the Cordillera Central. It has a core of Cretaceous and older rocks, flanked by Tertiary and younger sediments. The lower peninsula's structure and stratigraphy are similar.

GEMINI VII DECEMBER 13, 1965 S65-64027

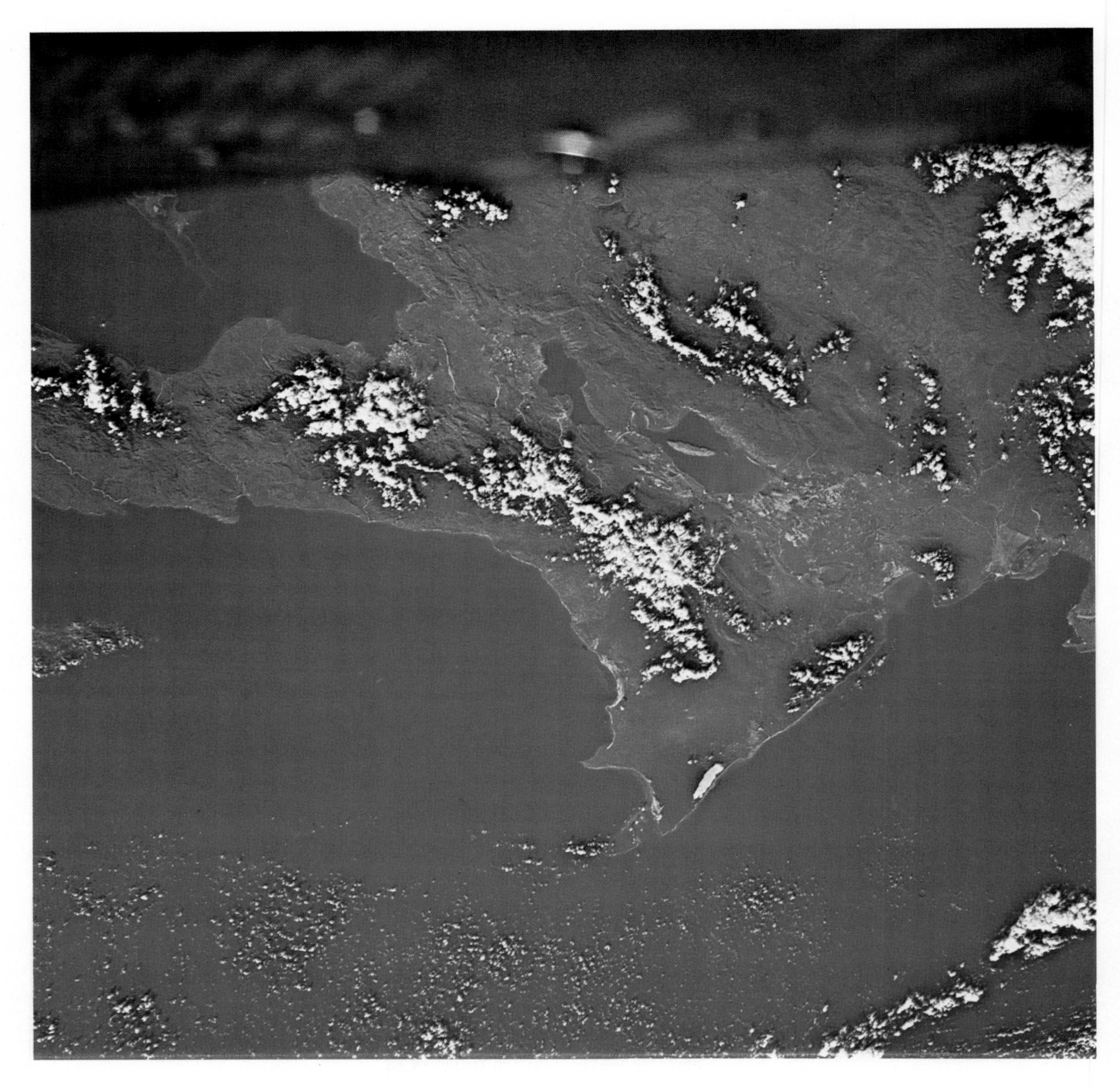

The southernmost tip of Hispaniola is now in the foreground. The large lake above the peninsula is Lago Enriquillo in the Dominican Republic. The smaller lake above it is the Étang Saumâtre in Haiti. Lago Enriquillo is 131 feet below sea level and contains a large island. The Valle de Neiba is to the right. The big valley in the upper center is the Plaine du Cul de Sac, adjacent to the harbor of Port au Prince, Haiti's Capital. Graben faulting along a major wrench fault on the south side of the island produced this coast-to-coast valley and lake system. To the north, another mountain mass is also bordered by a fault valley.

GEMINI VII DECEMBER 13, 1965 S65-64028

Crooked and Acklins Islands are in the center, and Long Island above them in this photo taken north of Cuba's eastern tip. Part of Mayaguana Island is in the lower right. Thin white lines along the northern shores of the islands are surf from long waves coming from the open Atlantic Ocean. Variations in color in the Bight of Acklin reveal calcareous sand and spillover bars. The small cumulus clouds are in lines parallel to low-level northeast winds. Several large-scale cloud bands are alined in northwest winds aloft. An upper air trough moved through this area a few hours before the picture was taken.

GEMINI VII DECEMBER 8, 1965 S65-63857

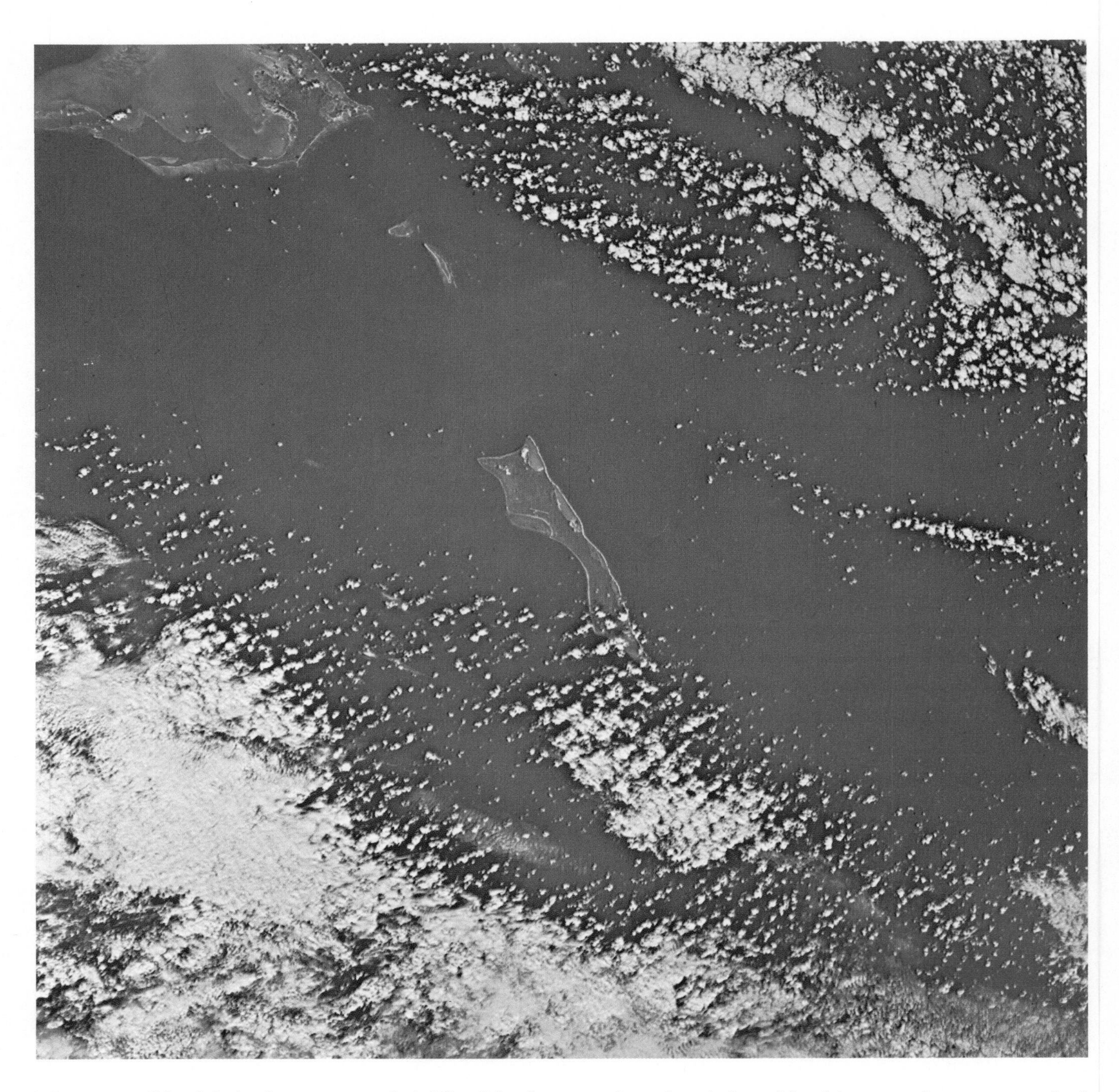

Mayaguana Island is in the center, and Acklins Island in the upper left of this photo taken as the spacecraft proceeded east over the Bahamas. Abraham's Bay is on the left side of Mayaguana. Although no ocean currents can be seen around the islands, strong surf and wave action is visible off their northeastern shores. A heavy surf produced the white fringe on the eastern end of Mayaguana. Surf also sharpens the image of the Plana Cays that rise from the sea between the two large islands; waves were rolling over a reef half a mile offshore, while the winds were from the east.

GEMINI VII DECEMBER 8, 1965 S65-63858

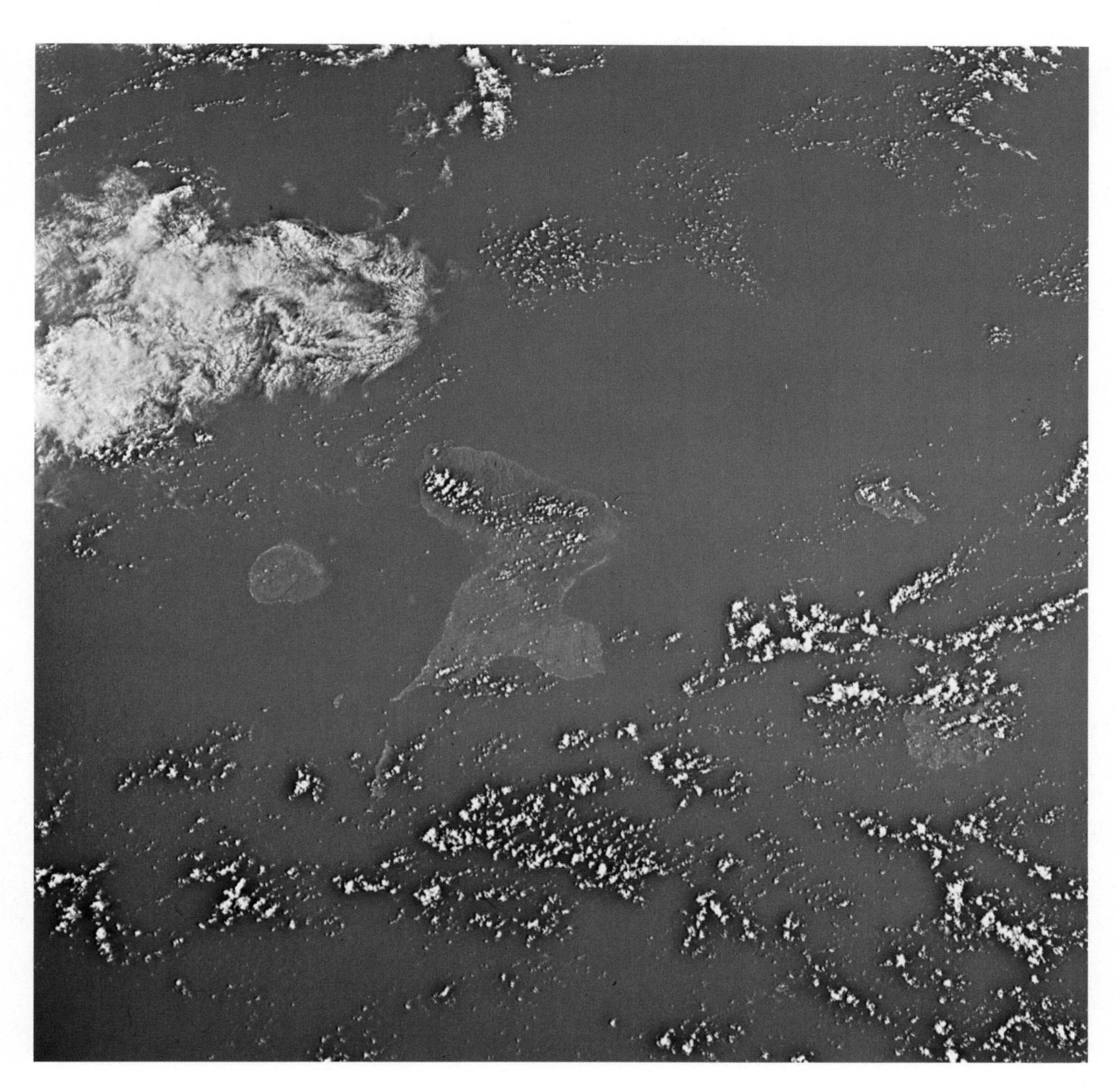

Guadeloupe's twin islands, Grande Terre and Basse Terre, are in the center of this photo of the French West Indies between the Caribbean Sea and the Atlantic. Marie Galante is to the left of the 583-square-mile main islands. One also can see La Désirade, Iles des Saintes, and Îles de la Petite Terre. The Dominica Channel is left of Guadeloupe and the Guadeloupe Passage is to the north. Montserrat is in the upper right and Antigua in the lower right. The cloud distribution is typical of a fair-weather regime in the subtropics, and the weak alinement of the clouds indicates light, low-level winds from the southeast.

GEMINI VII DECEMBER 8, 1965 S65-63855

Meteorology has been one of the first and greatest beneficiaries of man's recently acquired ability to view the weather from high altitudes. This cyclonic circulation over the Atlantic Ocean was photographed about 400 miles southeast of Bermuda, while a Gemini spacecraft was docked with an Agena target vehicle. The storm's center was near the circular clouds that you see around the antenna of the Agena. Dense cirrostratus formed the cloud shield at the left, north of the center. The winds in the lower and middle troposphere were blowing counterclockwise about this center.

GEMINI XII NOVEMBER 12, 1966 S66-62913

This is a southeasterly view of the same cyclonic storm over the Atlantic southeast of Bermuda that was shown in the preceding picture. It covers the region to the right, and again the center of the disturbance is shown near the antenna of the Agena. Numerous cumulonimbus clouds can be seen throughout the right half of this photo. Their anvillike tops usually point with the wind direction at their level. A few cellular-shaped lines of cumulus are seen near the right center. Operational use of data from cameras and other sensors in satellites has become routine in the first decade of man's exploration of space.

GEMINI XII NOVEMBER 12, 1966 S66-62914

What appears to be a large break in these clouds, associated with a cold front about 2000 miles east of Cape Kennedy, is really a shadow cast by a high cloud deck upon a lower one in early-morning sunlight. Such dark bands have been seen frequently in pictures transmitted from operational weather satellites and interpreted as shadows from higher clouds, often oriented parallel to the upper wind flow. The Gemini astronauts were asked to look for and obtain pictures such as this, and their pictures have helped to convince students and skeptics that the operational weather-satellite pictures can be diagnosed correctly and beneficially.

GEMINI VI DECEMBER 16, 1965 S65-63143

This vast network of stratocumulus clouds lay near 20° N and 20° W. These are open cellular-type convective clouds in which air rises along the cell walls and sinks in the centers. This is the opposite of what occurs when a closed cellular pattern is formed. The surface wind in the foreground here was from the northeast, right to left, at 15 to 20 knots. Downwind the cloud openings decreased, and in the background they tended to aline themselves in rows parallel to the wind. This type of organized convection is typical of fields in which the wind's speed increases with height. The blue band along the horizon is the Earth's troposphere.

GEMINI VI DECEMBER 16, 1965 S65-63264

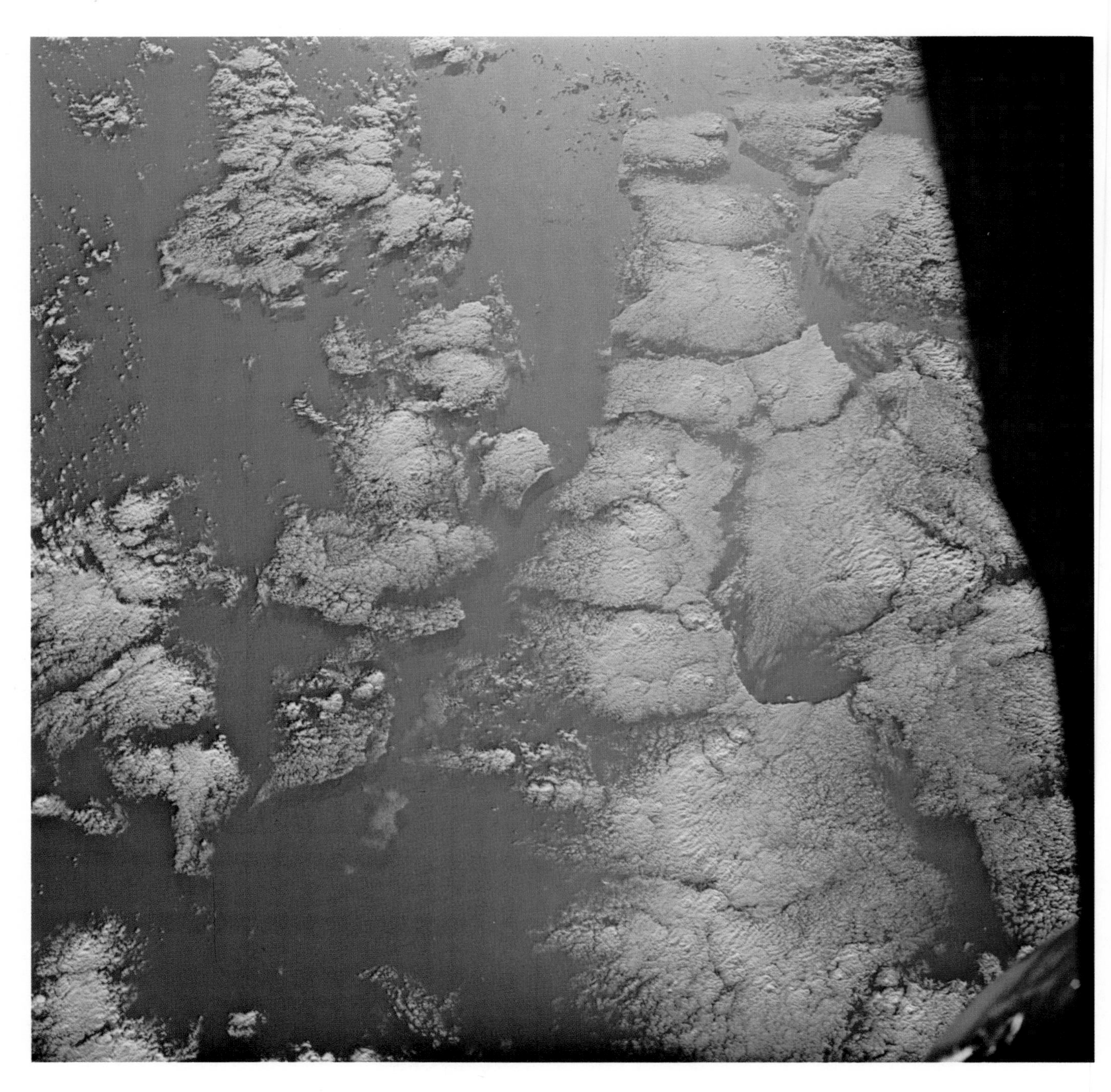

These stratocumulus clouds organized in approximately polygonal closed cells were seen southwest of the Canary Islands. To produce this type of pattern, there is a general weak rising motion below and in the cloud patches up to a stable layer, perhaps 1000 or 2000 feet above sea level. This stable layer inhibits further vertical motion, so there is an outflow from the cloud area and a descending and, hence, drying, motion in the clear bands between the clouds. This type of mesoscale convection frequently occurs in an oceanic anticyclone. The large hole at the lower right was an eddy caused by wind blowing past one of the islands.

GEMINI VI DECEMBER 16, 1965 S65-63146

Here, on a June day, the Canary Islands come into view. The tiny one at the left is Hierro. Geographers once drew the first meridian there because they knew nothing of the world west of it. The dark circular spot as your eyes swing to the right is Gomera. Above it is La Palma. That big arrow in the sea is Tenerife. Below its tip is Gran Canaria. The day that this photo was taken, cumulus clouds were piled on the windward, northeastern slopes of the three Canary Islands that lay closest to Africa, and clouds connected with an upper-air, low-pressure system were at the right near the horizon.

GEMINI IX JUNE 6, 1966 S66-38442

This and the next picture of the Canary Islands were taken in morning light, actually on the revolution before the previous picture. The patch of cirrus and cirrostratus clouds off the Morocco coast and the streaks of cirrus over the land are alined with a southwesterly upper-level wind. The large bright area in the lower left is sunlight reflected from the sea. Apparently the sheltering effect of the Islands calmed the surface and greatly reduced the reflection towards the camera southeast of the Islands. The most conspicuous dark "tail" extends from Gomera, which lies between Tenerife, the largest island in this view, and La Palma and Hierro.

GEMINI IX JUNE 6, 1966 S66-38404

Centuries ago the Canary Islands were known as the Fortunate Islands. They are less than 100 miles from Africa, and this photo shows both the islands and the coasts of Morocco and Spanish Sahara. The Sun rising over Africa made the sea glisten and small lines of cumuli at the left cast shadows on the water. The reflective pattern to the right of the Sun glitter was caused by waves on the surface of the sea. The crest-to-crest distance of the waves was about a nautical mile, which is unusually long. The sea was smoother and darker to the southeast in the lee of the islands.

GEMINI IX JUNE 6, 1966 S66-38405

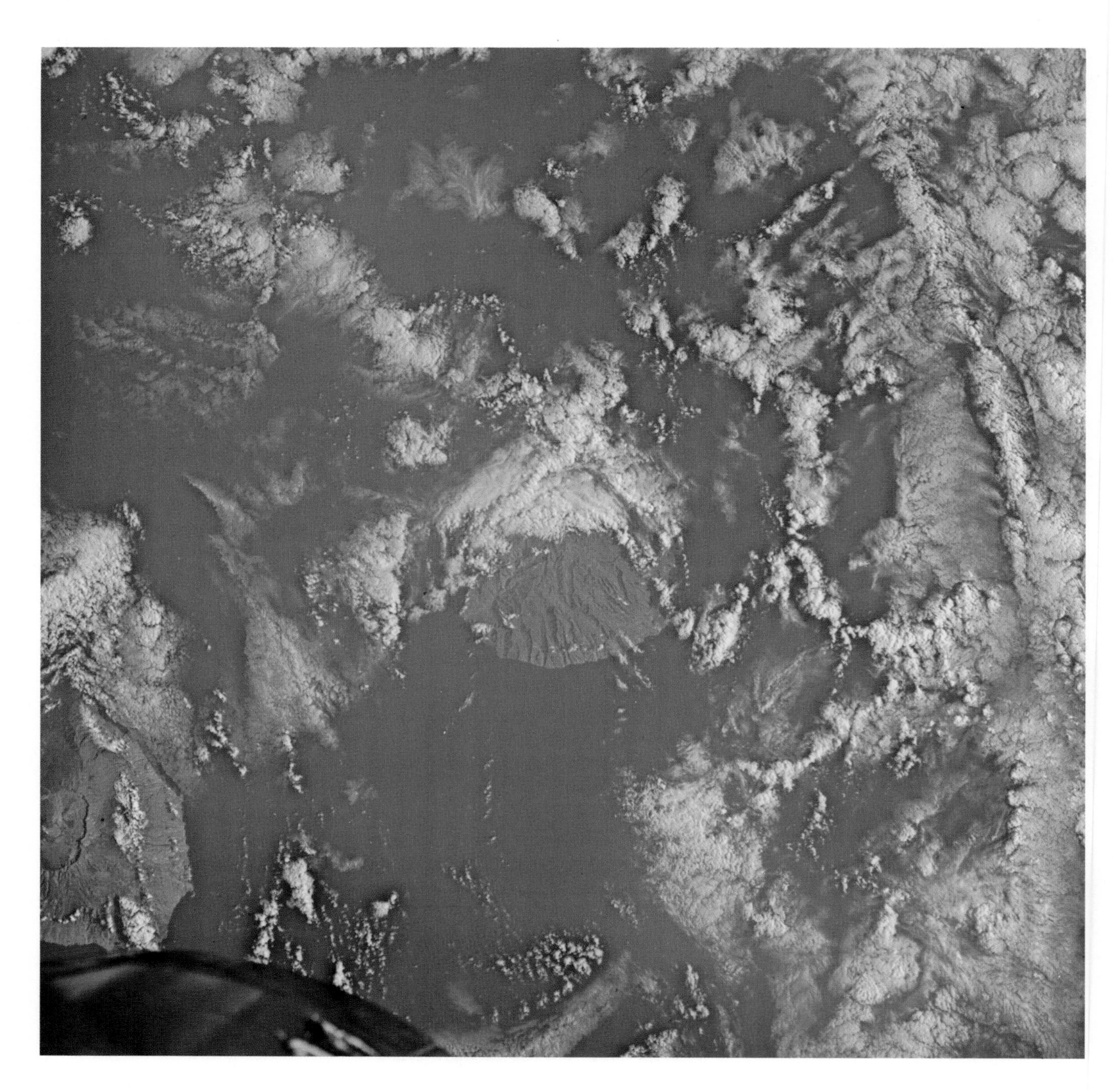

This and the next three pictures of the Canary Islands and their environment were taken in December. They reveal how such mountainous islands interrupt the flow of air over the sea and create eddies downstream in the lower atmosphere. Gran Canaria is in the center here, and part of Tenerife is visible. Clouds cover the upwind slopes of Gran Canaria's 6394-foot peak. Las Palmas, the islands' largest city, is on Gran Canaria. The climate is warm and pleasant. Rainfall on the coast reaches 10 to 15 inches annually, and vegetation at the lower levels includes the species found throughout the North African Mediterranean littoral.

GEMINI VI DECEMBER 16, 1965 S65-63151

Tenerife is in the center of this view of the Canary Islands. Its Pico de Teide crater is 12 198 feet high. These islands rise from great depths and present precipitous cliffs to the sea at many places. They consist of trachytes and basalts erupted intermittently from the ocean floor. They emerged toward the end of Cretaceous time and subsequent volcanic activity has increased their size. The last reported eruption was in 1909 on Tenerife. The stratocumulus clouds seen here are typical of the area. Dark, parallel lines in some of them are billows caused by undulations in the wind flow at the altitude of the clouds.

GEMINI VI DECEMBER 16, 1965 S65-63150

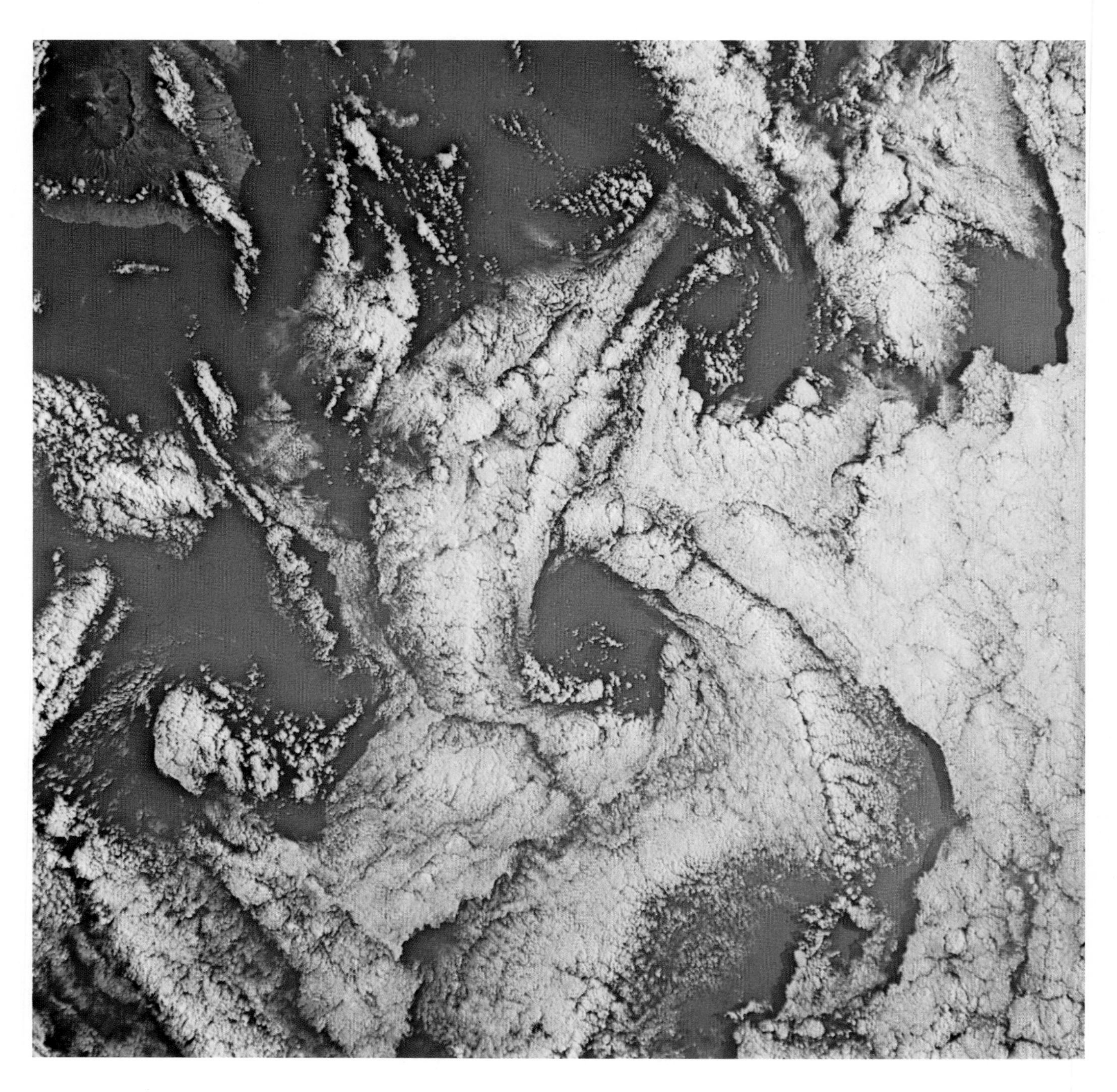

"This beautiful vortex is typical of the varied weather phenomena that can be seen from space," Astronaut Thomas P. Stafford wrote of this photo taken over the Canary Islands. Tenerife is in the upper left here. When northeast winds, under a temperature inversion layer, blow past the mountainous islands, the air is frequently swirled into a chain of eddies similar to a Von Kármán vortex street. The eddies become visible when stratocumulus clouds are present. The center eddy here was 60 miles from Tenerife and its eye was 13 miles wide. Alongside it, about 35 miles away, other eddies rotated clockwise.

GEMINI VI DECEMBER 16, 1965 S65-63149

This photo shows clouds west of those in the preceding picture. The island of Hierro was at the lower edge of the eddy eye in the lower right center, but was almost entirely obscured by stratocumulus clouds. The eddy chain reaching from the top to bottom was a part of a Von Kármán vortex street formed in the lee of the larger Canary Islands. This phenomenon is also found frequently near Guadalupe Island off Baja California. By studying photos of these eddies, researchers can obtain data to relate the physics of the natural vortex streets to their laboratory experiments. This is the last view of the Canary Islands area in this series.

GEMINI VI DECEMBER 16, 1965 S65-63148

This unusually fine display of cirrus clouds was photographed during an approach to Africa about a dozen degrees south of the Canary Islands. These clouds lay off the coast of Senegal and Gambia. Cap Vert can be seen jutting into the ·Atlantic Ocean at the lower left edge. A radiosonde ascent at Dakar, which is on that cape, indicated that the winds were east-southeast at 20 knots at an altitude of about 6 kilometers, and becoming southwesterly at 25 to 40 knots above 8 kilometers at the time this picture was taken. The clouds in the foreground were probably 9 or more kilometers high.

GEMINI VII DECEMBER 11, 1965 S65-63754

Ilha de Madeira is north of the Canary Islands, and about 535 miles southwest of Lisbon. On an approach to this island, noted for wines and embroideries, the astronauts found a cyclonic eddy in the stratocumulus clouds at the right. The island is a tiny dark spot about an inch to the left of the eddy. It is 35 miles long, up to 13 miles wide, and has a peak elevation of more than 6000 feet. It obstructs the broad northeasterly wind flow, and thus can induce eddies in the low-level wind similar to those caused by an obstruction in a wind tunnel. In this case the result was a fairly simple vortex in the sky near it.

GEMINI X JULY 20, 1966 S66-46040

"Europe and Spain enjoying good weather," Gemini X reported on one approach to Africa, "but not for long if that storm off Gibraltar is an indicator." Actually, the cyclonic circulation southwest of the entry to the Mediterranean was only an eddy on the edge of a large-scale northerly wind flow over the Atlantic, induced by the configuration of the land and revealed by stratocumulus clouds. Portugal and Spain are at the left and Morocco is at the right. The geologic unity of southern Spain and Africa is suggested in this photo by the evident continuity of the Sierra Nevada and related mountains in Spain with the Riff Atlas in Morocco.

GEMINI X JULY 20, 1966 S66-46044

# Part III. Northwest Africa

ASTRONAUT James A. Lovell, Jr., thought that the broad western bulge of Africa was "truly the most interesting area of the world" to see from a spacecraft. Its dry and desolate terrain was nearly always free of clouds, and he found it a delight to photograph because there was so little haze to dim its beauty.

The atmosphere's heat and aridity over the sands of the Sahara is less welcome to travelers on the surface. For centuries this land was as hostile a barrier to explorers as the Atlantic Ocean. Men went around rather than across Africa to learn about the world, and the chroniclers of their journeys dubbed it the "Dark Continent." In photographs taken from very high altitudes, it now often seems to be the most brilliantly lighted continent.

Photographs spanning vast areas can be obtained more quickly and frequently from orbiting spacecraft than mosaics can be produced. They are increasing the geologists' knowledge of the structure of Africa. They can help engineers estimate the volume of flow in its watersheds. They can facilitate surveys of the distinctive resources available to the people of Africa's many ambitious new nations. Such photographs, as you will see in the pages that follow, are also often remarkably beautiful.

Africa's westernmost point, Cap Vert, is in the upper center here. The camera was pointed west, the spacecraft was starting over the Sahara, and the view includes part of Mauritania and all of Senegal and Gambia. Here one can clearly see the transition from tropical rain forests to open savanna and the desert. The Senegal River flows through the prominent valley in the upper half of the photo. The escarpment in the lower right is between the Aouker Basin and the barren land of the Tagent Plateau. Senegal's glittering capital, Dakar, on Cap Vert is an historic port, about halfway between Europe and South America.

GEMINI VI DECEMBER 16, 1965 S65-63251

Here you see the Atlantic coast of Africa north of Dakar and the most western part of Mauritania. There the dunes of Azefal and Akchar extend far inland and cross part of Spanish Sahara. The white spots in the upper left are salt flats called Sebkha de Ndrhamcha. Toward the right is the Baie du Lévrier, flanked by Cap Timiris on the south and Cap Blanc on the north. Port Étienne is on the latter, at the northern end of Mauritania's portion of the coast. Note the prominent fault in the right center of this photo. You will see more of northwestern Africa's geological structure in the next few pictures.

GEMINI VI DECEMBER 16, 1965 S65-63255

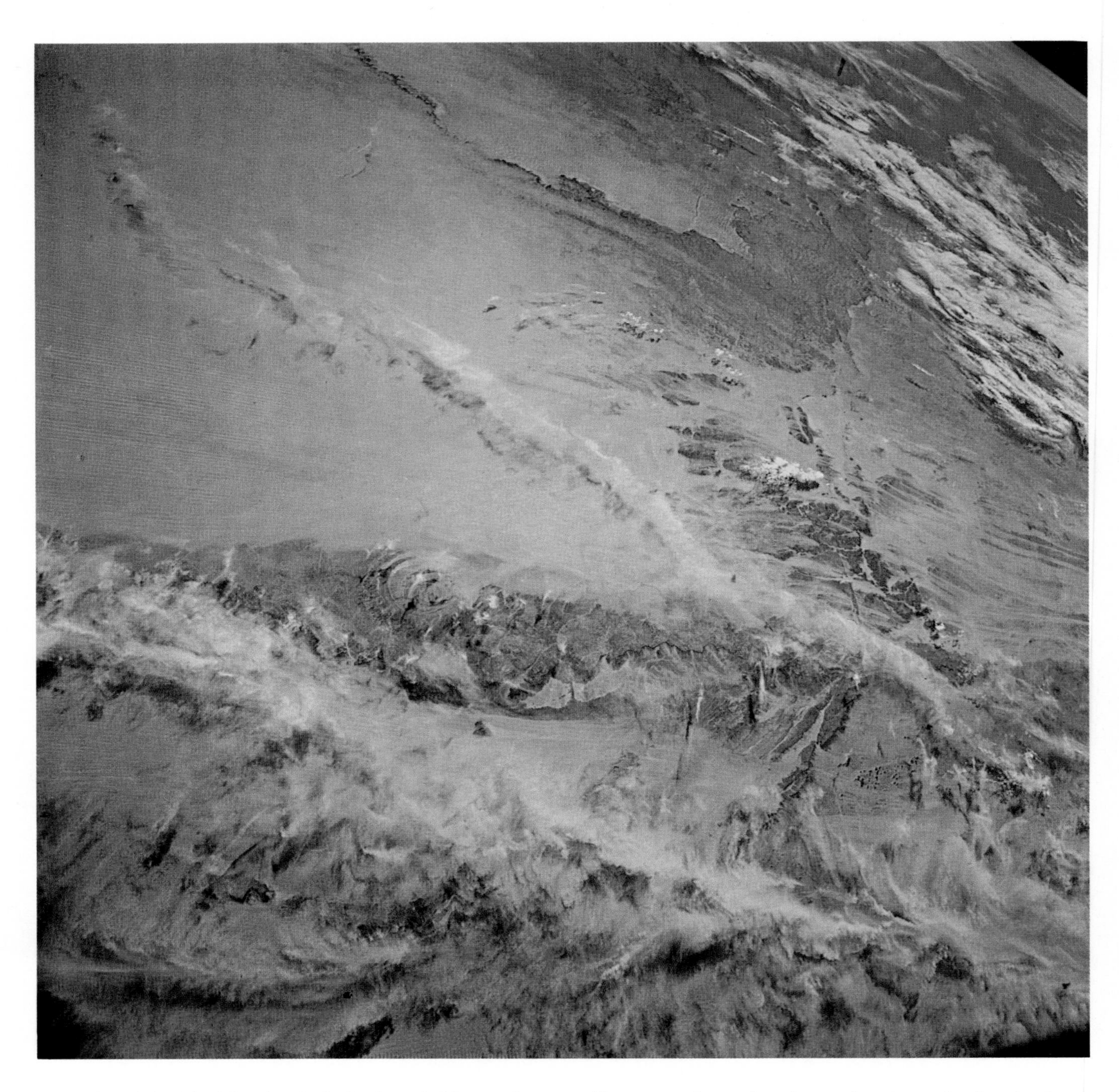

The Dhar Adrar in Mauritania is the broad ridge under cirrus clouds in the lower center of this picture. Near its center are the circular Richat structures that intrigue geologists. One is more than 25 miles wide, the other only 5 miles wide. These structures have been ascribed to meteoritic impact, partly on the basis of a reported discovery of coesite, but volcanic rocks in the large structure throw doubt on this theory of their origin. Igneous instrusions such as laccoliths may have produced them. Under the clouds at the top of the picture, vegetation darkens the view of the terrain of Mauritania and Senegal.

GEMINI XII NOVEMBER 13, 1966 S66-63471

This is one of the best photos yet obtained of the Dorsale Reguibat. Geographers know it as the Yetti and Karet Plain. The south limb of the Tindouf syncline, at lower left, borders it on the north; and the Hank and El Hank bluffs, at upper right, border it on the south. The latter are a limb of the Taoudeni syncline, of Hercynian age (Late Paleozoic), which has been listed among the world's largest. The apparent dip in the horizon at the right was caused by the window of the spacecraft. The long streaks at the left center are the southwestern end of the Erg Iguidi, which extends into Algeria from northern Mauritania.

GEMINI XII NOVEMBER 15, 1966 S66-63083

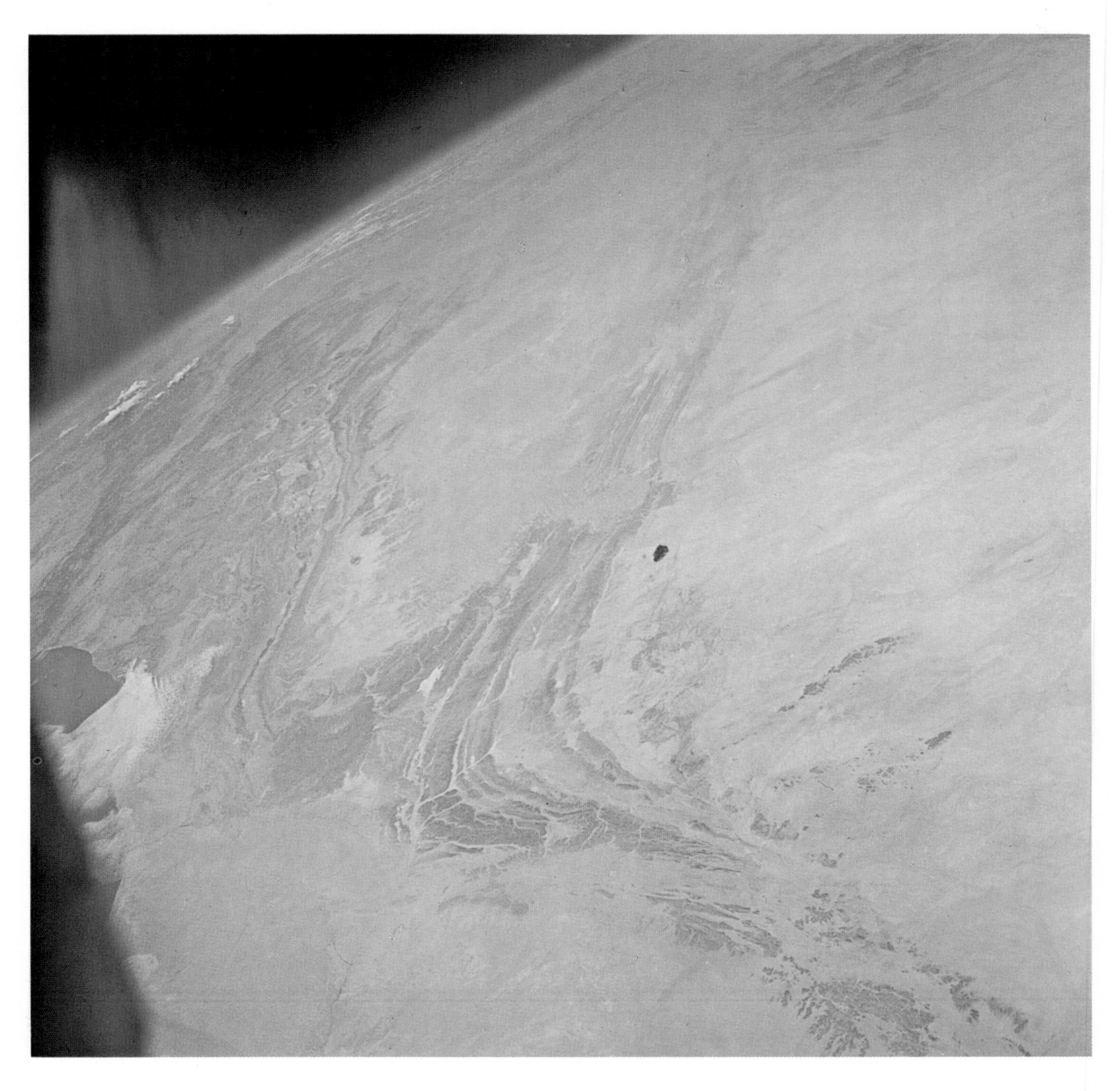

This view to the northeast over parts of Mauritania, Spanish Sahara, and Morocco includes some of the coast south of Agadir at lower left. A few cirriform clouds are along Morocco's southern coast. The view is approximately along the axis of the Tindouf syncline. Outcrops of rocks on each side dip inward, forming limbs of the syncline. The immense uplift of Precambrian rocks at the right is the Dorsale Reguibat. It may have resulted from removal of Paleozoic and younger rocks by erosion, or may have been a positive area that did not receive a great volume of sediments. Faint dark ridges show where it is cut by dikes.

GEMINI X JULY 21, 1966 S66-46063

Morocco's Cap Juby is near the lower center here. Light spots near it are salt flats. Its annual rainfall is less than 10 inches and comes mostly in the winter, but the cool Canaries Current produces summer cloudiness that resembles California's stratus. Note how the cloud-cell size changes over the sea. Streaks of cirrus in the upper left are over the Atlas Mountains. At the right is the Hamada du Dra, a plateau underlain by the Tindouf syncline. Discordant geologic structures on each side of the Atlantic are often cited to support the theory of continental drift, but this photo of Morocco and Spanish Sahara shows concordance to the African shore.

GEMINI IX JUNE 6, 1966 S66-38408

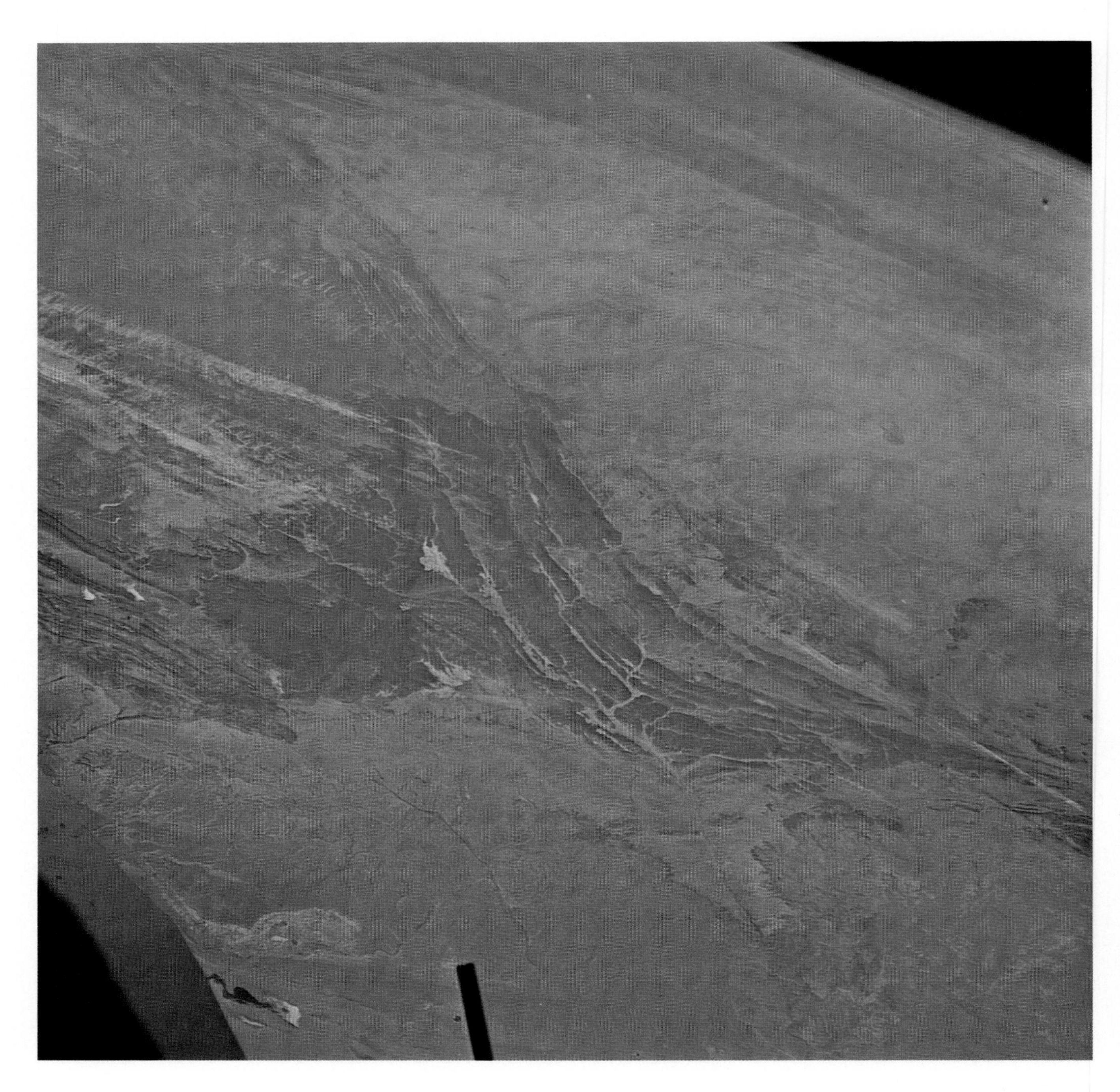

This is part of the area shown in the photo on the preceding page. At the left is the Hamada du Dra's western end; in the center is the south limb of the Tindouf syncline. These are Paleozoic (chiefly Devonian) sedimentary rocks that have been folded, tilted, and eroded. The broad desert at the right is the Dorsale Reguibat. It is a large eroded area of Precambrian rock in Spanish Sahara and Mauritania. The deflection of the Tindouf syncline is apparent here, but the reasons for it are not clear. A major wrench fault may pass through the area in the foreground and be partly responsible for this deflection.

GEMINI IX JUNE 6, 1966 S66-38409

The Atlas Mountains extend southwest of Gibraltar to Cap Rhir, at the top in this photo. The clouds near it are over a major tectonic boundary, the south-Atlas line coincident with the Agadir fault. This fault geologically separates Mediterranean Africa from the bulk of the continent. The Atlas Mountains were formed in the Tertiary age with the Alps, Zagros, Caucasus, Himalayas, and others on the site of the former Tethys geosyncline. The contorted ridges at right are eroded remnants of older (Paleozoic) structures. Air flowing past Cap Rhir from the northeast may have caused the eddy-like pattern offshore.

GEMINI XI SEPTEMBER 14, 1966 S66-54764

The bright lines across this photo are sand dunes of the Erg Iguidi (an erg is a sand-covered part of the desert) in western Algeria. They parallel the dominant northeast trade winds and are formed by reworking of alluvial sands. The bands at the left are the topographic expression of Paleozoic sedimentary rocks in the south limb of Sebkha de Tindouf. The black areas above the dunes are rhyolite intrusions of El Eglab, a Precambrian massif composed chiefly of igneous and metamorphic rocks. Photos taken of this part of Africa during a Mercury flight in 1961 have increased scientific knowledge of the area.

GEMINI VI DECEMBER 16, 1965 S65-63155

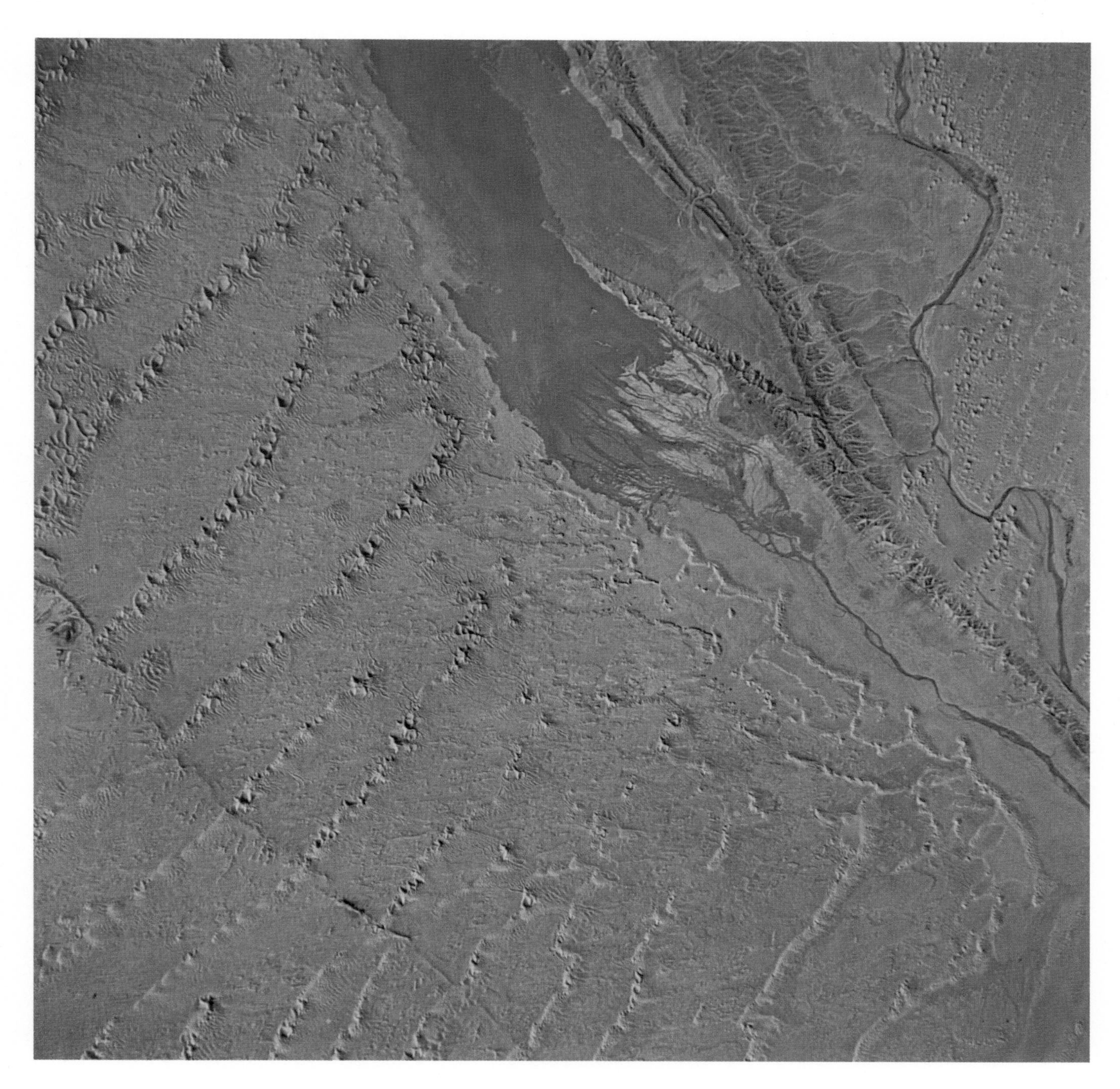

This picture of the Oued Saoura, a wadi in western Algeria, was taken through a longer focal length lens than the photo that precedes it. This area is usually dry and a source of sand for long dunes, but at the top you see an ephemeral lake that was produced by runoff from the Atlas Mountains northwest of this regïon. The desert absorbs water before it can flow much farther south. The bedrock structure resembles that of the Atlas Mountains, but is considerably older and is perpendicular to the northeasterly Atlas trend. It consists of sedimentary rocks with minor volcanics that were folded in the Paleozoic era.

GEMINI VII DECEMBER 5, 1965 S65-63830

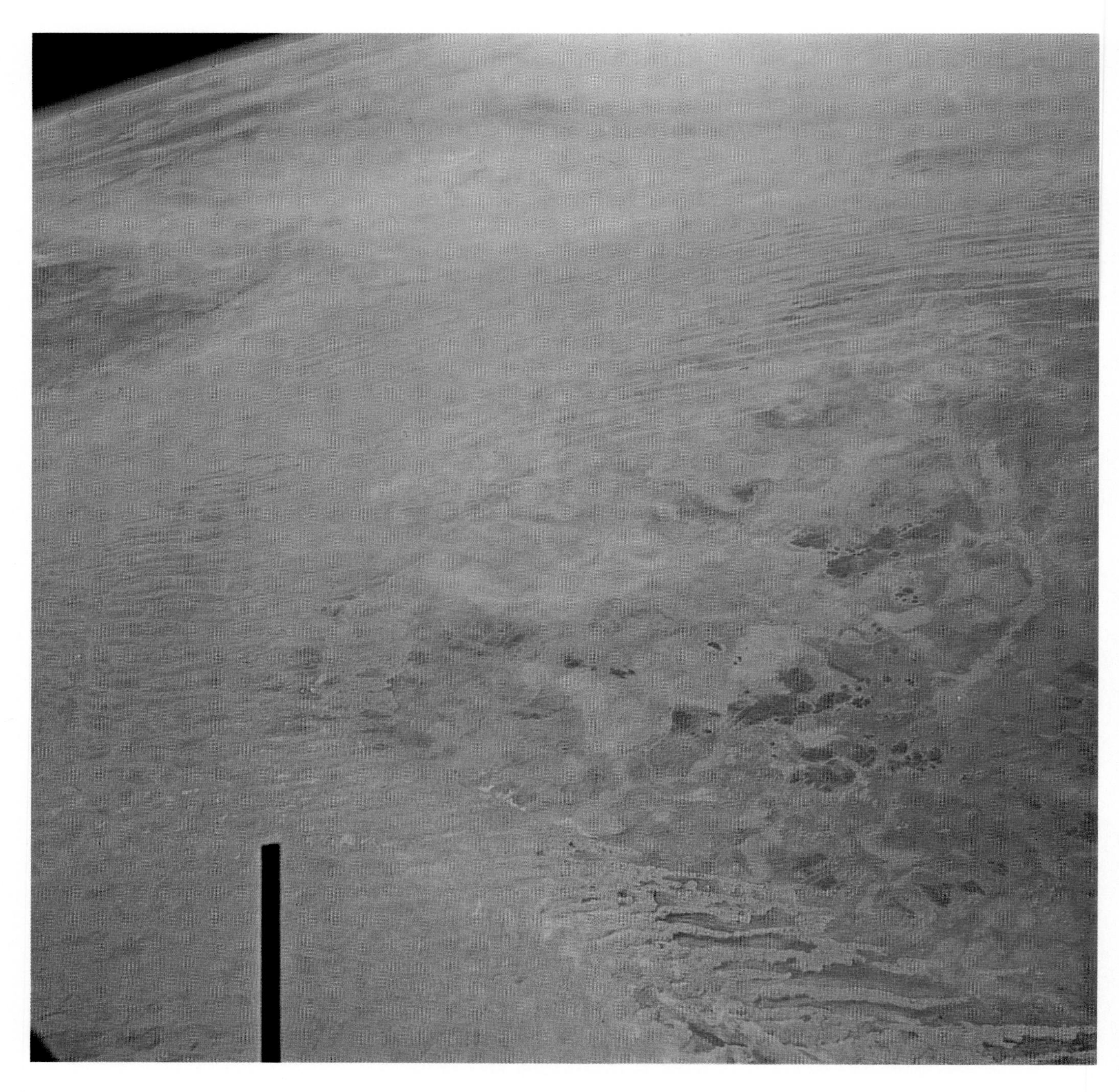

The Erg Iguidi dunes rule the foreground, and a duststorm farther east whitens the top of this photo. The dark area at the right is the Eglab Massif. It is one of northern Africa's three major Precambrian highlands (the others are the Ahaggar and the Tibesti). These massifs were uplifted and erosion removed whatever Paleozoic or Mesozoic rocks had been deposited on them. Volcanic activity often accompanies such uplifts. Interpreters of earlier photos such as this believe that the dark blotches at the lower right may be rhyolite intrusions, with lighter toned microgranite aureoles.

GEMINI IX JUNE 6, 1966 S66-38413

Centered here you see a small dune field resembling a cluster of tents. This photo was taken over central Algeria and shows the southern edge of the Plateau du Tademaït, which extends more than 600 miles from the Dhar Adrar to the Libyan border. Its easternmost part is called the Hamada de Tinrhert. The plateau is underlain by Cretaceous limestone. This dark rock has been moderately deformed by basin-and-swell movement accompanied by faulting. The long, straight watercourses that locally cut the plateau probably follow faults. Wind erosion of sedimentary strata produced the closed basins in the left foreground.

GEMINI VII DECEMBER 7, 1965 S65-63784

Earth presented this colorful view when the astronaut-photographer looked down on the central Tassili-n-Ajjer, at the junction of Algeria, Niger, and Libya. The broad, brushlike streaks across the photo appear to be incipient wind-erosion features, and the prominent curving cuesta at the top is the western border of the Marzuq Sand Sea. Overlapping pictures of this area, taken from spacecraft, are increasing knowledge of wind-erosion phenomena. The physiography of this area reflects the prevailing basin-and-swell geologic structure of this part of northwest Africa.

GEMINI XI SEPTEMBER 14, 1966 S66-54773

This photo includes both the area shown on the facing page and the Mediterranean's southern shore. The Gulf of Sirte is under the cumuliform clouds in the upper left, Egypt is on the far horizon, and the Tassili-n-Ajjer in Algeria is in the foreground. The yellowish circular area in the center is the Marzuq Sand Sea. The dark spot between it and the gulf is Al Harūj al Aswad, a 200- by 100-mile Quaternary volcanic field. Few geologists outside of Africa are familiar with this impressive field because such a thinly populated area has long been difficult to visit. This picture clearly shows the basin-and-swell tectonic structure.

GEMINI XI SEPTEMBER 14, 1966 S66-54525

This view is along the southeastern end of the Tassili-n-Ajjer in eastern Algeria. The Marzuq Sand Sea of Libya is in the upper left corner. The black formless feature in the lower center is the Telut, a large Quaternary basalt field. Its linear features extend toward the upper right and are probably the reflection of structure in the metamorphic rocks of the Ahaggar Massif. The ridges cutting across this structure nearly at right angles are products of erosion and indicate the direction of the prevailing winds. The rocks at the lower right constitute the edge of the Ahaggar Massif and probably are Precambrian.

GEMINI IX JUNE 6, 1966 S66-38418

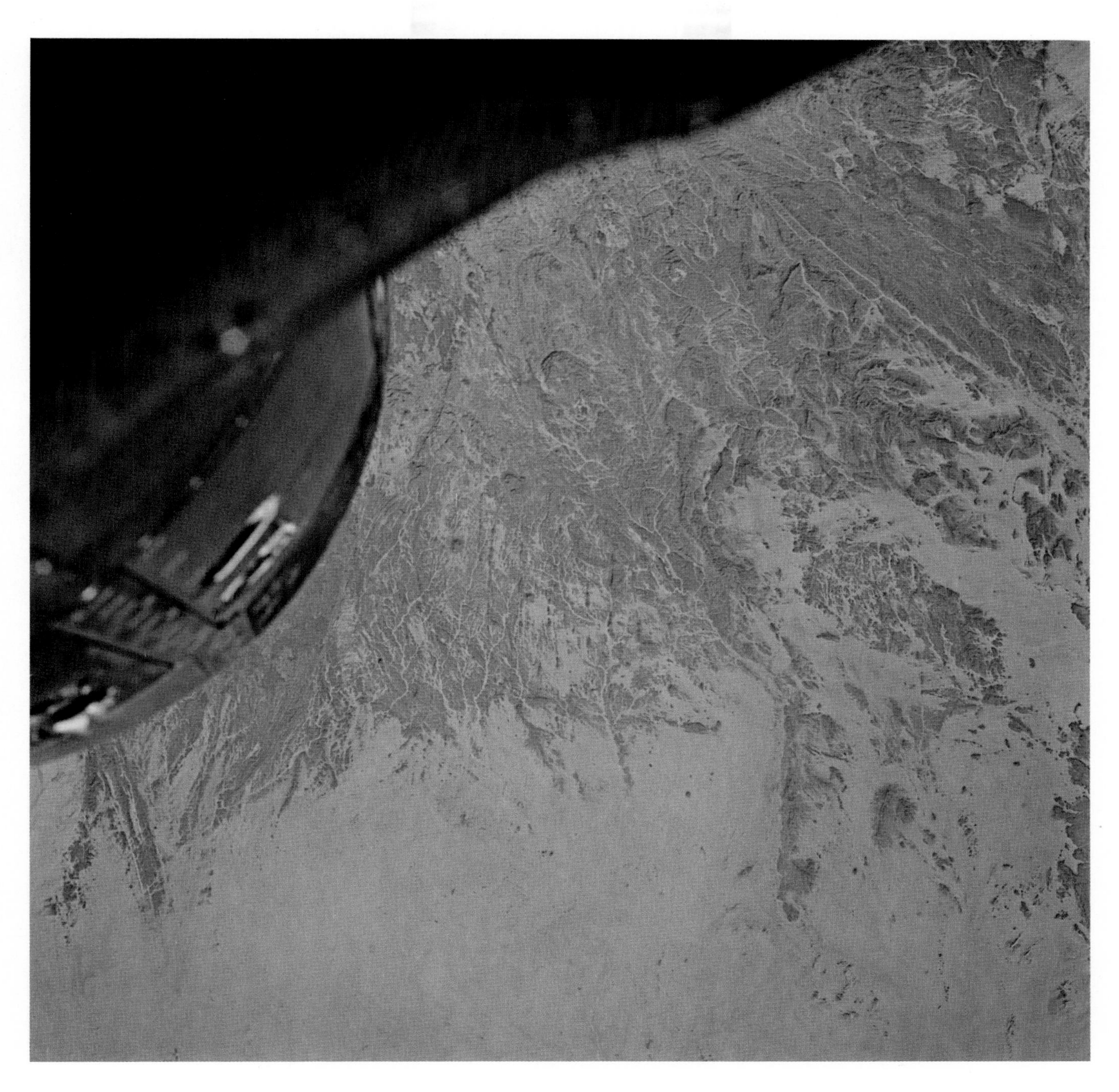

This photo was taken as the spacecraft approached the southern slope of the Ahaggar Massif in southern Algeria. The Ahaggar is a rugged mass of Archean and Paleozoic rock that rises high above the Sahara. One of its peaks is partly visible in the upper right corner of the picture. A small outpost called Tamanrasset is just below the spacecraft. The light area in the foreground is part of the sandy wasteland known as the Tanezrouft, or "Land of Thirst," south and west of the mountain massif.

GEMINI VI DECEMBER 16, 1965 S65-63157

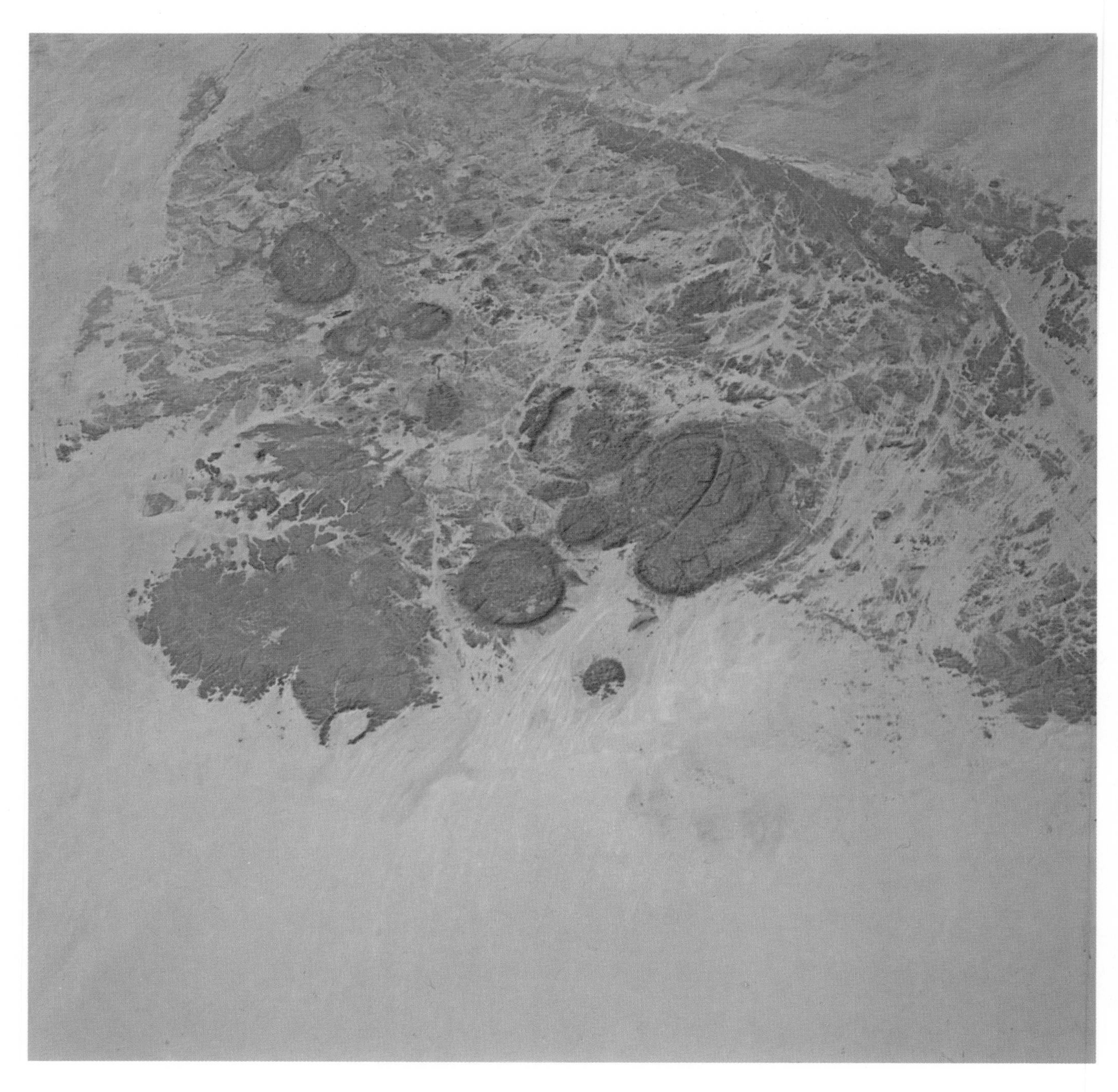

The Aïr mountain range in the north-central part of Niger, Africa, is an outlier of the Ahaggar, and is underlain by Precambrian igneous and metamorphic rocks. The big, dark, roughly circular areas so prominent in this picture of the range are plateaus of resistant masses of granite, intruded as ring complexes. The curved, fracturelike feature cutting the plateau at the right is shown on an unpublished map by R. Black and others as a gabbroic ring dike. A crater in the lower left is probably a volcanic feature associated with Quaternary massifs. Niger is in a part of the Sahara where rain may evaporate before reaching the surface.

GEMINI VI DECEMBER 16, 1965 S65-63158

Mali and Niger, south of Algeria, have no seacoast. The Niger River flows through them on its way to the Gulf of Guinea, and this photo shows it in central Mali. The long dart above and to the right of the striated area is Lac Faguibine. The city of Timbuktu, which Christians formerly were forbidden to enter, is between the lake and the river. The dark linear pattern south of the river is the result of flooding of stabilized sand dunes. El Djouf Desert at the upper right is still one of the least known parts of the Sahara. A cuesta separates this sandy desert from the Aouker region to the west.

GEMINI VI DECEMBER 16, 1965 S65-63247

Parts of several African countries are in the foreground, and Mali and northwest Niger are in the background of this view. The area shown includes northwest Nigeria, southwest Niger, northern Dahomey, eastern Upper Volta, and northern Togo. This part of the world was not explored in detail by Europeans until many years after America was discovered. The remarkably straight lines of cirrus-cloud tufts are oriented east-west over Nigeria, although their filamentlike structures are nearly perpendicular to this direction. The filaments in the lower left corner of the picture extend for distances up to 30 or 40 miles.

GEMINI VI DECEMBER 16, 1965 S65-63240

Cumulonimbi of various sizes dominate the center of this view of the northern part of the Central African Republic and the southern part of Chad. Both nations are landlocked, and the rainfall in this region is produced mainly by thunderstorms. Several smoke plumes emanate from the tropical savannatype forest in the lower right quadrant of the picture. To the north the desert land gives a reddish hue to the area between the thunderstorms and the horizon. The blue band along the horizon is the lower, more dense region of the atmosphere called the troposphere.

GEMINI IX JUNE 6, 1966 S66-38445

This southwesterly view over Lake Chad shows the sands of the Sahara encroaching on it. Chad is in the middle of Africa between the desert and the Sudan grassland. The lake is much smaller now than when Europeans first saw it. Progressive desiccation has left only a remnant of what was an extensive lake system in recent geologic times. Lac Fitri, in the upper left, is only about 20 feet higher than Chad. The Chari River, at the upper right, drains a large basin ringed by the Mbang, Chaine des Mongos, and Jabal Marrah Mountains. Isolated, water-filled depressions can be seen between many of the sand dunes.

GEMINI VII DECEMBER 17, 1966 S65-63969

This northwesterly view includes most of Lake Chad. Four countries—Niger, Nigeria, Cameroon, and Chad—share its shores. In early June when this photo was taken, the lake was shrinking as the flood waters from December and January rains evaporated. The submerged dunes show how it becomes progressively smaller as the desert robs it of water. Its principal affluent, the Chari River system, flows northward to enter the lake below the spacecraft. The only other affluent of significant size is the Yobe River, visible here at the left, which drains a small basin in Nigeria. Few roads lead one to its shores.

GEMINI IX JUNE 6, 1966 S66-38444

This and the next photo are overlapping views of the mountains in western Sudan. Here one sees the northern end of the Jabal Marrah range on the Darfur plateau. These volcanic mountains form the divide between the area around Lake Chad and the Nile Basin. In the lower left here, Jebel Gurgei rises 7864 feet. The town of Kutum is on a wadi near it and the provincial capital, El Fasher, is 50 miles southeast of Kutum. Sudan is Africa's largest country, and its boundaries touch Libya, Chad, Central African Republic, the Democratic Republic of the Congo, Uganda, Kenya, Ethiopia, and the United Arab Republic.

GEMINI VI DECEMBER 16, 1965 S65-63159

This second view of western Sudan shows the southern end of the mountains there. The volcanic crater of Jebel Marra, in the center of this picture, is at an elevation of more than 10 000 feet and contains two lakes, known as the Deriba Lakes. The town of Nyala is located along the prominent stream that can be seen flowing west at the left side of the picture. The clouds in the lower right are high cirrus. These mountains stand between the area depicted in this section of the book and the photographs of the countries around the Nile that are presented in the next section.

GEMINI VI DECEMBER 16, 1965 S65-63160

The contrast between western Egypt and the Nile Valley is sharp in this photo. Libya is in the foreground, and the Red Sea is above the river near the horizon. The large elliptical feature in the upper center is the Gilf Kibir Plateau. Gently dipping sandstones underlie it and there is a **V**-shaped escarpment to the left. The larger of two dark circles below the Gilf Kibir is the Jebel Uwaynāt, which is bisected by the border between Libya and Egypt. These jebels were formed by erosion and are said to consist of Precambrian rocks with aegerine syenites and granites dominant. The desert here gets less than 2 inches of rain annually.

GEMINI XI SEPTEMBER 14, 1966 S66-54529

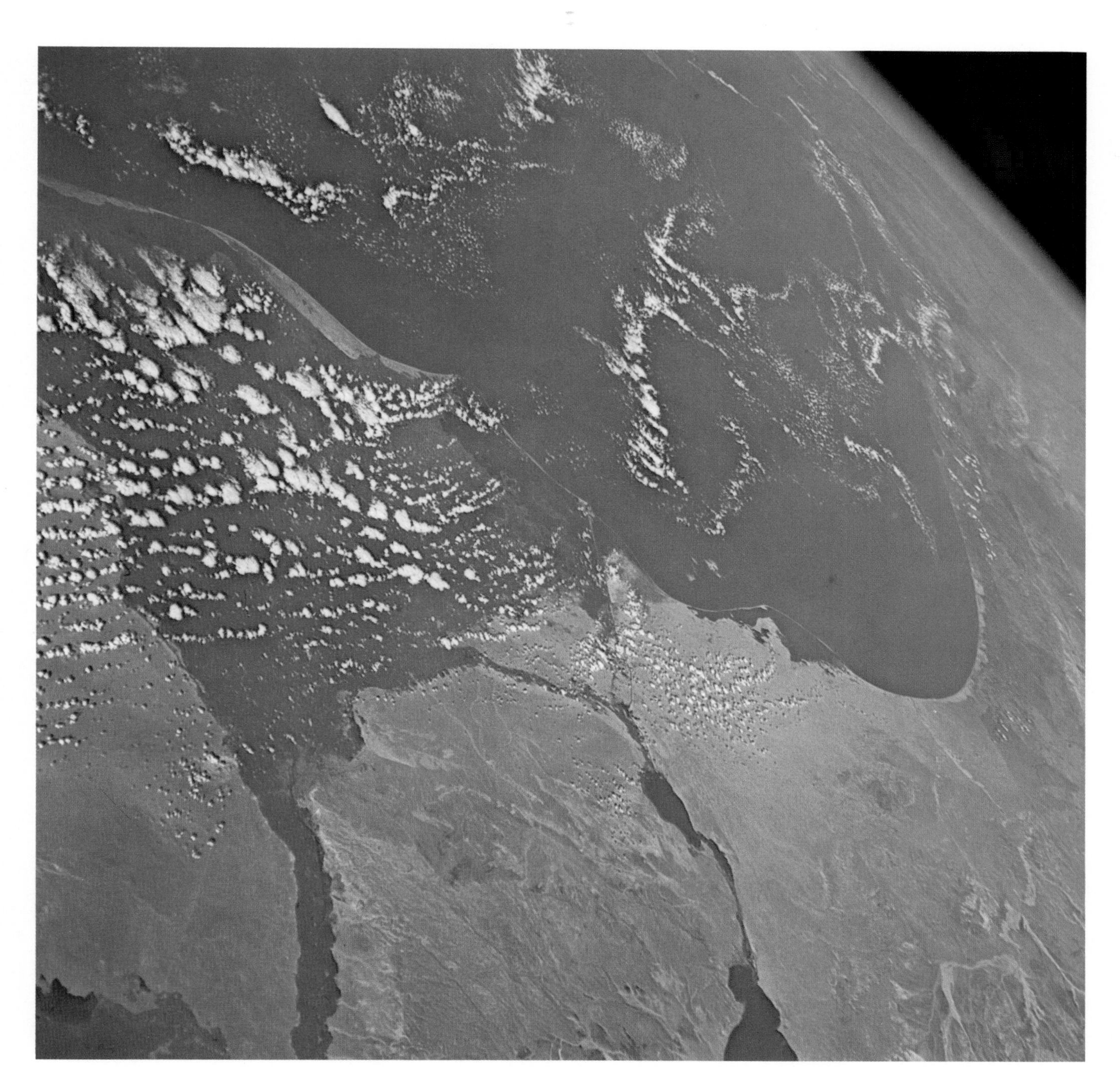

This is the eastern end of the Mediterranean. The Nile River and its delta dominate the left half of the view; the right half includes Israel, Lebanon, and parts of Cyprus, Jordan, the Syrian Arab Republic, Iraq, and Turkey. The Suez Canal is in the lower center, and the Gulf of Suez in the foreground. The narrow body of water on the right edge is the Dead Sea. The smaller waterbody in the fault extending northward from the Dead Sea is the Sea of Galilee. A lake, the Birkat Qarun, is in the dark lower left corner of the picture. A light northerly wind had alined cumuliform clouds over Egypt in parallel rows when this picture was taken.

GEMINI VII DECEMBER 8, 1965 S65-63849

"This picture, accentuating the blue of the Red Sea separating Egypt from Sinai and Saudi Arabia, was taken while inverted, pointing south and moving sidewise in orbit," Astronaut Edwin E. Aldrin, Jr., reported. "The radar transponder pointing toward the Nile River and the wire loop of the tether are on the Agena which was docked to Gemini XII at this time." The Gulf of Suez at the bottom of the photo extends northward from the Red Sea, and the Gulf of Aqaba to the left edge. A few cirrus clouds lay east of the Nile, and cumuliform clouds can be seen over the Red Sea and Saudi Arabia at the upper left.

GEMINI XII NOVEMBER 13, 1966 S66-63481

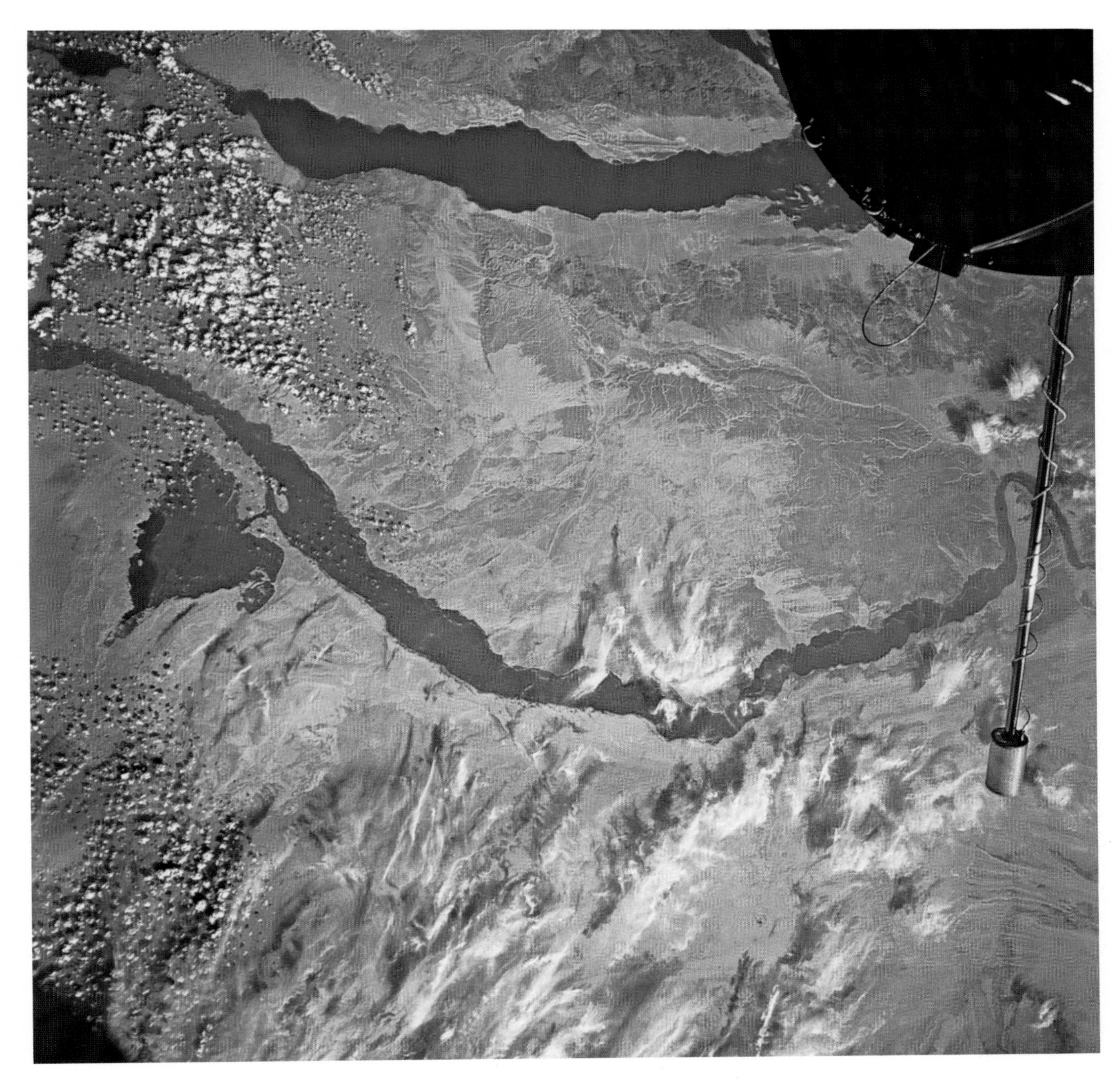

North is at the left in this view of Egypt's Nile Valley. The dark triangle at the left is El Faiyum, a natural depression 148 feet below sea level. It contains the lake, Birkat Qarun, and a large irrigated area. Amenenhet I of the XII Dynasty controlled the level in the lake to attain some control of Nile floods. The pronounced bend in the river under the antenna has been ascribed to the same major fault system that probably influenced the shape of the Gulf of Suez and the northern Red Sea. The cirrus clouds in the foreground are embedded in southwest winds from Libya and the cumulus clouds at the left are in winds sweeping in from the north.

GEMINI XII NOVEMBER 13, 1966 S66-63477

Only a few cumuliform clouds covered the northern end of the Red Sea between Egypt and Saudi Arabia the morning this photo was taken. The Nile can be seen in the lower left. The spacecraft transponder points to the tip of the Sinai Peninsula, the Gulf of Aqaba, and the Dead Sea in the upper left corner. The dark Precambrian rocks on the far shore of the sea in this view are part of the Arabian-Nubian Massif. An Nafud, a large sand desert, is in the upper right. This photo shows distinct dune trends that are alined in the dominant direction of the wind.

GEMINI XI SEPTEMBER 14, 1966 S66-54664

At most points the Red Sea is less than 200 miles wide. This is a closer view of part of the Arabian shore seen on the preceding page. This photo shows the coast of Saudi Arabia between Dubā and Ras Bariji. The dark massif towering above the blue water is a complex of Precambrian igneous and metamorphic rocks that is parted by graben faulting below the Red Sea. The black, crablike feature at the far right is a Tertiary-Quaternary lava flow. The lightly colored sediments are stream deposits of alluvium and related surficial deposits of Quaternary age. The shadows of the clouds indicate that they were at a great height.

GEMINI XI SEPTEMBER 14, 1966 S66-54895

This is a photo of the Red Sea taken from east of it. Yemen and Saudi Arabia are in the foreground; Ethiopia, Sudan, and the United Arab Republic are on the far shore. Oceanographers have found gold, silver, zinc, and copper associated with sediments in a 7000-foot-deep part of the Red Sea northwest of Jiddah, a city near the shore in the right center. In the depths the water is 56° C and has 10 times normal salinity. Submarine eruptions and ancient salt beds probably explain these conditions. Jiddah had a west wind of 15 knots, and Port Sudan, across the sea, a 10-knot southeast wind when this photo was taken.

GEMINI VII DECEMBER 13, 1965 S65-64006

Ethiopia is in the upper left and the Arabian Peninsula in the foreground of this photo taken east of the Red Sea. The dark area in Ethiopia is the Danakil Depression, a below-sea-level part of the Great Rift Valley. Islands and reefs are visible off R'as Isa, the cape on the near shore. Dark areas in the lower left are volcanic rock. The prominent fault in the lower right is in Yemen. It brings granitic rocks into contact with Jurassic sediments of the Amran Series in the light central part of the photo's lower half. There are batholiths of Mesozoic or Cenozoic age in the Amran Series which darken parts of the picture.

GEMINI VII DECEMBER 13, 1965 S65-64007

For this view of the Nubian Desert east of the Nile, the camera was pointed east from over southern Egypt and Sudan. The Red Sea waters at the top are in the northern part of the Great Rift Valley of Africa, which has been shown to be a graben or downfaulted block. The dark areas bordering it are Precambrian igneous and metamorphic rocks. The dark linear depression at the right is north of Kassala, Sudan, and is undoubtedly a subsidiary structure related to the main Rift Valley faulting. Thin cirrus filaments hide the nearby desert and several cumulonimbi rise amid the cumulus clouds at the right.

GEMINI XI SEPTEMBER 14, 1966 S66-54779

Before flowing north into Egypt, the Nile curves southward in northern Sudan. To the right of the antenna rod, where the river is relatively straight and there are no clouds, is its third cataract. Most of the area in the foreground is underlain by Nubian sandstone. Circular features here are similar to those of the Jebel Uwaynāt. Vegetation increases from left to right as the color of the landscape darkens. To the east the main structural features of the Nubian Ramp, the Precambrian highlands bordering the Red Sea, are visible. Some cumuliform and cirriform clouds are shown drifting over the desert on both sides of the Red Sea.

GEMINI XI SEPTEMBER 14, 1966 S66-54531

This and the next three pictures were taken only minutes apart from altitudes of more than 300 miles. Lake Tana in Ethiopia is in the lower right. Beyond is nearly the whole southern end of the Arabian Peninsula. The bare orange expanse there is the "Empty Quarter" of Saudi Arabia and Yemen. Showers apparently were falling on the lava-covered Abyssinian plateau from the clouds in the foreground. This plateau's average elevation is more than 6000 feet. Dark areas below the cumulus clouds along the Red Sea's far shore are part of the Arabian shield, which the Red Sea rift separates from the African shield.

GEMINI XI SEPTEMBER 14, 1966 S66-54533

The Red Sea is at the left. From it the Gulf of Aden extends to the Indian Ocean on the horizon. Between the spacecraft and the V-shaped Tadjoura Gulf in the lower center of this photo is Lake Abbe. The boundary between Ethiopia and the Somali Republic crosses that lake. Yemen occupies the left part of the Arabian Peninsula shown here, and Aden is along the shore to the east. Major structural lineaments of the Arabian shield, and the dendritic wadi system of the Hadramawt Plateau, can be observed in this and the next picture. The spacecraft was ascending when this and the next photo were taken from an altitude of more than 350 miles.

GEMINI XI SEPTEMBER 14, 1966 S66-54536

The resolution of this photo, showing some of the same area as the preceding two, is greater because the view is more nearly vertical. In the upper center the gently dipping Paleozoic and Mesozoic sediments that form the arcuate central interior homocline of the Arabian Peninsula can be seen emerging from below Ar Rab al Khālī. In September the Red Sea's warm waters pour into the Gulf of Aden over the sill of the strait you see beneath the spacecraft's transponder. A portion of that flow, about 150 miles long and 75 miles wide, can be detected by a difference in the water's hues, caused by its relative roughness.

GEMINI XI SEPTEMBER 14, 1966 S66-54537

The Red Sea and the Gulf of Aden are in a geologically important area. The Gemini photos show several major structural lineaments which traverse Precambrian and Cretaceous rocks in this area. The view includes the bifurcation of the Great African Rift valley—to the east under the Gulf of Aden and to the southwest under Africa to form the Abyssinian rift. The Afar depression in Africa, in the foreground, consists largely of volcanic rocks. It appeared to be raining on Ethiopia's highlands when this series of pictures was taken; air temperatures reached 100° F along the Red Sea coast 3 hours later.

GEMINI XI SEPTEMBER 14, 1966 S66-54783

Now our view is to the east across the dry lands of the horn of Africa toward the Gulf of Aden. The Indian Ocean shore between Eil and Garad is visible in the upper left. The cumulus-cloud streets shown here are parallel to the southwest wind and the clear swath is over the valley of the Nogal River which flows across the Somali Republic. A narrow Precambrian ridge extends eastward from the bottom of the photo and roughly parallels the coast of the Gulf of Aden in the foreground. The dark areas on the right represent Mesozoic deposits.

GEMINI IX JUNE 6, 1966 S66-38424

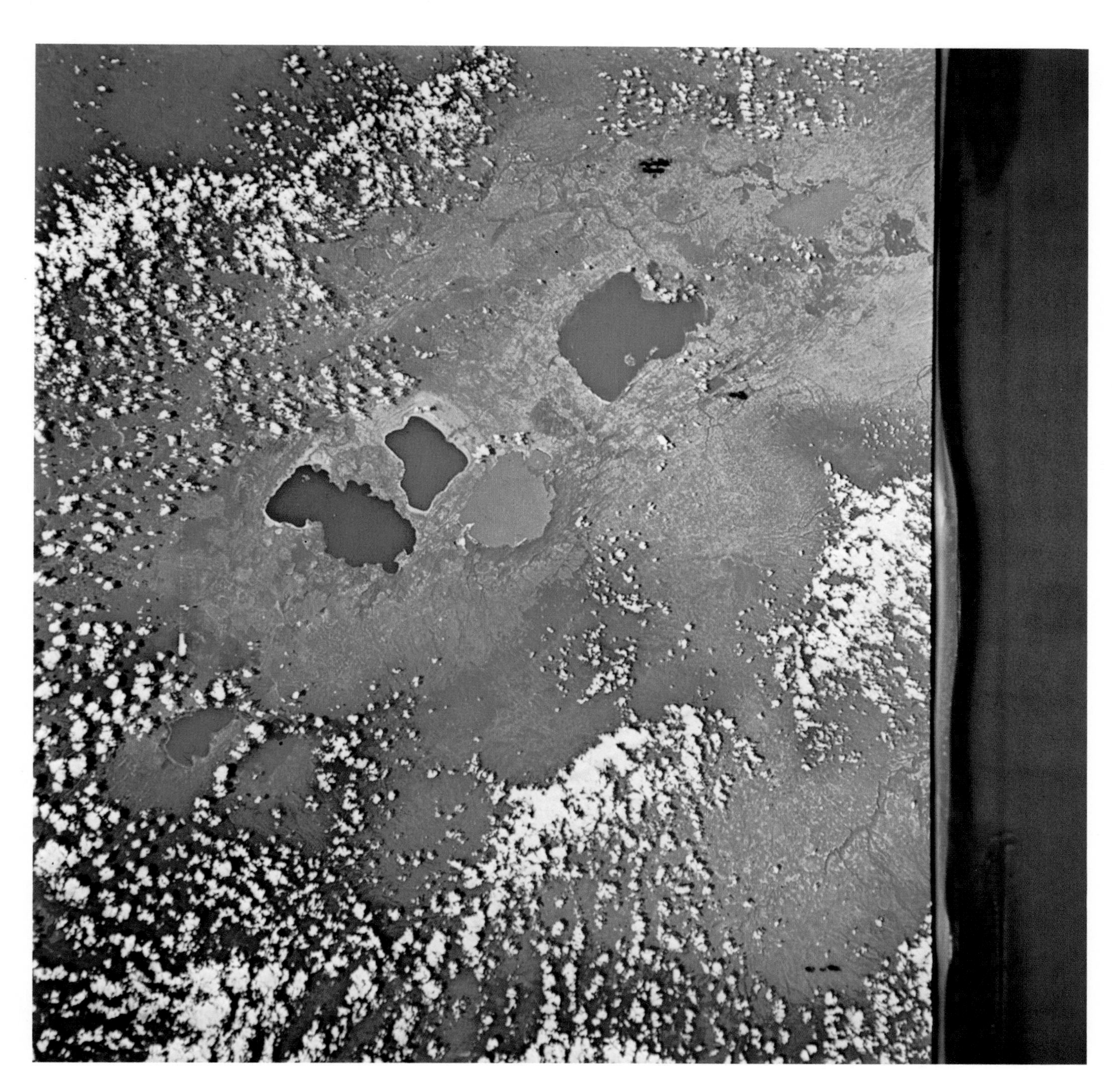

Ethiopia is dotted by large lakes south of Addis Ababa. They are in the northern part of the Great African Rift valleys that extend from Syria to South Africa, and are thought to be graben; i.e., large blocks of the crust that have been downdropped along fractures. The parallel lines northeast of Zeway, the northernmost dark lake here, are indications of these fractures. The three center lakes are Shala (left), Hora Abyata (middle), and Langana (right). Cumulus clouds partially hide Awusa lake at the lower left. The sharp brown marks at the upper right and a curlicue on Langana's shore are defects in the photographic film.

GEMINI VI DECEMBER 16, 1965 S65-63162

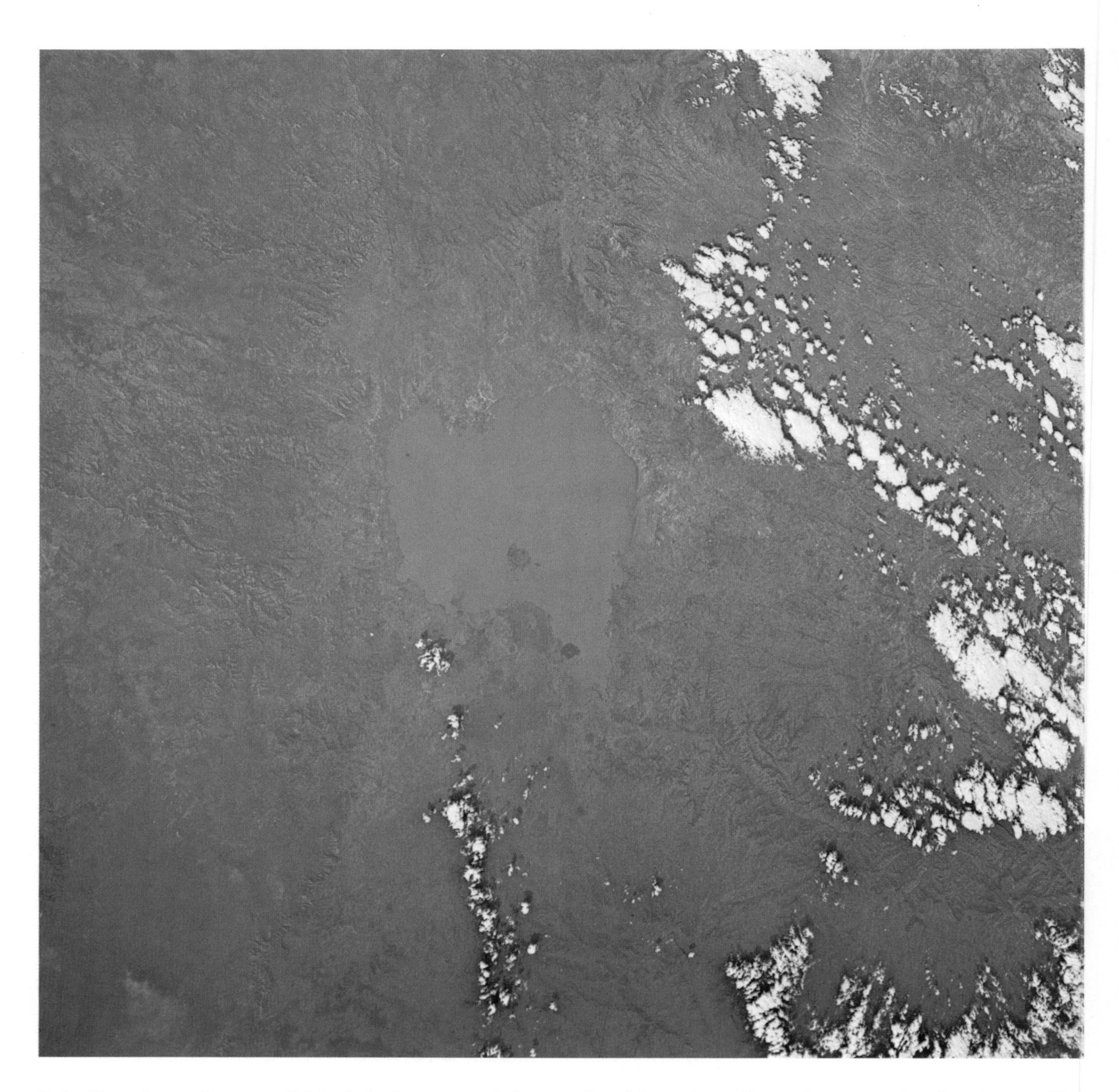

Lake Tana in northwestern Ethiopia is the source of the Blue Nile. It is on a plateau more than 6000 feet above sea level, and its water flows to the southeast (lower right) before curving west to irrigate farms in Sudan and Egypt. Monasteries on the islands in Lake Tana date back to the 14th century. Extensive lava flows of late Mesozoic or Cenozoic age overlay the plateau. The lineament left and above the lake may be the expression of a fault, suggesting that the lake is of tectonic origin. Mountains rise nearly 13 000 feet in the region near the pancake-shaped cumulus clouds to the right of the lake.

GEMINI VII DECEMBER 13, 1965 S65-64014

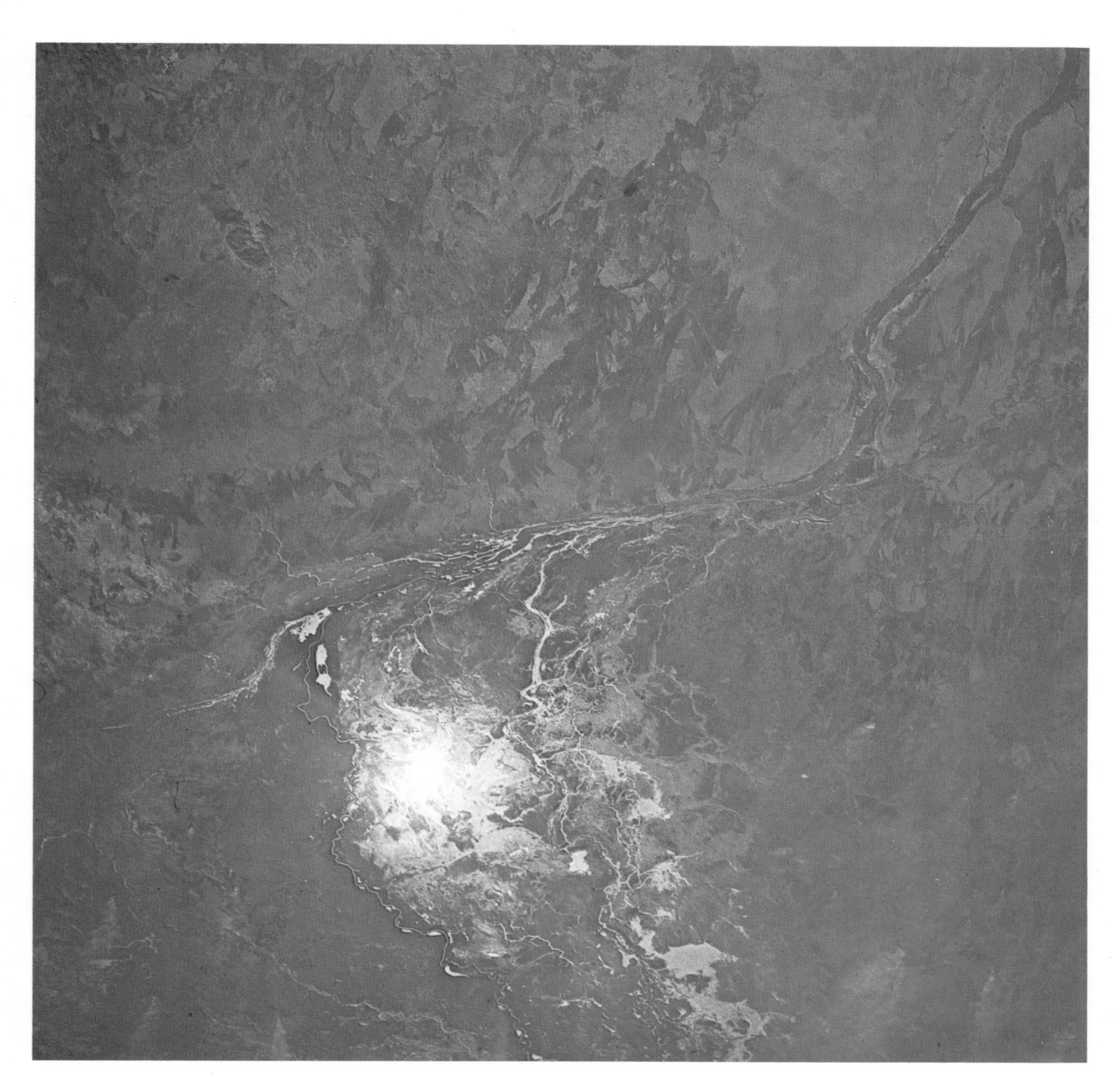

This photograph shows the Sun brilliantly reflected in the immense swamp called As Sudd through which the White Nile flows in Sudan. During Mid-Tertiary time the Sudd region was an enclosed drainage basin. Then tilting of the east African plateau during Pleistocene time changed the direction of drainage of Lake Victoria and additional waters were supplied to the lake here. This lake soon overflowed, draining off most of the water and leaving the swamp which exists today. Smoke from clearing operations on farms is visible at the bottom of the picture.

GEMINI VI DECEMBER 16, 1965 S65-63161

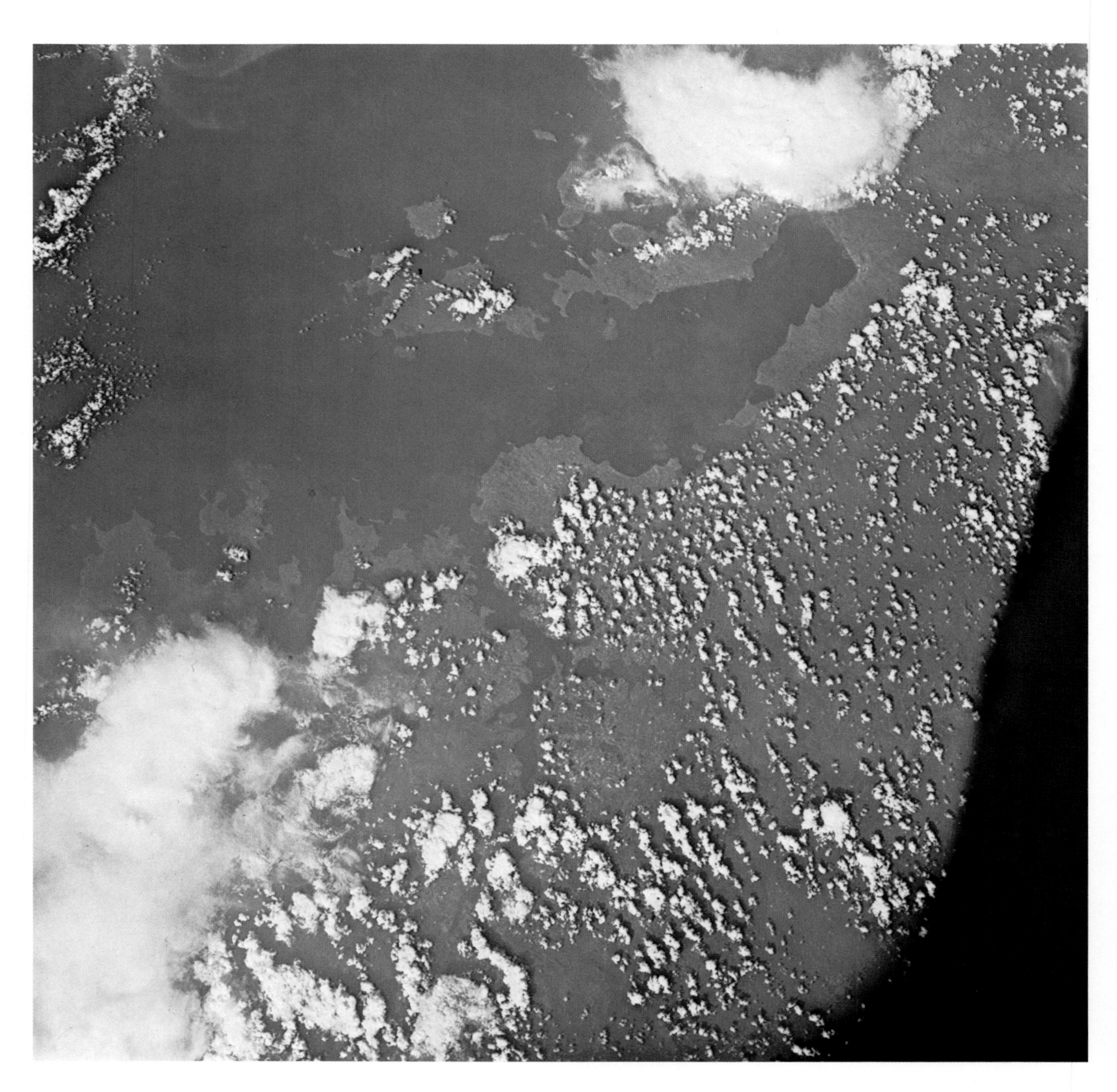

Lake Victoria extends southward from the Equator. This is its southern shore in Tanzania, where it has many deep inlets and steep bluffs. The rows of cumulus clouds running northward direct your eye to Speke Gulf in the upper center of the picture. The large island at its entrance, called Ukerewe, rises 650 feet above the lake water and is densely populated. The town of Mwanza is at the head of the inlet below the gulf. There were thunderstorms northeast of Speke Gulf when the spacecraft passed over this tropical region in December on its way to the Indian Ocean shore of the continent.

GEMINI VI DECEMBER 16, 1965 S65-63232

Thunderstorms had generated a canopy of cirrus, penetrated by turrets from upward currents of air, when the astronauts took this picture of Africa's east coast south of the Equator. The spacecraft was over the northern end of the Mozambique Channel. The view extends from south of Vila do Ibo, Mozambique, to north of Mtwara, Tanzania. The boundary between the two countries is the Ruvuma River, which can be seen entering the Indian Ocean to the right of the center of this picture. High rocky headlands and steep cliffs on this part of the coast consist of marine sediments, and tiny coral islands stud the sea near the shore.

GEMINI VI DECEMBER 16, 1965 S65-63228

For this photo of eastern Africa, the camera was pointed west from off its shores. Kenya's coastal lowlands are in the foreground, and Tanzania's famous safari lands are near the horizon. Mount Kilimanjaro is the dark object left of center, flanked by Lake Eyasi on the left and Lake Natron on the right. The clouds suggest how the mountains disturb air flowing from the southeast. Several isolated cloud patches to the right lay near high peaks; the one farthest right is around 17 050-foot Mount Kenya. Although these volcanic mountains are close to the Equator, ice fields and glaciers are found on their summits.

GEMINI IX JUNE 6, 1966 S66-38453

This view is similar to the preceding one, but the coastal strip shown is farther north and is part of the Somali Republic. The Equator crosses this area from the upper left to the lower right. Here the sea-surface temperature in the Somali Current is about 79° F in June, and you see fewer clouds over the water than over the land. The convective cloudiness covers the coastal lowlands and extends into northeastern Kenya, but over the highlands at the upper left—the region between the Indian Ocean and Lake Victoria—the sky is mostly quite clear.

GEMINI IX JUNE 6, 1966 S66-38454

Several cloud decks are discernible in this picture of Africa's Indian Ocean coastline. East-west banding has occurred in the highest deck of cirrostratus, while cumulus-cloud streets have been embedded in a southwesterly airflow parallel to the coast at a low level. The camera was pointed northwest and a strip of the coast of the Somali Republic near Eil is visible in the clear zone at the right. Beyond the cloud field, the mainland has a reddish hue because the landscape is arid here. Eil is on the Baia del Negro at the mouth of the Nogal River, which flows eastward from higher areas inland.

GEMINI X JULY 21, 1966 S66-45878

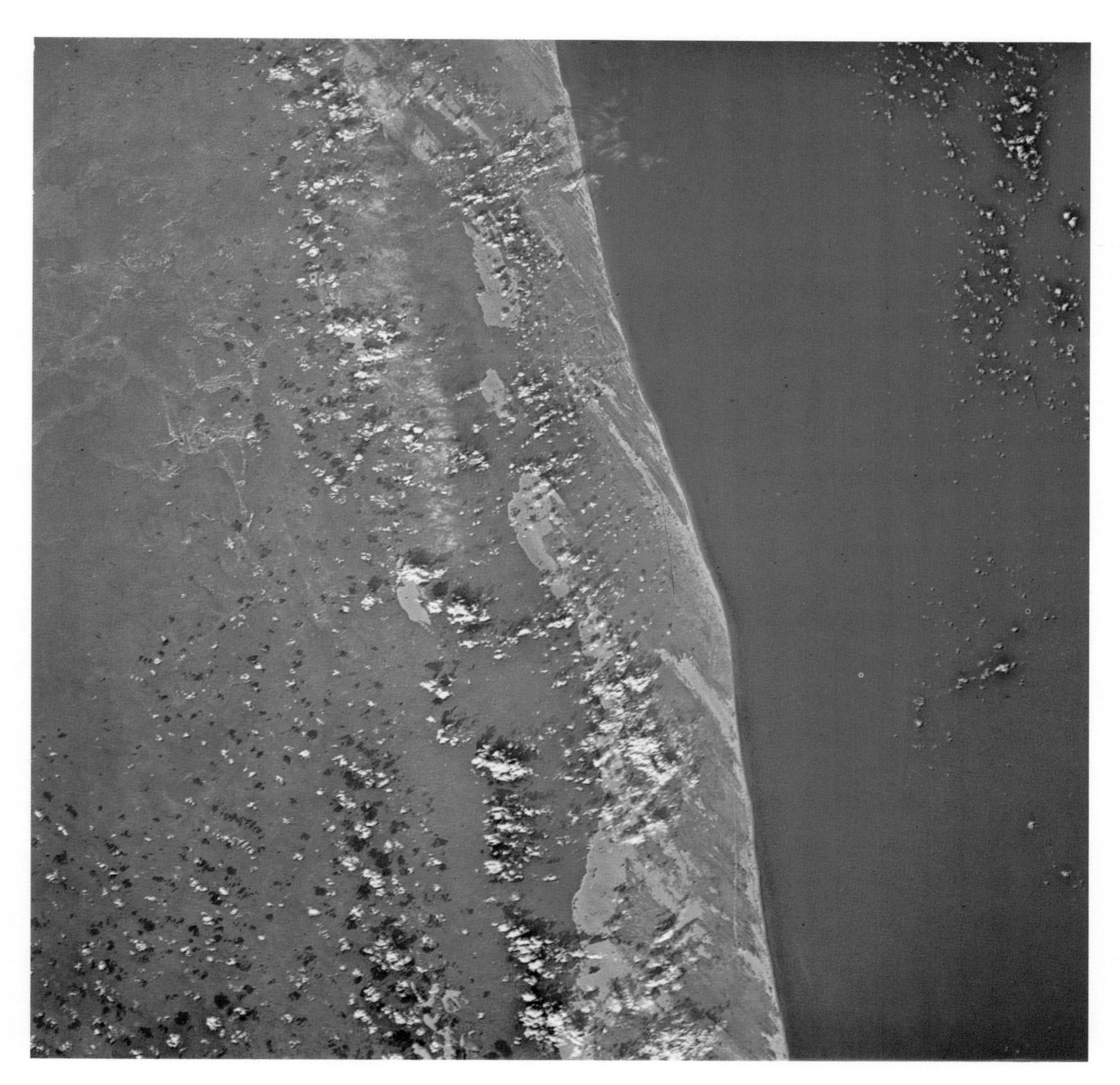

South of Ras Hafun and just north of the city of Mogadishu, the capital of the Somali Republic, this vivid image of the Indian Ocean shore of Africa was recorded by one of the astronauts. The sand dunes extend inland and show a typical increase in red coloration as the distance from the shore becomes greater. The orientation of the dunes follows the dominant winds along this portion of the continental shelf along the shore. This strip of the coast is only a few degrees north of the Equator.

GEMINI VII DECEMBER 13, 1965 S65-64021

Near Africa's eastern tip, the Indian Ocean nearly surrounds Ras Hafun, as you see in the center of this photo of the coast of the Somali Republic. A narrow strip of land connects it to the continent. Tidal action on river affluents has discolored the water of the bay. The smaller cape at the left is Ras Binnah. It is near the eastern entrance to the Gulf of Aden. The river running from the lower right corner of the picture is the Uadi Giael; it flows into the sea south of Ras Binnah. Two more pictures of this area follow. They were taken at nearly the same time as this one. Ras Hafun illustrates what geologists call a tombolo.

GEMINI VI DECEMBER 16, 1965 S65-63130

This is a closer view of some of the area shown on the preceding page. Ras Hafun is in the upper left. The river draining into this large bay is the Darror. The Uadi Giael crosses this picture near the center. Cumulus clouds cast shadows on the Earth in the foreground. The desert here is underlain by Cenozoic marine and continental sedimentary rocks. The ancient Egyptians called this northeastern horn of Africa "the land of aromatics" because in their time, as in ours, Somalia was a principal source of frankincense and myrrh.

GEMINI VI DECEMBER 16, 1965 S65-63131

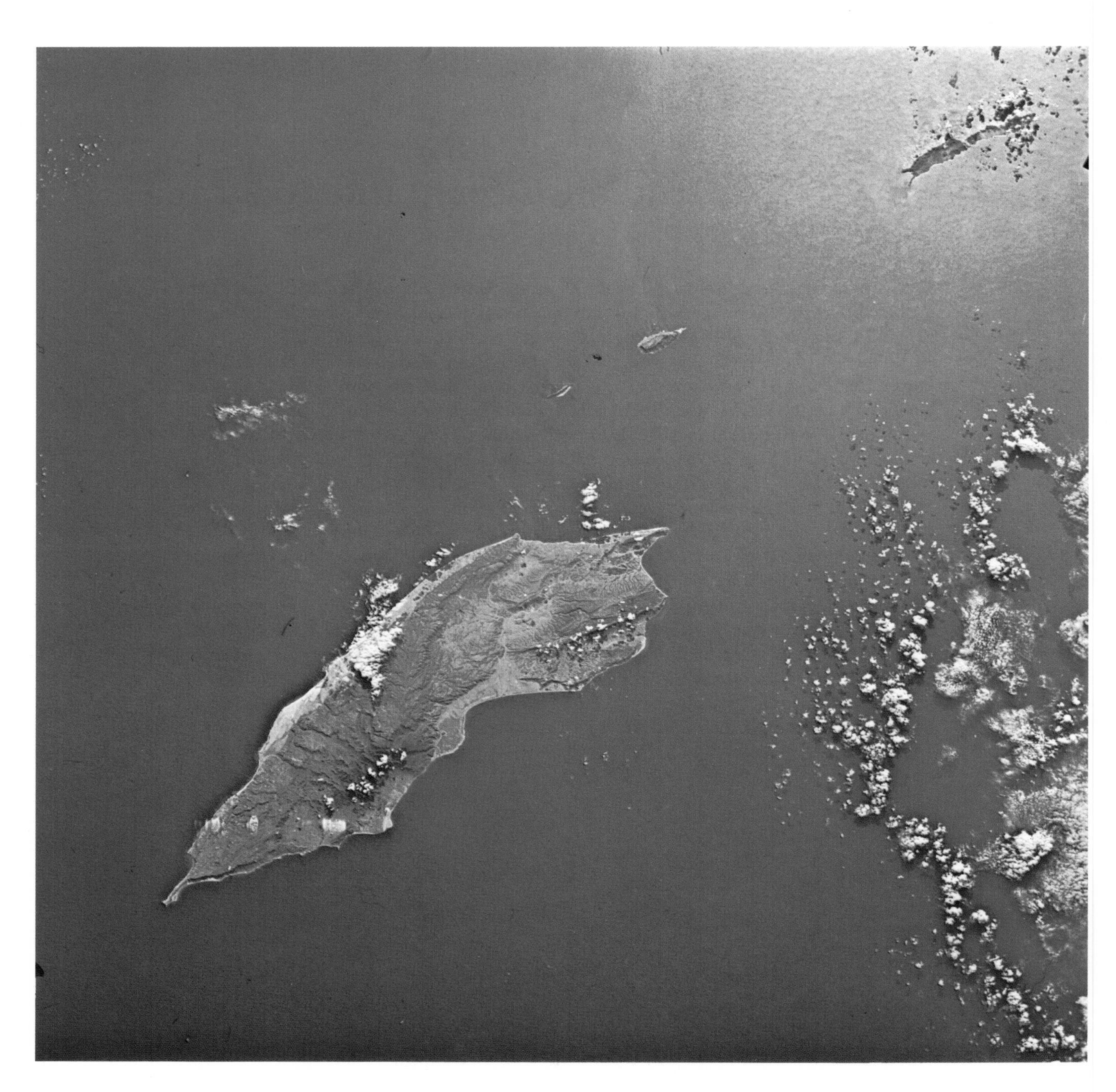

Little is known about the geology of Socotra, an island about 75 miles long in the Indian Ocean south of Aden and Muscat and Oman. A British party resurveyed it a few years ago for the first time in more than a century. The surf often makes landing difficult, but it was moderate when this photo was taken and shows as a mere white line. The light, northerly winds typified those of the early monsoon season. The tiny islands above Socotra here are The Brothers, and the slender one in the Sun's glitter at the top is 'Abd Al Kūrī. The Brothers lie on an insular shelf around Socotra, but the channel is deep between them and 'Abd Al Kūrī.

GEMINI VII DECEMBER 13, 1965 S65-64013

This panoramic oblique view from over the Indian Ocean embraces nearly the whole Arabian Sea. The horn of Africa and parts of Dhufar, and Muscat and Oman are at the left. On the right the view extends past Pakistan, and well down the coast of India. The low-level wind was southwest in the foreground and northwest off India south of the Gulf of Cambay. The Gulf of Oman is near the upper left. South of it one can see the archlike structure of the Oman Range, and to the north the general trend of the Makran range in Iran is visible. The relationship between these mountains has long been an enigma.

GEMINI XI SEPTEMBER 14, 1966 S66-54670

In this view to the east over the Indian Ocean off the coast of the Somali Republic, one sees long rows of cumulus clouds. Some small rows appear to be enhanced, others have been suppressed, and the larger cloud elements form other rows at an angle of approximately 30° to them. A broad line runs from the top center to the lower right where the clouds have been suppressed. The mechanisms that produce such phenomena in the atmosphere are poorly understood. Wind shear, atmospheric stability, and sea-surface temperature may all enter into the creation of patterns such as these. The next photo was taken much farther south.

GEMINI IX JUNE 6, 1966 S66-38429

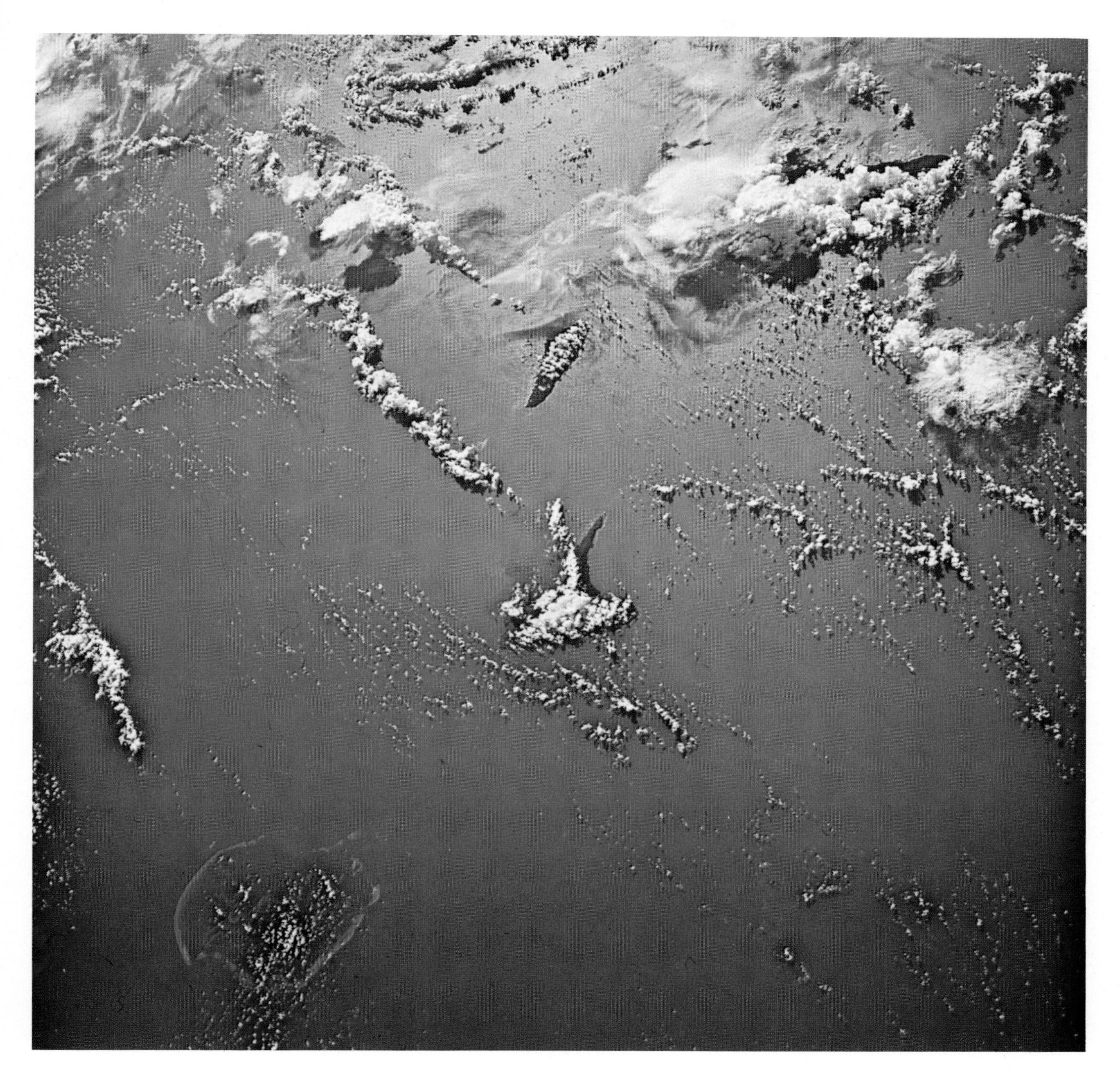

The Mayotte Archipelago is in the Mozambique Channel between Africa and the Malagasy Republic. This is a westward view of the Comoro Islands there. At the lower left is Mayotte, surrounded by an extensive, dangerous coral reef. In the center is Anjouan, which has a central peak 5170 feet high. Moheli, directly above it, is the smallest of these volcanic islands. Grande Comore is at the upper right, but covered by cumulus congestus clouds. The varied alinement of cumulus indicates a complex low-level wind pattern. A small cloud eddy induced by the light flow of air past the islands can be seen near the top of the picture.

GEMINI VI DECEMBER 16, 1965 S65-63227

Shadows and curving lines of cumulus clouds broke the Sun's glitter on the Indian Ocean between the Malagasy Republic and the Mascarene Islands farther east. The curvature of the rows of cumulus may have resulted from the eddy effect generated by air flowing past mountainous islands. The island of Réunion is barely visible in the lower left. The coastline of the Malagasy Republic is near the horizon where the flattened tops of thunderstorms rise high into the atmosphere. Several bands of cirrus clouds are to the left of the Sun glitter. The reddish image at the top was caused by reflections within the camera.

GEMINI VI DECEMBER 16, 1965 S65-63283

Several hundred miles east of the Malagasy Republic, the camera recorded this view of the Mascarene Islands in the Indian Ocean. Mauritius, in the center, is a roughly oval island composed of basalt and surrounded by coral. Uninhabited when discovered in the 1500's, its population now exceeds 500 000. The rows of cumulus clouds over it are alined east-west. At the left, south of the island, is an outstanding example of the classic open convective cloud cell. Réunion, the island in the upper center, is dominated by two volcanic masses, the largest of which, Piton des Neiges, rises 10 069 feet.

GEMINI VI DECEMBER 16, 1965 S65-63284

This and the next two photos of clouds were taken far east of Africa, almost directly south of the tip of India. The clouds in this photograph belonged to a weak tropical vortex that was visible near 13° S and 80° E. You can see several decks of clouds in it, from high-level cirrus to low-level cumulus, arranged in distinct lines. Tropical storms are frequently spawned on both sides of the Equator in this lonely part of the Indian Ocean. Some of these storms grow to be vigorous, destructive typhoons; others remain weak, tropical circulations.

GEMINI VI DECEMBER 16, 1965 S65-63280

This picture overlaps the one on the preceding page and includes the same clouds along its left edge that were shown in the photo there. This is an eastward look at the southern edge of a tropical vortex seen over the waters of the southern Indian Ocean. The alinement at different altitudes shows the changes in the wind direction with height. Of particular interest here is the apparent alinement of the lower clouds. This suggests that there was a diverging northeasterly flow, but because such a flow is not likely so near to storms, the apparent alinement may have resulted from the perspective of the photograph.

GEMINI VI DECEMBER 16, 1965 S65-63279

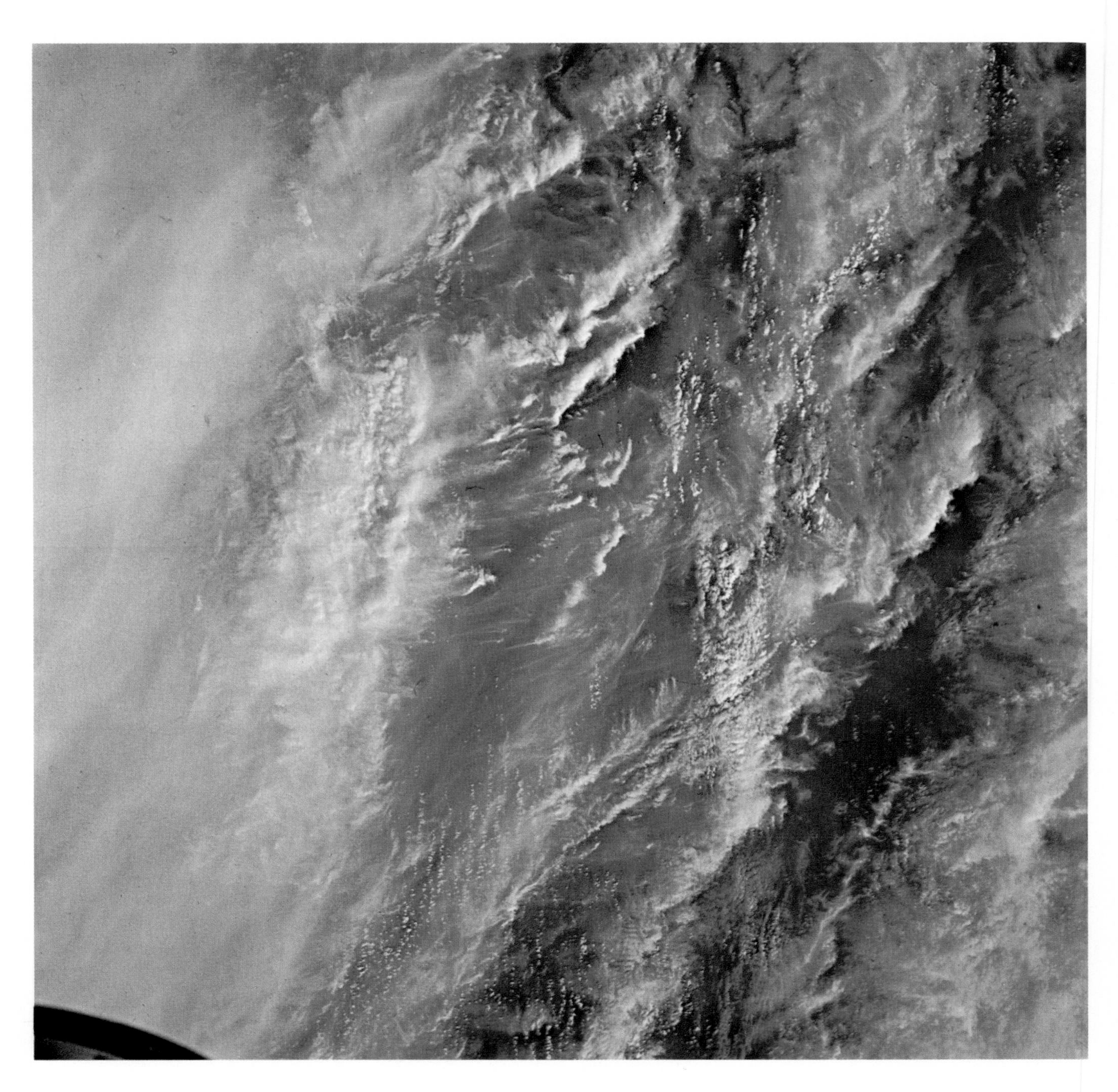

This is a nearly vertical view of a part of the area shown in the two preceding photographs of clouds in a tropical vortex over the southern Indian Ocean. The fine streamers of cirrus clouds in the center are being blown in a direction perpendicular to the rows of low cumulus clouds. A canopy of cirrus obscures the lower levels at the left. Many of these storms originate over the tropical seas west of Sumatra, and some of them travel for several weeks before striking land or curving into higher, colder latitudes to fade away.

GEMINI VI DECEMBER 16, 1965 S65-63278

All scales of convective clouds can be seen near the Chagos Archipelago. The clear area at the lower right was over the Egmont Islands. The cirrus anvil tops of several cumulonimbi in the Sun-glitter area project toward the southwest. Small cumulus-cloud streets in the boundary layer are alined with the southeast trade winds. The large area of cirrus and cirrostratus in the foreground is a small part of a massive cloud volume of convective activity. Weather-satellite photos have revealed similar masses. Their lifetime is 1 or 2 days and their role in the circulation of the equatorial atmosphere is not well understood yet.

GEMINI X JULY 21, 1966 S66-45846

The Chagos Archipelago, about 250 miles south of the Maldive Archipelago, consists of five main coral atolls called the Oil Islands. Two of them, Egmont and Three Brothers, can be glimpsed between the clouds in the foreground. The small cumulus clouds there are alined with southeast trade winds at the surface, while in the background a vast area of cumulus clouds is organized in various patterns. These islands are in the equatorial counter current; fish are plentiful, and green turtles thrive on their shores. The largest atoll in this group, Diego Garcia, totals only 11 square miles and had only 650 local residents in 1960.

GEMINI X JULY 21, 1966 S66-45848

Five atolls of the Maldive Islands, a group north of the Chagos Archipelago, are in the foreground here. From the right edge they are Nilandu, Kolumadulu, Haddummati, Suvadiva, and Addu. The Equator is between Suvadiva and Addu. Winds from different directions are warping the towering cumulus clouds west of Addu at the lower left. At low levels the trade wind bends the towers toward the northwest; at an intermediate level they are being bent to the southwest; and at high levels, plumes containing ice crystals are being carried westward. The convection that dominates a large area near the horizon is producing more cirrus clouds.

GEMINI X JULY 21, 1966 S66-45853

Suvadiva is the large atoll here, Addu Atoll is below it, and the small island and reef of Fua Mulaku Island is between them. Within the lagoon of Suvadiva, the white spots are cumulus clouds, and the dark ones are coral knolls typical of Pacific and Indian Ocean atoll lagoons. The white, pearllike fringe on the shores of both Suvadiva and Addu is the reflectance from strong surf produced as waves approach from the south. The prominent large white cumulonimbus in the foreground had reached the upper levels of the atmosphere, and the tops of these clouds were being blown to the southwest when this picture was taken.

GEMINI X JULY 21, 1966 S66-45851

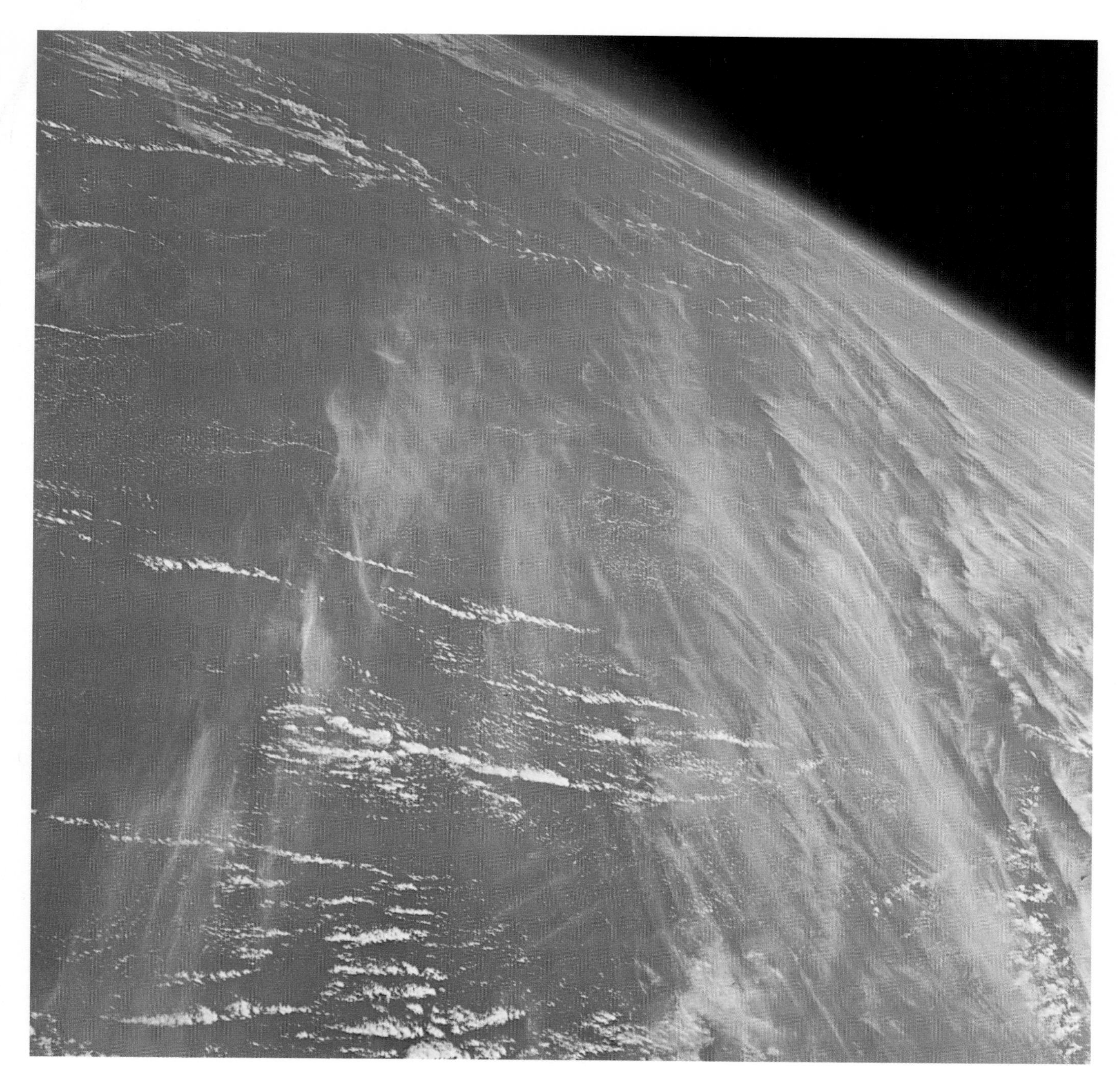

This picture shows a thin veil of cirrus clouds being swept along by high-altitude east winds over the Indian Ocean south of Ceylon. The camera was pointed west, and the Maldive Islands are near the horizon, but too small and far away to be seen. Thunderstorms spew out long cirrus streamers which may extend for hundreds of miles in this tropical region. A different, lower level wind regime had alined the cumulus clouds in the foreground in a north-south line at the time this picture was taken.

GEMINI X JULY 21, 1966 S66-45859

Only about 200 of the 2000 small Maldive Islands southwest of Ceylon are inhabited. They are grouped in 12 atolls. Suvadiva Atoll is near the center of this early-morning photo, for which the low Sun brightened the sides of high towering cumulus clouds. The cirriform clouds were in thinner, less dense layers and appear darker. The Maldive Islands are coral caps on the high, central portions of a long, submerged, partly granitic ridge. It begins at the approximate latitude of Bombay and extends southward along the west coast of India. This Chagos-Laccadive Plateau joins the Mid-Oceanic (Carlsberg) Ridge near the Chagos Archipelago.

GEMINI XII NOVEMBER 14, 1966 S66-62974

These stratocumulus clouds seen over the southeastern Indian Ocean looked like floating fields of ice, but the orbits of the Gemini flights kept them well away from the polar regions of the Earth. Similar cloud forms frequently are seen off the coasts of California and Peru where the waters of the Pacific are relatively cool. Some cellular patterns are discernible in this stratocumulus, indicating that a Bénard cell-type circulation might be found in the lower atmosphere. A few cirrus clouds also are scattered throughout the photo.

GEMINI IX JUNE 6, 1966 S66-38440

A late-afternoon Sun spread dark shadows of cumuliform clouds over Western Australia the day that this and the next photo were taken. The Ashburton River valley is in the upper left, and the Indian Ocean shore in the lower right. The large light area near the sea is Lake McLeod, a dry salt lake (visible again in the lower left corner of the next photo). Lake McLeod is a short distance south of the Tropic of Capricorn, and the town called Winning Pool is north of it. Many nations helped to assure the safety of the American astronauts; Australia contributed to the cost of operating a tracking station on its western coast.

GEMINI VI DECEMBER 16, 1965 S65-63135

Shark Bay and Denham Sound dominate the center of this view of Australia's westernmost shore. The Carnarvon Tracking Station, a part of the NASA worldwide network used to track manned space flights, is near the mouth of the Gascoyne River in the lower left corner of the picture. The cumulus and cumulus congestus in the upper half of the photo are over the higher parts of the mainland between this shore and Australia's great deserts. In the central foreground are Dorre Island and Bernier Island. The city of Wooramel is on the left side of the large bay in which the topography below the shallow water is discernible.

GEMINI VI DECEMBER 16, 1965 S65-63136

This is a wide-angle photo of Australia's northwestern coast with Eighty Mile Beach in the foreground. Inland is the Great Sandy Desert; the Lake Mackay is near the center of the right edge. In the upper left, parts of Timor are visible despite dense clouds such as persist over Indonesia much of the year. The Gulf of Carpentaria is near the horizon on the right. Cumulus-cloud patterns cover hilly regions below it. A vast Precambrian shield extends across Australia from Perth to the Gulf of Carpentaria. The area is a broad complex of pillow lavas, tuffs, and greenstones, flanked by metasediments, all of which are intruded by granites.

GEMINI XI SEPTEMBER 14, 1966 S66-54700

In this view of Australia's Eighty Mile Beach, three coral reefs stand out at the left below a fine-structured network of cumulus clouds over the sea. The shore here shows the simple contours and sand beaches of a mature coast. In the desert inland, long linear dunes cover a basin of Permian rocks. The V-shaped bay in the upper center is King Sound, filled with muddy, silty water by the Fitzroy River. At Tampi Point, above it, much iron has been mined from Precambrian granites and pegmatites. Collier Bay, Brunswick Bay, Prince Frederick Harbor, and York Sound are indentations in the coastline at the top of this photo.

GEMINI XI SEPTEMBER 14, 1966 S66-54918

Here is Australia's Northern Territory from Joseph Bonaparte Gulf, in the upper left, east to Cape York. On the far side of the gulf are Bathurst and Melville Islands, which shield Darwin from the Timor Sea. The prominent river entering the gulf is the Ord. The King Leopold ranges curve across the lower part of this photograph. Gregory Lake is in the lower center. The plain area in the upper center is Arnhem Land, a plateau capped by Jurassic shale and sandstone, with important mineralization of granodiorites and pegmatites around Pine Creek on its western end. The next picture is a more nearly vertical view of this area.

MINI XI SEPTEMBER 14, 1966 S66-54925

This picture overlaps the preceding one. Cold ocean currents sweep along Australia's coast here and through the straits to the Timor Sea. Winds from the Great Sandy Desert were blowing turbid water away from the shore when this picture was taken. The light-blue areas near the center, left of King Sound and Joseph Bonaparte Gulf, are shoal waters around islands and archipelagos. The coastline here is one of submergence, with tides of 15 to 30 feet, and up to 46 feet in King Sound. In the right center, the Margaret River joins the Fitzroy River. The King Leopold Ranges cross the upper right center of the picture.

GEMINI XI SEPTEMBER 14, 1966 S66-54924

# Part VI. Southern Asia

GEMINI XI rose farther above the Earth's surface on September 14, 1966, than men ever had gone before. Astronauts Charles Conrad, Jr., and Richard F. Gordon, Jr., first realized how high they were when the whole subcontinent of India came into view. Commander Conrad was so impressed by "how small the world is" that the sight always will be one of his sharpest memories of the flight.

When photographed from an altitude of more than 400 miles, India's whole coast was nearly cloudless. A small low-pressure system lay in the north, the wind was toward the shore on all coasts, and there for India's people it was a pleasant sea breeze. The air temperature along the coast was about 80° F and only from 7° to 10° higher in the interior.

Man's newly acquired ability to "see" such a system in toto can be very helpful in quantitative studies of his environment. Not only can the seaward extent of the ocean breezes be measured, but the sea-surface wind drift, areas of potential upwelling, and convergences can be plotted for an entire coast. Were such a view available daily, the value to fisheries, shipping, and meteorology would be incalculable.

Some of the pictures in this volume were taken at the request of the U.S. Navy Oceanographic Office and the U.S. Geological Survey. They contain information that is frequently lost when photos taken from aircraft are combined to show large areas.

You are looking directly down now on 100 000 square miles of the Arabian Peninsula's Hadramawt Plateau. The dark areas near the Gulf of Aden in the upper left are igneous and metamorphic rock including Quaternary volcanics, and the light area is a sand-dune field. The Hadramawt Plateau's sedimentary rocks dip gently to the north, and stream piracy is evident in the foreground. Several tributaries of the immense wadi in the lower right have lost their headwaters to the stream in the center. This dendritic drainage pattern is typical of a morphologically youthful stage of erosion on nearly flat strata.

GEMINI VII DECEMBER 13, 1965 S65-64010

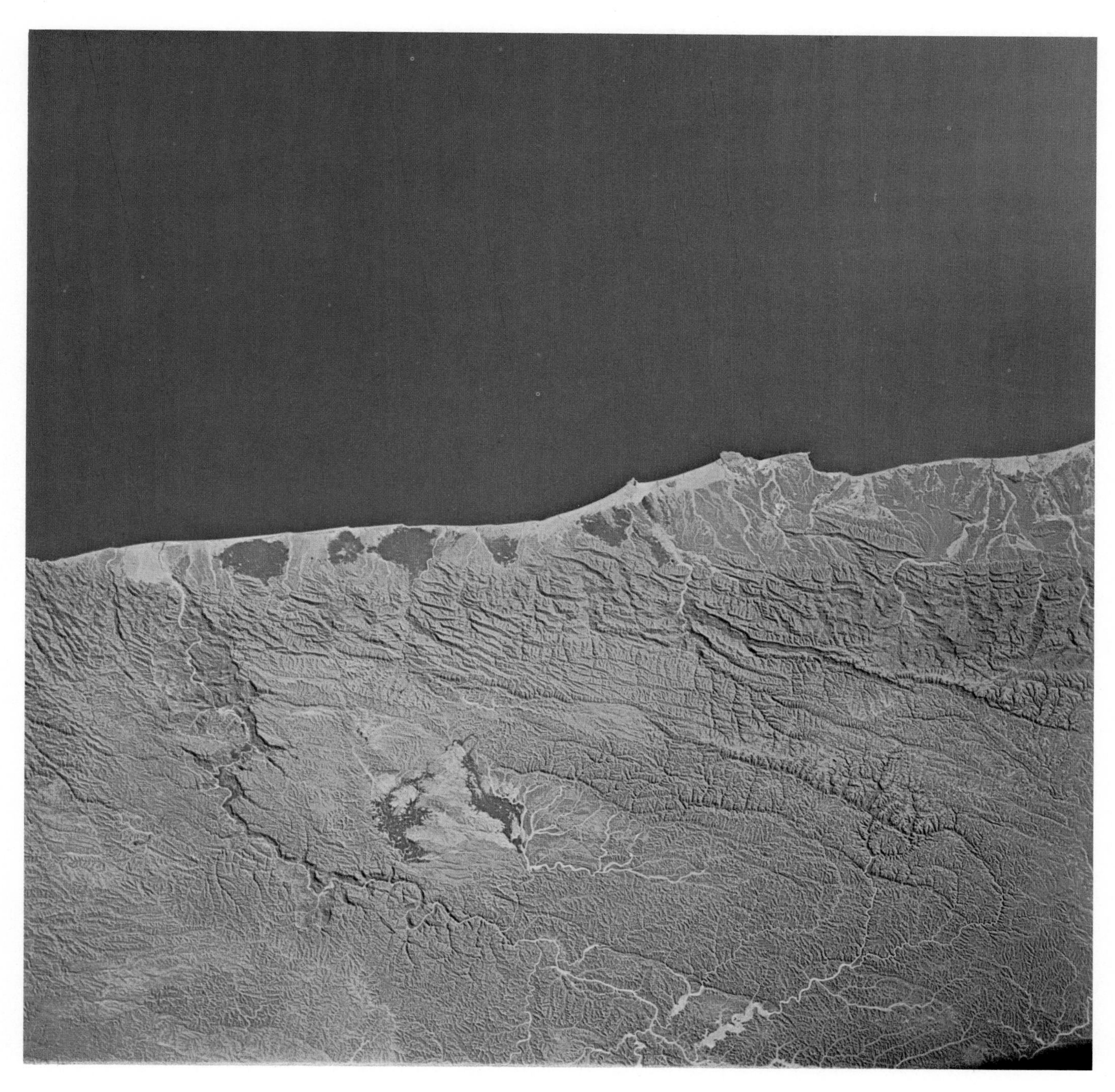

This view spans about 150 miles of the southern coast of the Arabian Peninsula, and partially overlaps the preceding picture. The Hadramawt Plateau is in the foreground and the Gulf of Aden in the upper part of the photo. The drainage is partly dendritic, but shows a trellis pattern near the shore, which may have resulted from the dip of strata or from faulting. The dark areas near the water are Quaternary volcanics of the Aden Volcanic Series. Five old lagoons have been filled and their inlets closed by depositions that contrast with the sharp coastal features of the erosional headlands. This area is immediately east of Al Mukalla.

GEMINI VII DECEMBER 13, 1965 S65-64011

The strait between the Persian Gulf and the Gulf of Oman is directly above the antenna in this photo, taken from an altitude of about 300 miles. Near the horizon the folded mountain systems forming the Zagros-Makran Ranges of Iran and West Pakistan can be seen, as well as the great depression containing the Baluchistan Desert, Siah Reg, of northern Pakistan and southern Afghanistan. Over the Empty Quarter in the foreground, cumuliform clouds were widely dispersed. Along the shore of the Gulf of Oman they were more prevalent in a sea-breeze circulation. Beyond the Arabian Sea, India is faintly visible at the far right.

GEMINI XI SEPTEMBER 14, 1966 S66-54669

This photo shows the whole Gulf of Oman. The southeastern end of the Persian Gulf is in the foreground and the Arabian Sea can be seen at the top. The large island at the lower left is called Qeshm, and the light area above the spacecraft nose is the Trucial Coast. In the distance, northeasterly winds can be seen carrying dust out over the Gulf of Oman for 150 miles near the border between Iran and West Pakistan. This and the next photo are of considerable geological interest because of the clarity with which they show the Strait of Hormuz. In a geological sense, this strait separates Africa from Asia.

GEMINI XII NOVEMBER 13, 1966 S66-63486

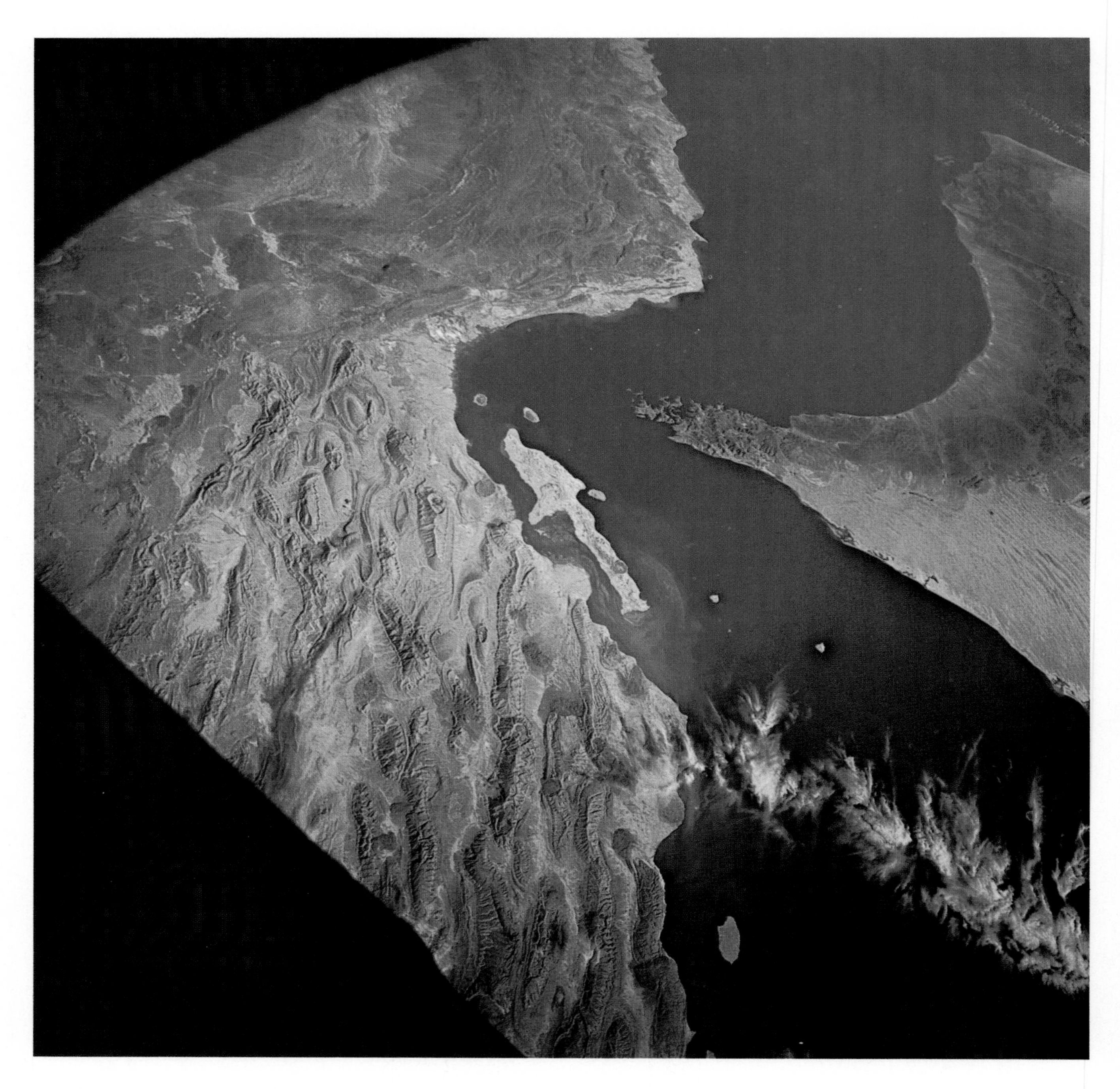

In this view to the east, Iran is at the left and Saudi Arabia at the right. The peninsula that juts into the Strait of Hormuz is the northern end of the Oman Range on the Arabian Peninsula. It points to a sharp discordance, called the Oman line, at the left, in the Makran Ranges in Iran. These ranges seem to have been moved to the south by an immense thrust fault. There are reasons to doubt this, but a considerable dislocation of fold axes is certainly apparent, and the concept is of interest because of the insight regarding the nature of the Oman line that geologists may gain from high-altitude photography.

GEMINI XII NOVEMBER 15, 1966 S66-63082

This view of the Zagros Mountains in Iran and the Persian Gulf shows anticlines generally composed of Cretaceous or Tertiary sedimentary rock cores, surrounded by upturned younger strata. The uplift of these mountains began in the Pliocene era and has outstripped erosion thus far. Salt beds have figured in their history by forming plugs and flowing upward as rheids in many places. Some have penetrated thousands of feet of rock to reach the surface. The dark circular or elliptical masses near the coast at the upper left are salt plugs that are exposed at the surface. They would dissolve soon in a wet climate, but here they survive.

GEMINI XII NOVEMBER 13, 1966 S66-63483

This is the front of the Himalaya Mountains in India and Nepal. This is a fascinating area geologically because the Himalayas here are an extremely complex assortment of igneous, sedimentary, and metamorphic rocks, ranging in age from Precambrian to Recent, that have been thrust southward where the Indian Peninsula begins. The city of Rampur, India, lies near the lower center of this view, and the mountains at the upper right are in Nepal. The rivers, including the Sard at the upper right, are tributaries of the Ganges, which flows into the Bay of Bengal east of Calcutta. The next photo shows the Himalayas from another vantage point.

GEMINI VI DECEMBER 16, 1965 S65-63128

Mount Everest is about an inch to the right of the center of the view of the Himalayas from west of Nepal to Bhutan, and 8 more of the world's 12 highest peaks are visible. Over India at the left the air is hazy, and thunderstorms catch early-morning sunlight south of the mountains. In the clear area at the right edge is the Brahmaputra River. The central peak of the forked range in the right foreground is Kula Gangri. The Himalayas were formed by thrust faulting along the margin of the central Asia tableland. As they were thrust southward, the crust folded to form the sub-Himalaya chain in front of the main mountains.

GEMINI XI SEPTEMBER 15, 1966 S66-54840

Notice the great **U**-shaped cloudline around India in this photo. Subsiding air in a sea-breeze circulation resulted in the suppression of convective clouds off the peninsula's coast for 30 to 50 miles on the west and 120 to 150 miles on the east. The occurrence of polygonal convection cells of cumulus clouds indicates heating of the air by the water and a lack of winds. Vegetation darkens the mountainous regions of Western and Eastern Ghats, but the reddish soil of southern India can be seen between these ranges.

GEMINI XI SEPTEMBER 14, 1966 S66-54677

The Coleroon River and other topographic features of the tip of India can be seen here, as well as typical daytime cumulus-cloud activity, with many cloud elements in long lines parallel to the winds. Southern India was included in the synoptic terrain photography experiment because the Indian Upper Mantle Project is focused on it, and photos such as this show more than mosaics. Between India and Ceylon, at the far right, the sea is so shallow that a small drop in its level would rejoin the two areas. The islands and shoals there are known both as Adam's Bridge and as Rama's Bridge. The next two pictures show more details of Ceylon.

GEMINI XI SEPTEMBER 14, 1966 S66-54904

This picture overlaps the previous one. It includes all of Ceylon, yet the Himalayas, roughly 2300 miles away, are faintly visible on the horizon. Ceylon is 270 miles long. Its people are clustered on the moist southwestern third of the island. Dry areas elsewhere were irrigated and productive 2000 years ago, but later were neglected until recent times. At the upper right, cirrus clouds can be seen streaming westward toward Ceylon from a convective area in the Bay of Bengal. At top center there is another region of cloudiness near Calcutta. It is associated with a weak depression.

GEMINI XI SEPTEMBER 14, 1966 S66-54678

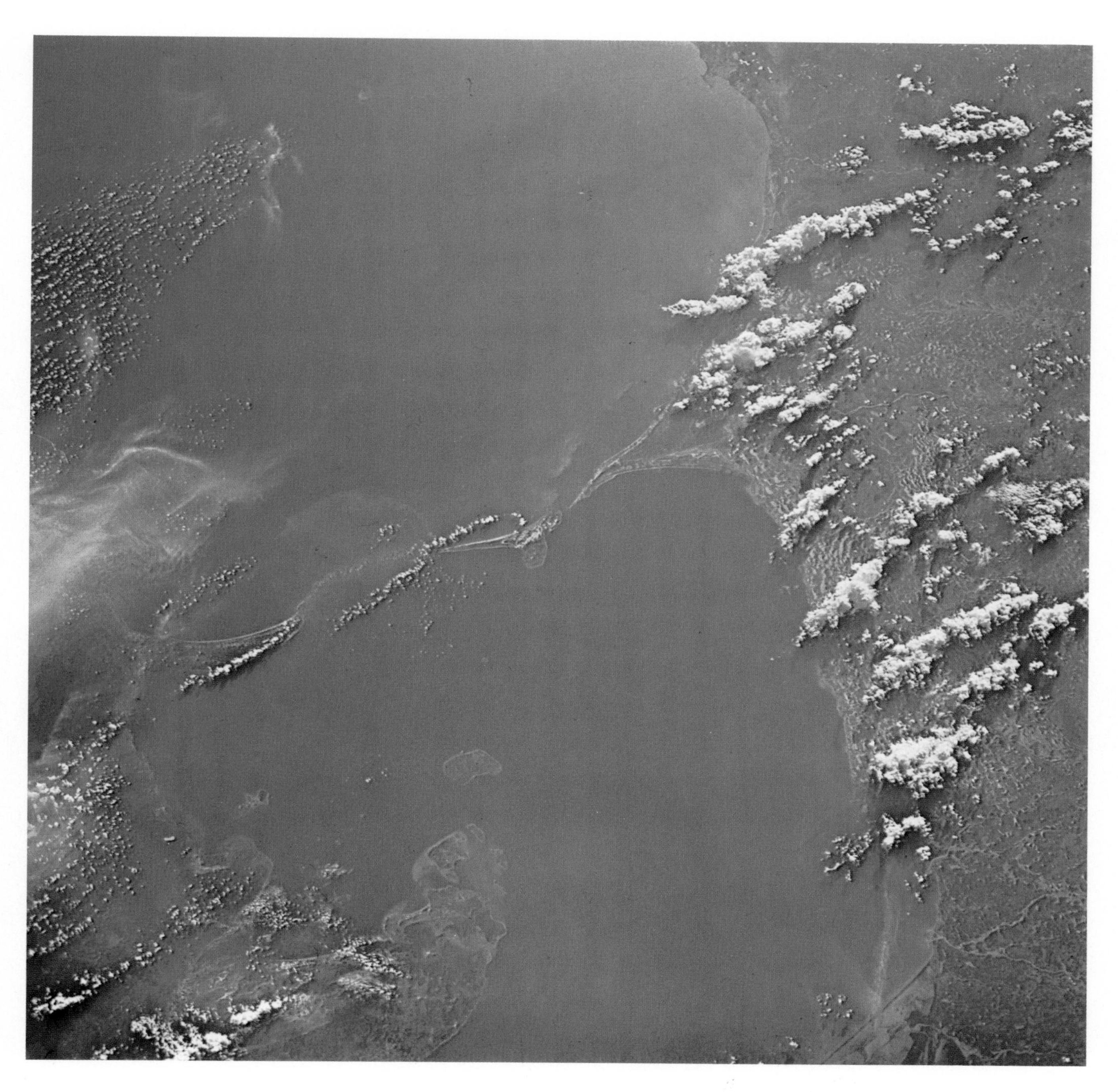

You are looking south now at the shallow water between Ceylon, on the left, and India, at the right. Palk Bay and Palk Strait are in the center and the Gulf of Mannar at the top of the picture. Rama, the hero of Ramayana, is said to have built a bridge here to take his army from India to Ceylon. A road-railway-ferry system now crosses this shallow area. The high thin clouds over Ceylon are probably associated with a tropical storm in the Bay of Bengal. Ceylon is within 450 miles of the Equator, but oceanic winds temper its hot, humid climate. At the lower right, the Coleroon River at Thanjávúr is visible.

GEMINI VII DECEMBER 11, 1965 S65-63743

About 90 minutes after the Gemini XI photos on preceding pages were taken, the spacecraft crossed the Indian Ocean again and obtained this view. In it one can see how the clouds developed and changed in the brief time it took the spacecraft to circle the world. India and Ceylon are near the horizon at the left. Cumulus congestus over Ceylon had become cumulonimbi, with elongated, anvillike tops extending nearly 100 miles to the Indian coast, by the time this photo was taken. Over the equatorial Indian Ocean in the foreground, dense cirrus and cirrostratus clouds hid many of the low-level convective clouds.

GEMINI XI SEPTEMBER 14, 1966 S66-54544

This picture was taken through an 80-mm lens at about the same time that the preceding one was taken through a 38-mm wide-angle lens. India and Ceylon are at the upper left, and meteorological features that were visible in previous pictures can be seen in greater detail in this one. Easterly winds were carrying cirrus streamers great distances at the time of this photo, and the thunderstorms over Ceylon had grown considerably since the astronauts first saw them. In the foreground, cirrus and cirrostratus obscure much of the lower convective cloudiness typical of this equatorial ocean area.

GEMINI XI SEPTEMBER 14, 1966 S66-54793

Southeastern Ceylon is in the lower left corner of this picture of long fingers of cirrus clouds reaching west across the Bay of Bengal. The thick cirrus near the top of this northeasterly view is emanating from convective storms over the Malay Peninsula. The cloudiness near the upper center is west of the Nicobar Islands, and is typical of that seen in tropical Southeast Asia. Details discernible in Gemini color pictures such as this have helped the meteorologists who interpret the photographs televised to Earth from unmanned satellites.

GEMINI XI SEPTEMBER 14, 1966 S66-54681

This view eastward across Sumatra shows the great quantities of cirrus produced by cumulonimbus clouds in this equatorial monsoon climate. The intense convective activity, which produces more than 100 inches of rain a year in much of this area, is particularly evident over northern Sumatra in the upper left, and along a line which cuts across the lower right corner of the picture. In the lower levels the undeveloped cumuli show open cellular patterns in some areas, as well as a suggestion of a vortex in the right center of the photo. Monthly mean temperatures average about 80° F at sea level in this part of Indonesia.

GEMINI XI SEPTEMBER 14, 1966 S66-54686

The long shafts of cirrus clouds at the left here trended southwest from northern Borneo. The view is to the northeast and includes many of the Indonesian islands. They are the spice islands that Columbus sought. The clouds above them in this photo were predominantly convective in a moist, unstable atmosphere. Southern Sumatra is at the left behind the antenna; Java is the long, narrow island in the center, and the Sunda Islands stretch toward the horizon. Borneo is in the upper left corner. Celebes, across the Makassar Strait, is to the right of Borneo and well cloaked in clouds.

GEMINI XI SEPTEMBER 14, 1966 S66-54691

This is a view to the northeast from over the Indian Ocean near the Equator. The photo shows several extremely long bands of cirrus clouds lined up northeast-southwest at a time when cumulus clouds were sparse in the lower atmosphere. The dark mass discernible through the thin clouds at the upper left is northern Sumatra. The islands off its west coast here are Simeulue, at the left; Banjak, in the upper center; and Nias, in the right center. Notice how the moist equatorial atmosphere obscures the eastern lowlands of Sumatra bordering the Strait of Malacca more than it does the central highlands.

GEMINI X JULY 21, 1966 S66-45782

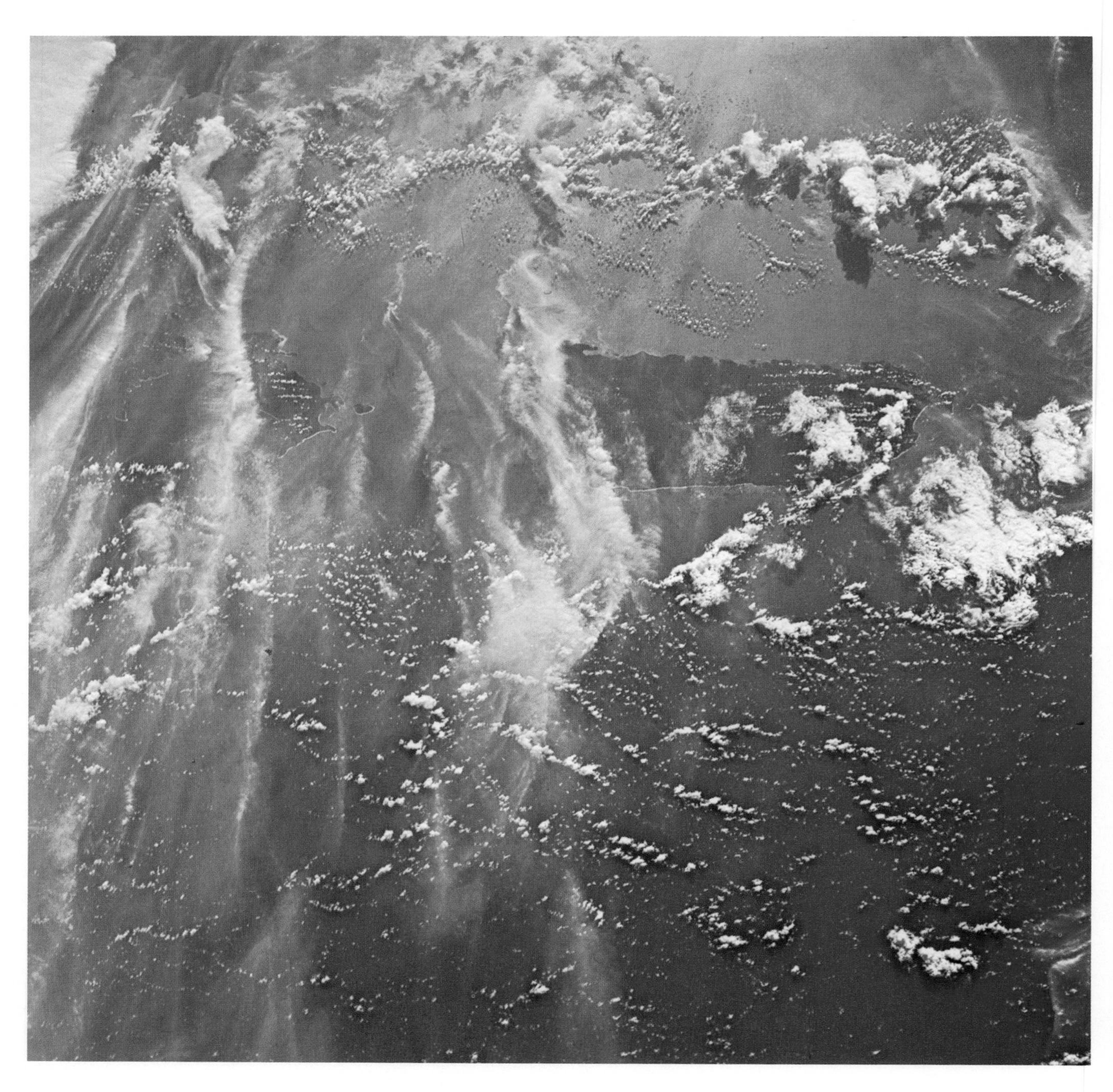

Off Sumatra's southwestern coast many large volcanic islands, with small ones scattered among them, rise from a submarine platform in the Indian Ocean. They are part of a chain that extends on toward Java and Australia. Thin cirrus clouds veil the upper part of this view, but Tanahbala, the southernmost of the Batu group, can be seen at the left, and Siberut, the largest of the Mentawai Group, is near the center. Some of Siberut's peaks rise more than 1000 feet. The cumulus-cloud streets at the lower right trend north-south, west of Siberut. Thick forests cloak many of the islands in this chain and coral reefs have risen around them.

GEMINI X JULY 21, 1966 S66-45785

This photo of the Mentawai Archipelago overlaps the preceding one. Siberut Island is at the left, Sipora Island in the center, Utara and Selatan Islands are at the right, and numerous other small islands are included. Sumatra's west coast along the southern slope of the Barisan Mountains is at the top. The surf was creating bright lines along the western and southern shores of the islands when this picture was taken, suggesting that an onshore wind was blowing. Cumulus clouds were lined up in a southwest wind over the islands, while cirrus plumes were blowing from the northeast at a higher level.

GEMINI X JULY 21, 1966 S66-45787

Sumatra sprawls across the Equator south of Burma and Malaysia. In the middle of this photo, cumulus clouds alined with southeasterly winds rib its central lowlands. The Strait of Malacca is at the right of boomerang-shaped Bengkalis Island. The narrower Pandjung Strait in the upper center separates several large islands from the mainland. The Siak and Kampar Rivers, flowing north and east from Sumatra's mountains, fill this strait with mud and silt. Thin cirrus clouds shroud forests and jungles on the hot, humid islands. A denser band of cirrus partly conceals a cumulus-cloud line that extends upward at the right.

GEMINI X JULY 21, 1966 S66-45791

This view northward over the Bay of Bengal shows the Irrawaddy River delta in Burma. The Gulf of Martaban in the lower right is 150 miles wide, and some of the river's several mouths are visible left of it. Rice is grown on the alluvial lowlands of this fertile delta. The brown, silt-laden water being discharged into the Andaman Sea is evidence of denudation upstream that has been estimated to be 1 foot in 400 years. At the left the northern part of the Andaman Islands can be seen. Cumulus streets prevail over the bay and sea, but there are also a few scattered cirrus clouds.

GEMINI XII NOVEMBER 14, 1966 S66-62976

The Gulf of Martaban is in the center and Thailand is at the right here. The Irrawaddy River delta is at the left, and from it a valley runs north to a dry, light-colored region near Mandalay that is sometimes called the Purple Plain. The river to the right of the Irrawaddy is the Sittang, and the Pegu Yoma separates the two valleys. The view is up the strike of the Arakan Yoma and other mountains in Burma. Geologically these mountains are continuous with the island arcs of Indonesia. Many geologists consider such arcs peripheral to growing continents. The accretion underway here, however, is occurring along the strike of the arc.

GEMINI XII NOVEMBER 14, 1966 S66-62979

Cumulus clouds have grown to extensive heights here, pumping heat and moisture into the high levels of the atmosphere, where cirrus plumes are beginning to obscure the lower clouds. The many stages of cumulus development depicted here were producing summertime showers over Kwangtung Province in China when this photograph was taken. East is at the top of the picture. Nearly 75 miles of coastal southeastern China can be glimpsed in the upper right corner. Offshore, a line of cumulus clouds parallels the bay-indented, island-studded coast of the Asiatic mainland.

GEMINI X JULY 21, 1966 S66-45945

The camera was pointed northeast along the Formosa Strait to obtain this picture of Taiwan and the coast of China. The Pescadores Islands are slightly above and left of its center. Hot, humid air hangs over southeastern China in the summer, and an unstable southwesterly current of maritime air had converged with the North Pacific trade winds to produce the clouds and showery weather shown here. The cloudiness on the left preceded a weak cold front near the mouth of the Yellow River. The muddy water from river mouths is faintly visible at the upper left.

GEMINI X JULY 21, 1966 S66-45860

This view toward the west of northeastern China includes the 70-mile-wide Hangchou Bay, at the right, into which the Fuchun River empties. The larger clouds are thunderstorms which are effective generators of precipitation over this region during the summer. The cumulus clouds at the upper right are in a northeast-southwest alinement. The area shown is largely in Chekiang Province, and includes the large cities of Hangchou, Shaohsing, and Ningpo. They are not resolved because of the range and atmospheric scattering, but the distinctive sediment patterns off the Fuchun and other rivers can be seen clearly.

GEMINI X JULY 21, 1966 S66-45960

China is at the left, the Pescadores Islands in the center, and Taiwan at the right here. The mainland's coast is in a youthful stage of development, and jagged because erosion has not yet produced offshore bars or extensive coastal plains along it. The convective cloudiness at the right is in air coming from the southeast over Taiwan's 12 000-foot Chungyang mountain range. Tides complicate the currents in the Formosa Strait here. Astronaut John W. Young called this a "lucky" photo because it was made while the spacecraft was drifting in a random attitude over the strait.

GEMINI X JULY 21, 1966 S66-45866

Looking back toward Asia from over the Pacific, 180 miles of China's coast, from Fuchow at the left to Wenling at the right, were photographed. The river in the foreground, with an island in its mouth, is the Ou Chang. Sediments discolor the coastal waters near it. Along the right edge, sections of the Yangtze River between Kiukang and Siangfu can be glimpsed. The convective-type clouds, from some of which rain was falling, were over mountainous terrain that rises 5000 feet in places. The region at the left, where the clouds are thickest, is a climatic wind convergence zone during the summer.

GEMINI X JULY 21, 1966 S66-45958

Convective clouds cover much of Taiwan in this southerly view, but its shorelines are visible. Taipei is at the lower center. A tropical storm was dissipated east of the island the previous day. The cloud streets beyond the southern tip are alined now in an easterly wind near the surface. Cumulonimbi are in scattered groups elsewhere. Left of the big island, the tops of thunderstorms are directed toward the east, indicating that there is a west wind at their level, and an open cellular formation of cumulus clouds also can be seen. The cirriform undercast near the horizon conceals the northernmost of the Philippine Islands.

GEMINI X JULY 21, 1966 S66-45956

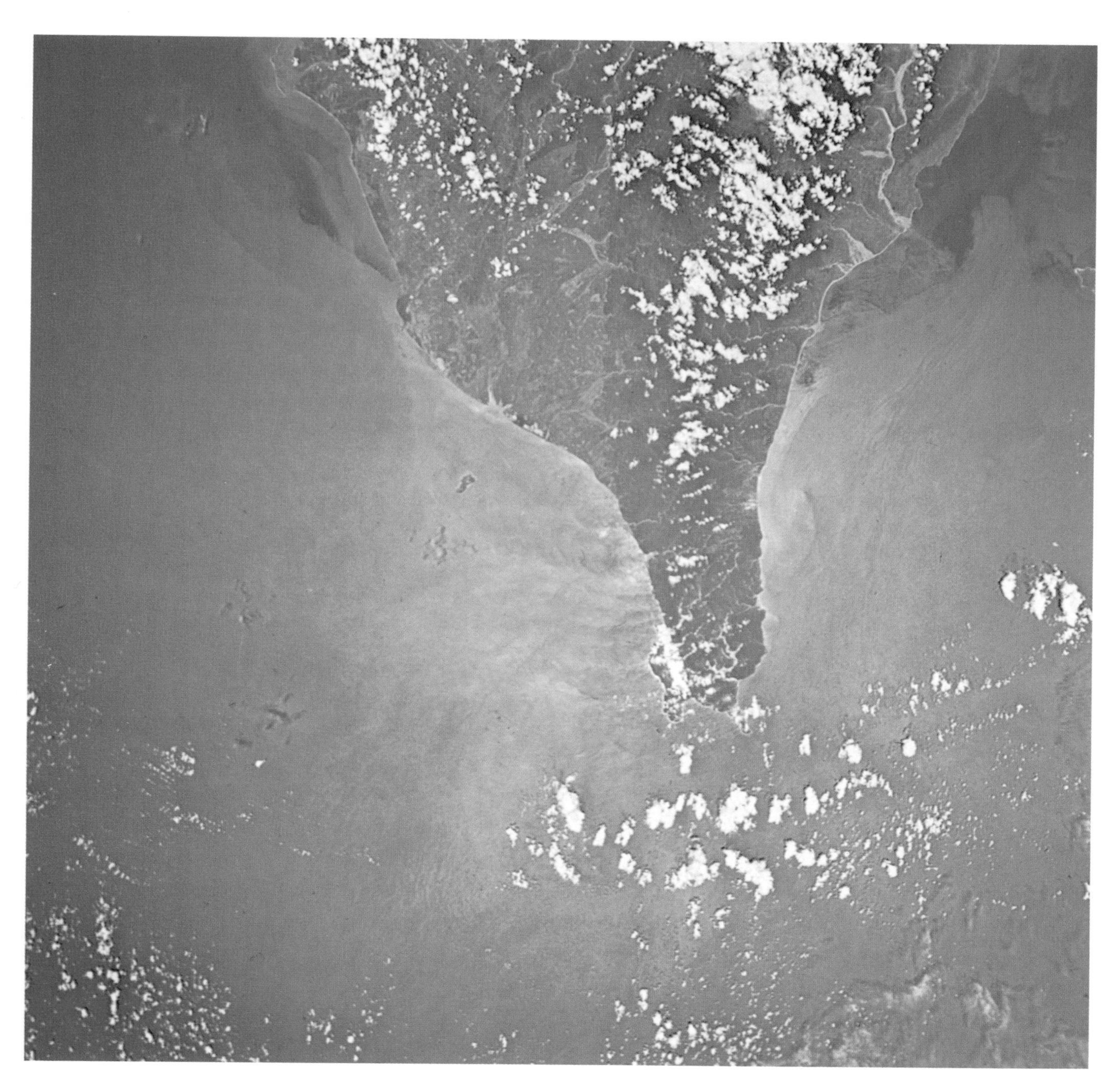

Taiwan is a rugged, forested island 250 miles long that parts the major current in the sea the way a ship does. As the "bow wave" spreads, the upwelling near the shore makes the sea darker blue above the island's southern tip, and lighter blue where an evenly roughened surface reflects the sunlight. More lowland shows west of the mountains than to the east. The braided patterns of the rivers are typical of streams issuing from steep mountainous areas. One of several wrench faults that ring the Pacific underlies the narrow eastern valley. "This picture," the astronaut noted, "shows many of the major features that we look for in Earth photography."

GEMINI X JULY 21, 1966 S66-45868

"The photo [above] was taken," said Astronaut David R. Scott, "during the second sunrise for Gemini VIII. I had hastily unstowed the camera and was anxious to make sure it functioned properly. . . . I was in hopes of capturing the magnificence of the scene, particularly the airglow and thunderheads. Unfortunately, the true fidelity of the view was not recorded by the camera." (More sensitive emulsion or longer exposure, or both, would be required to bring out the dim light features.) Study of twilight or dawn bands is of considerable interest to scientists. The spacecraft was near Guam when this photo was taken.

GEMINI VIII MARCH 16, 1966 S66-25771

"The Moon varied greatly during the 2 weeks of flight," Gemini VII's Command Pilot Frank Borman wrote afterward. "Jim [Lovell] took this picture of the full Moon as a symbol of our next goal in manned space flight, the lunar landing. I think it also dramatizes the difference between mere orbital flight and the future adventures that will take man a quarter of a million miles into the ocean of space." The two astronauts were over the Pacific on their 63d orbit. Trade-wind cumuli lay over that great body of water and extensive areas of cirrostratus were penetrated by the more active cumulonimbi.

GEMINI VII DECEMBER 8, 1965 S65-63872

These clouds came into view over the East Caroline Basin where seamen encounter northeast trade winds north of New Guinea in the western Pacific Ocean. A variety of convective clouds is shown here, some of which are forming open polygon-shaped cells with larger cumuli and cumulonimbi at the cell corners. Air generally sinks within the open region in a cell and rises near the edges where the clouds are found. The northern half of Murilo Atoll is just above the spacecraft nose. It is near Truk Island, and about 9° north of the Equator. The lagoon enclosed by this atoll is about 10 miles wide.

GEMINI X JULY 19, 1966 S66-45653

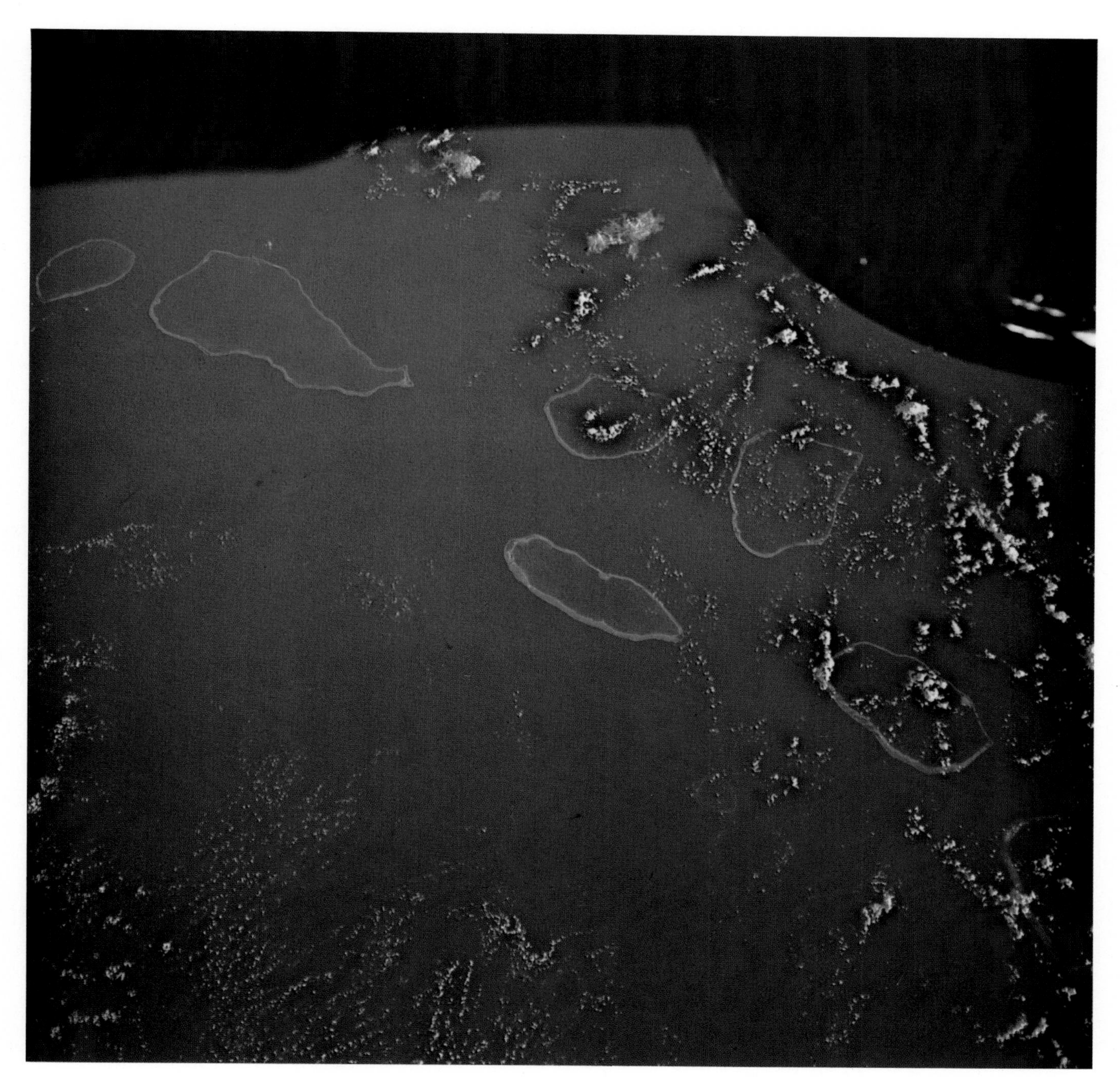

Here are 8 of the 80 coral islands in the 1300-mile chain of the Tuamoto Archipelago, a part of French Polynesia, about 16° S and 145° W in the South Pacific. The seven most prominent atolls are, from left to right, Tikehau, Rangiroa, Arutua, Kaukura, Apataki, Toau, and Fakarava. A thin line of clouds in the center points downward to Niau. The poorly organized cumulus activity is typical of the fair weather in this area. Coconut, breadfruit, and pandanus trees grow on these remote islands and the limpid waters of their lagoons yield pearl oysters. The islands shown in the next few pictures are far north of this archipelago.

GEMINI VII DECEMBER 5, 1965 S65-63827

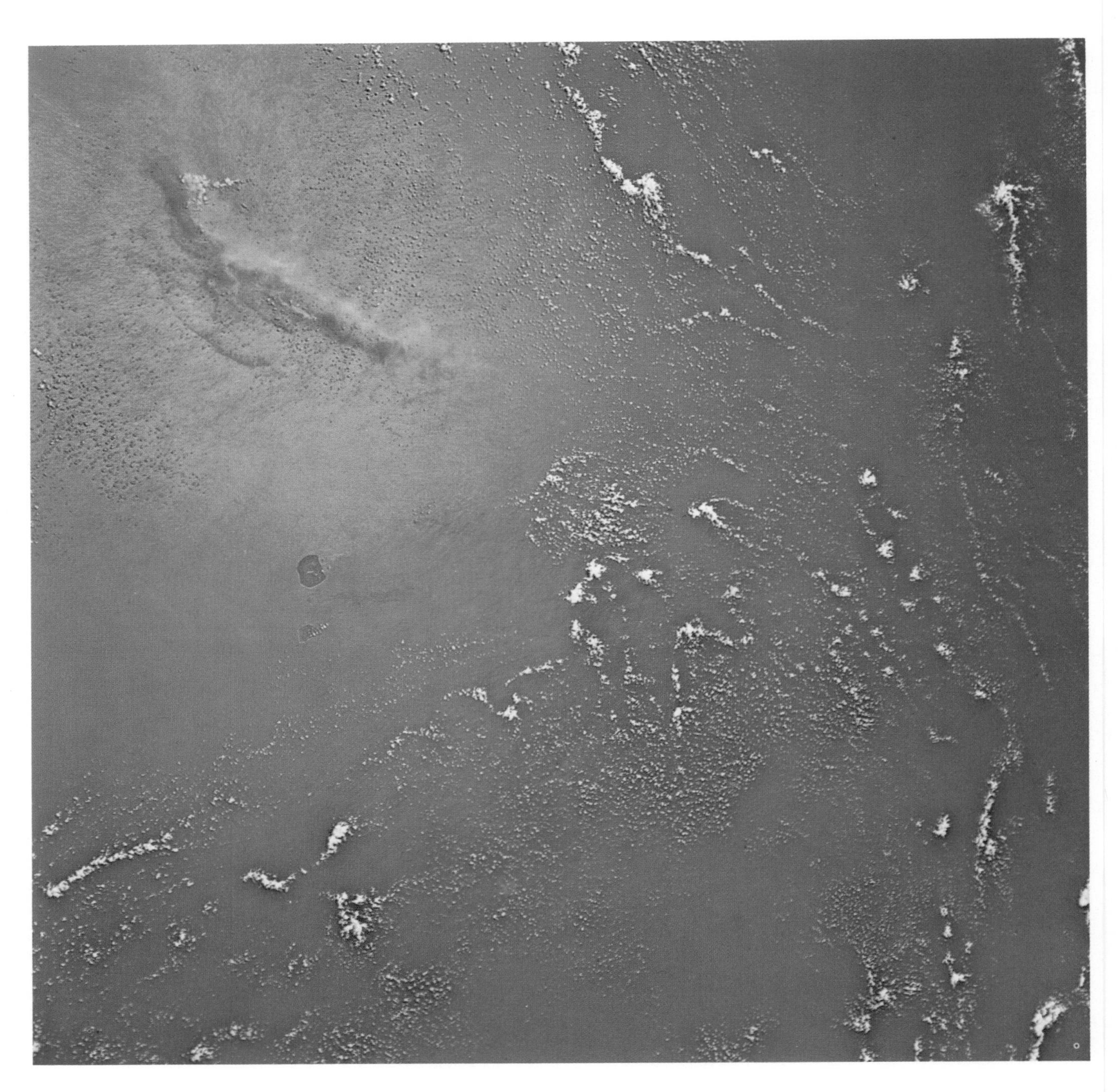

This is a nearly vertical view of two of the western Pacific's many volcanic islands, and shows both the motion of the clouds and the waters around them. These are the Daito Islands, about 200 miles east of Okinawa and 400 miles south of Kyushu, Japan. The larger one is Kita Daito Jima. The turbulence in the deep channel between it and the one below it in the photo and the cross-swell pattern behind them can be seen. In the original transparency of this picture, a typical wind slick, or "tadpole tail," behind the islands can be seen. It is mainly behind the larger island and indicates the wave action and water motion.

GEMINI X JULY 21, 1966 S66-45871

The most western part of the United States photographed on the Gemini flights was Kure Island, at the lower left here. The Midway Islands are in the center of the picture, and Pearl and Hermes Reef is at the upper right. Coral colonies built these gemlike dots in the sea on the summits of eroded submarine volcanoes that scientific studies indicate were active at this western end of the long Hawaiian chain before others erupted farther east. Test drillings have shown that the basaltic volcano base of the Midways subsided before the middle Miocene epoch.

GEMINI VII DECEMBER 9, 1965 S65-63726

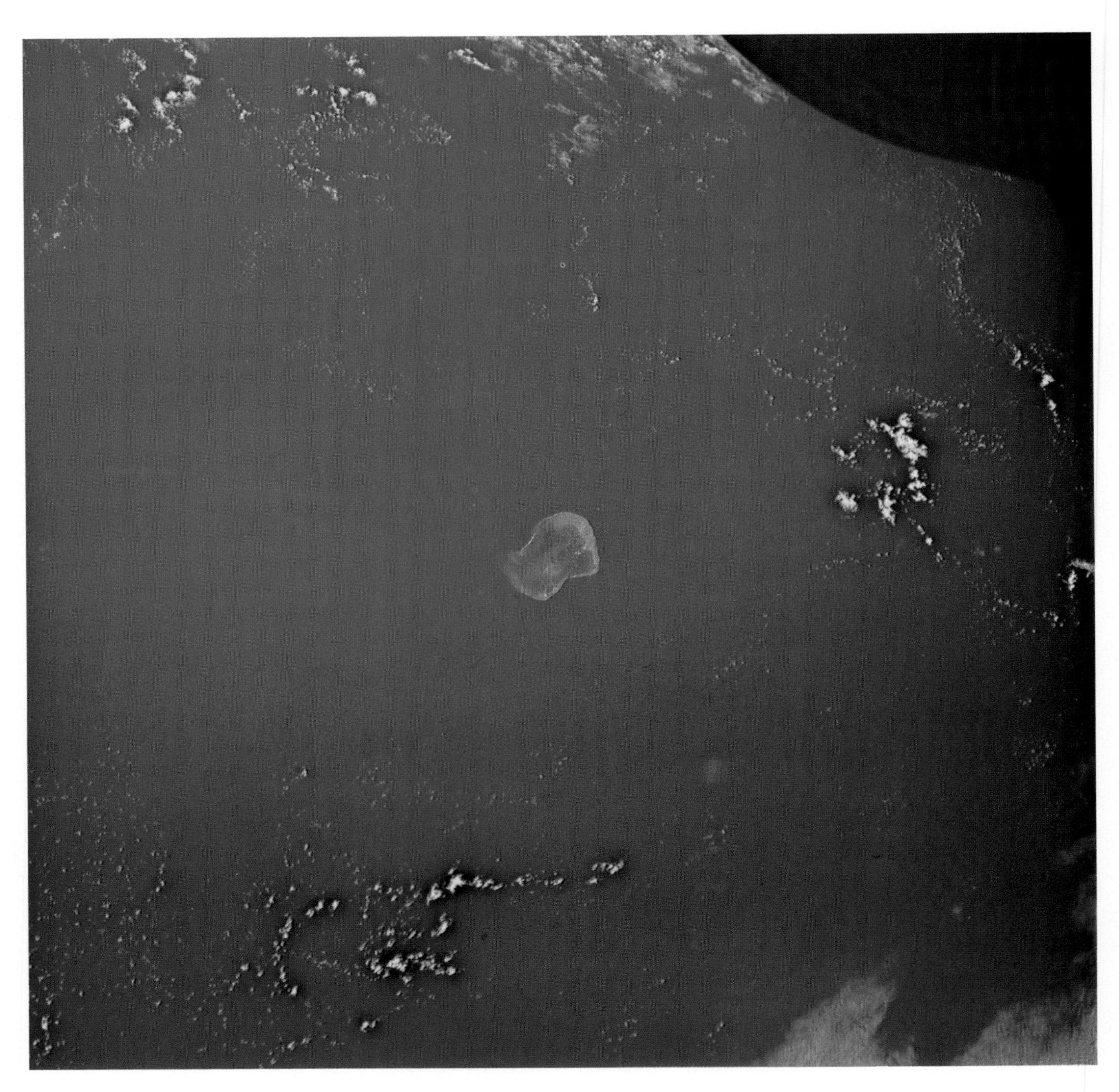

More details of Pearl and Hermes Reef and the lagoon that encloses its dozen islets can be seen in this photo than in the preceding one. Pearl fishermen once inhabited these beautiful protuberances from the Pacific, but these islands are now part of a national wildlife refuge. The islands from Nihoa to Pearl and Hermes Reef are often referred to as the "bird islands." Mark Twain called the Hawaiian chain "the loveliest fleet of islands that lies anchored in any ocean." Virtually all of the habitable islands of the Pacific were populated before the arrival of Europeans.

GEMINI VII DECEMBER 9, 1965 S65-63727

This cloud system was photographed over the Pacific Ocean about 400 miles west of Midway Island. The view was northeasterly along curving cloud lines that marked a cold front which extended into the cloud shield of a cyclonic disturbance at the upper right. The cool air behind the front was being heated by the surface of the sea, and cumulus clouds had formed a cellular pattern near the center of the photograph. Cirriform and cumuliform clouds can be seen preceding the cold front at the right. This picture was taken in November and the same cold front and cyclonic disturbance were photographed again the next day.

GEMINI XII NOVEMBER 13, 1966 S66-62951,

After taking the picture on the preceding page, the astronauts circled the Earth 15 times before taking this one north of Midway Islands. This is a view to the northeast along the same cold front that they had noted the day before. This front was part of a cyclonic disturbance, the center of which can be seen at the far end of the clearing. The more dense cloudiness near the center of the picture probably had thunderstorms embedded in it along the boundary between the warm and the cool air. Cirrus clouds are shown over the frontal clouds, stratus clouds are to the right of them, and cumuliform clouds to the left.

GEMINI XII NOVEMBER 14, 1966 S66-63076

This and the next photo were taken very soon after the one that immediately precedes them was taken. From the foreground to the center of this picture are Kure Island, Midway Islands, and Pearl and Hermes Reef, surrounded by blue-green lagoonal waters. The same low-pressure system over the Pacific that was shown in the preceding picture is shown here in different light. The cold front crosses the center of this picture from left to right in an arc of cumuliform clouds that touches Pearl and Hermes Reef. The cooler air in the foreground lay behind the cold front. Ahead of it, toward the horizon, the air was warmer.

GEMINI XII NOVEMBER 14, 1966 S66–63077

This is a southwesterly view along the same cold front near the Midway Islands in the Pacific that you saw in the three photos that have preceded this one. This shows the cold front from another vantage point. The blue-greenish spots, barely discernible, are, from the right center to the upper center, the images of Pearl and Hermes Reef, Midway Islands, and Kure Island. The surface winds at Midway Island were westerly at 10 knots when this picture was recorded. The bright region is Sun glitter from the surface of the Pacific. Several series of meteorological pictures such as these were obtained during the Gemini program.

GEMINI XII NOVEMBER 14, 1966 S66-63080

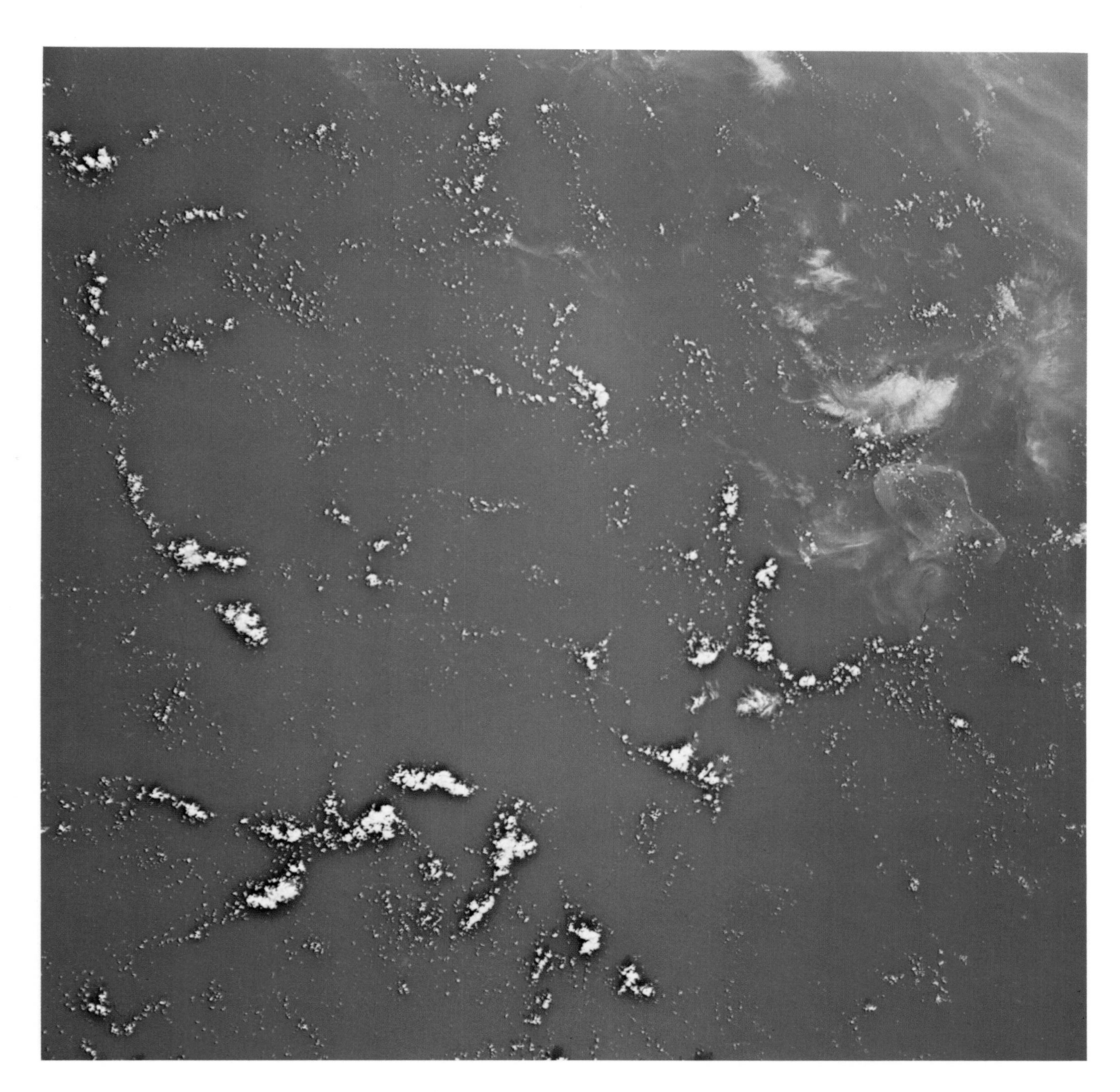

Few large areas of the marine atmosphere in and near the Tropics ever seem completely devoid of clouds. There is about one cloud for every 2 square miles of ocean surface in this picture, even though the total cover seems small. The blue-green outline of Pearl and Hermes Reef is detectable near the right edge of this photo under a few scattered cumulus and cirrus clouds. These reefs are near the western end of the chain of inlets and reefs that extends for approximately 1250 miles northwest from the main islands of the Hawaiian group. Most of these bits of the State of Hawaii are uninhabited.

GEMINI X JULY 21, 1966 S66-45844

Victor Hugo called clouds "the only birds that never sleep." This restless flock of them was photographed in the late afternoon over the eastern Pacific about 1000 miles southwest of Baja California. Vigorous convection in the cloud mass at the left was producing a cirrus cloud of ice crystals in the tropical sky, and thin cirrus was spread over wide areas elsewhere. Polygon-shaped open cells of cumulus clouds can be seen at the lower right, and there are a few cloud streets in the center of the photo. The camera was pointed toward the southeast.

GEMINI XII NOVEMBER 12, 1966 S66–63464

This is a southeasterly view of the eastern Pacific Ocean that includes the Baja California Peninsula and Mexico at the upper left separated by the Gulf of California. Guadalupe Island, in the left center, is surrounded by stratocumulus clouds. Downwind from the island, a chain of vortices has formed similar to eddy patterns found near the Canary Islands in the Atlantic. The patterns in the foreground indicate cellular convection was occurring in the air near the sea surface. The closed-cell type predominates here, but there are open cells in several areas in the foreground and the upper center.

GEMINI XII NOVEMBER 13, 1966 S66-63493

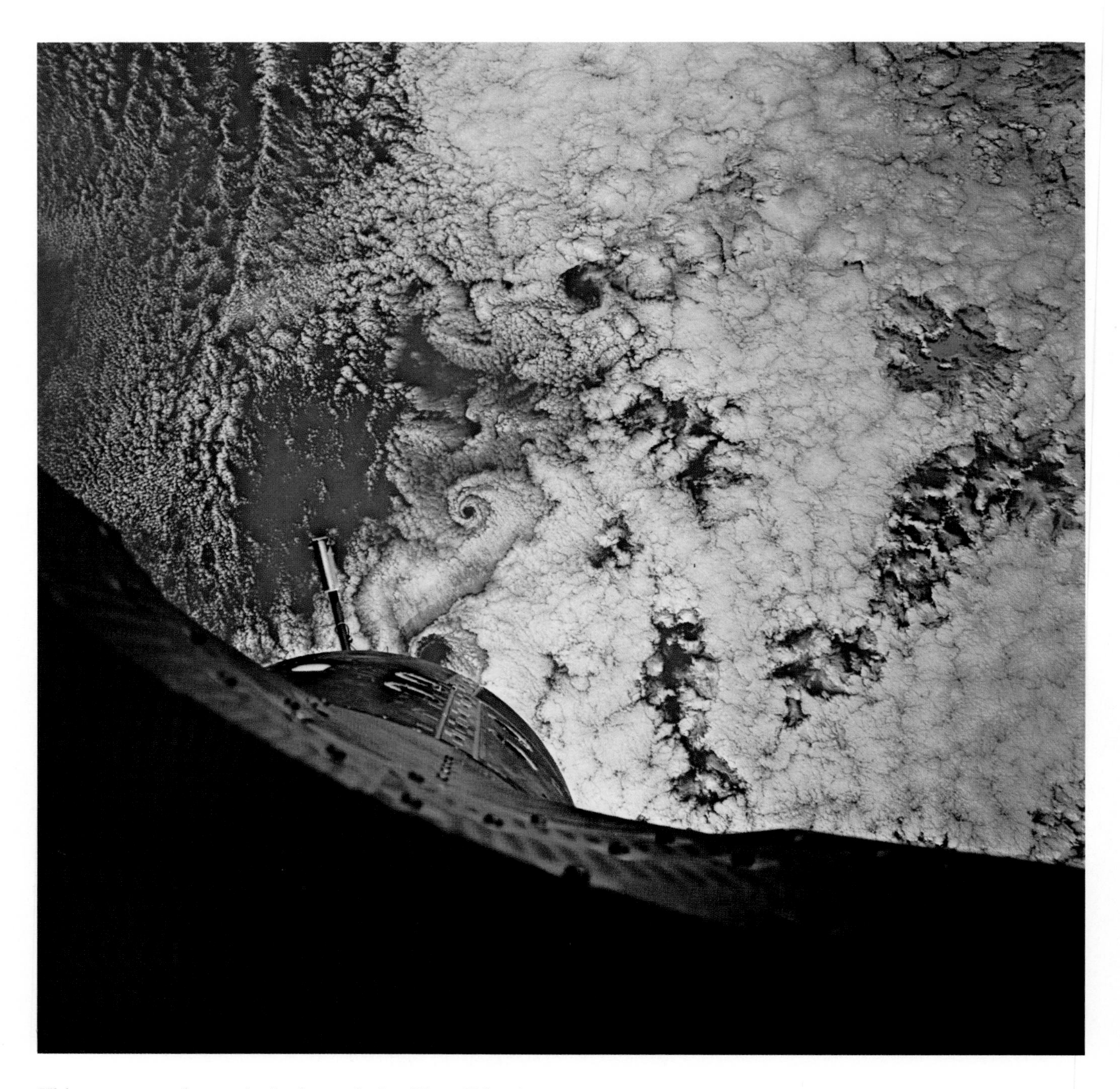

This more nearly vertical view of the Von Kármán vortices downwind from Guadalupe Island was obtained a minute after the preceding one, when the island was behind the spacecraft nose. These eddies over the eastern Pacific Ocean are disturbances caused in air flowing past its mountainous islands. Weak convective currents in the lower atmosphere give the stratocumulus clouds their cellular appearance. In a closed cell, the air ascends near the center and descends at its edges. The circulation is the opposite of this in an open cell, which has clouds for walls and a clear center. Both types of cells are represented here.

GEMINI XII NOVEMBER 13, 1966 S66–63494

Guadalupe Island is in the center of this photo, taken on a clearer day than the other pictures of it in this group. It is a game preserve for elephant seals, and is about 25 miles long. The winds on this day were northerly and aided in the formation of low stratus clouds over the island's northern coast and the development of counterrotating eddies downwind. The curved, poorly developed cumulus lines evident here follow, in part, the eddy system in the marine layer. Long, open waves approaching the island from the open Pacific developed the white surf on the island's western shore. The spacecraft window blurred an upper corner of this view.

GEMINI VII DECEMBER 8, 1965 S65–63870

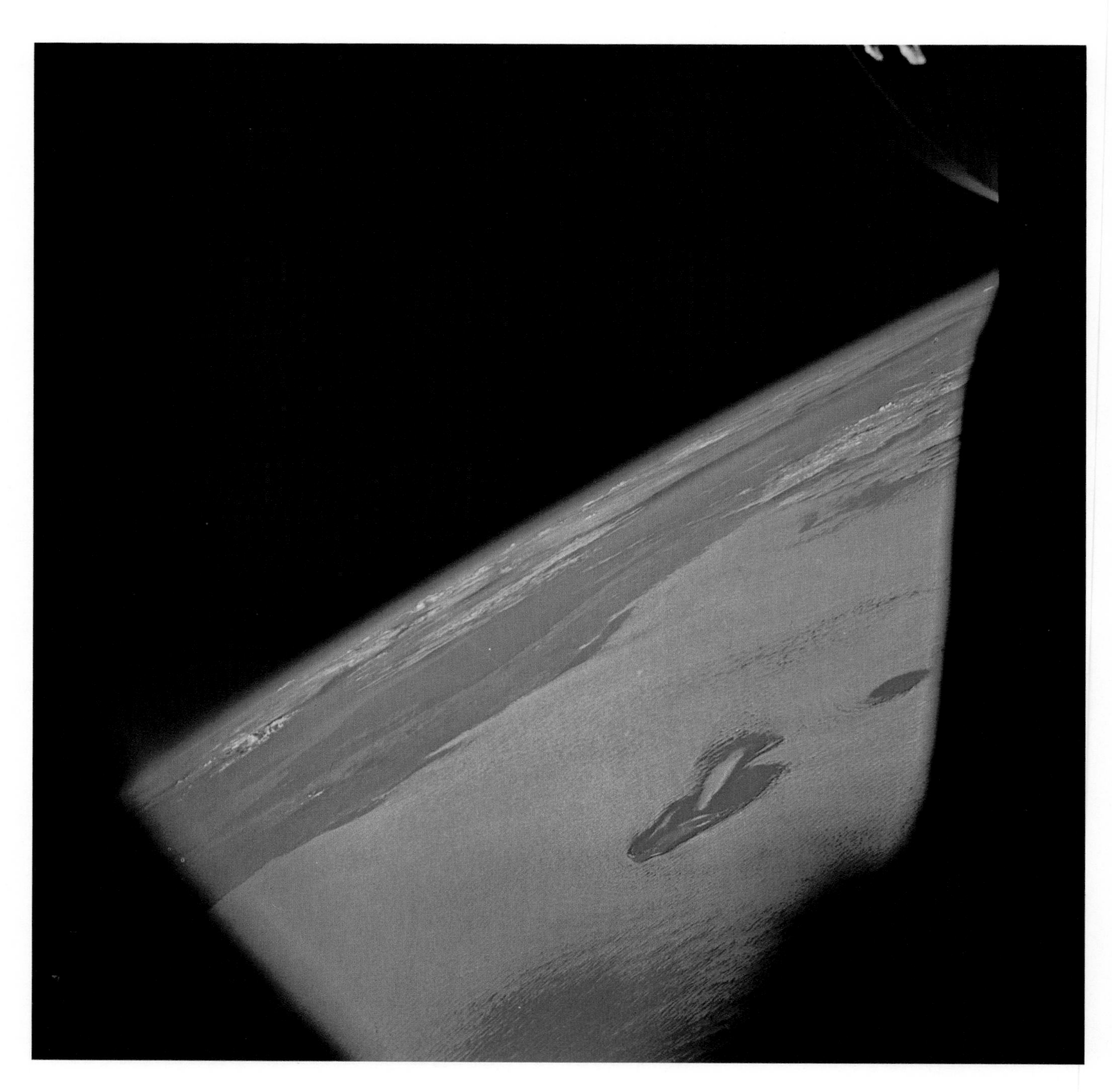

Guadalupe Island is in the opening in the clouds at the lower right. It is about 180 miles west of Baja California, the long peninsula visible in the center of the photo, beyond the clouds. The island is an extinct volcano that rises from a great depth to an altitude of more than 4900 feet. The large openings in these stratocumulus clouds are Von Kármán vortices that have formed downwind of the island. The cool California current produces a marine climate in this offshore part of Mexico. The Mexican mainland is visible along the horizon beyond the Gulf of California.

GEMINI X JULY 19, 1966 S66–45656

# Part VIII. South America

Astronaut Eugene A. Cernan took many of the photographs in this section on what he thinks was "the most fascinating and beautiful trip a man ever made across South America." The spacecraft carried him over the continent on a southeastward course that it would be arduous to follow on foot, and the weather was clear when he looked across Peru, Bolivia, Chile, and Argentina.

"Without blinking an eye," he wrote afterward, "I could see the high Andes, the Pacific Ocean, the great Altiplano with a jewellike Titicaca, the rain forests of the Amazon Basin, and the Chaco plains on down our orbital path." In addition to what he saw, this section contains pictures taken on three other Gemini flights.

These include some examples of photos taken on color infrared film. The camera has enabled men to use parts of the spectrum to which their own eyes do not respond, and this increases the information obtainable from afar about conditions on the Earth's surface. By combining the observations made in different spectral bands, scientists obtain still more information. This enables them to survey and study developments in parts of the Earth that are difficult and sometimes perilous to enter.

South America has been generous to bygone civilizations as well as to our own (e.g., the potato originated there), but our knowledge of many parts of it is still shamefully meager and can be enhanced by photographs such as these.

This is the towering Andean cordillera in Peru as seen from over the Pacific Ocean. The narrow coastal plain in the foreground is between Lima and San Juan. Península Paracus is nearly in its center. Beyond the peaks above it, the Río Ucayali, and the Vilcabamba Mountains, the view extends into the Amazon Basin. The snow and ice on many peaks are difficult to distinguish from cumulus clouds reflecting the setting Sun's light. The Peru Current brings relatively cool water to this part of South America's western coast and stabilizes the lower atmosphere. Stratus and stratocumulus clouds hover offshore here throughout much of the year.

GEMINI IX JUNE 4, 1966 S66–38281

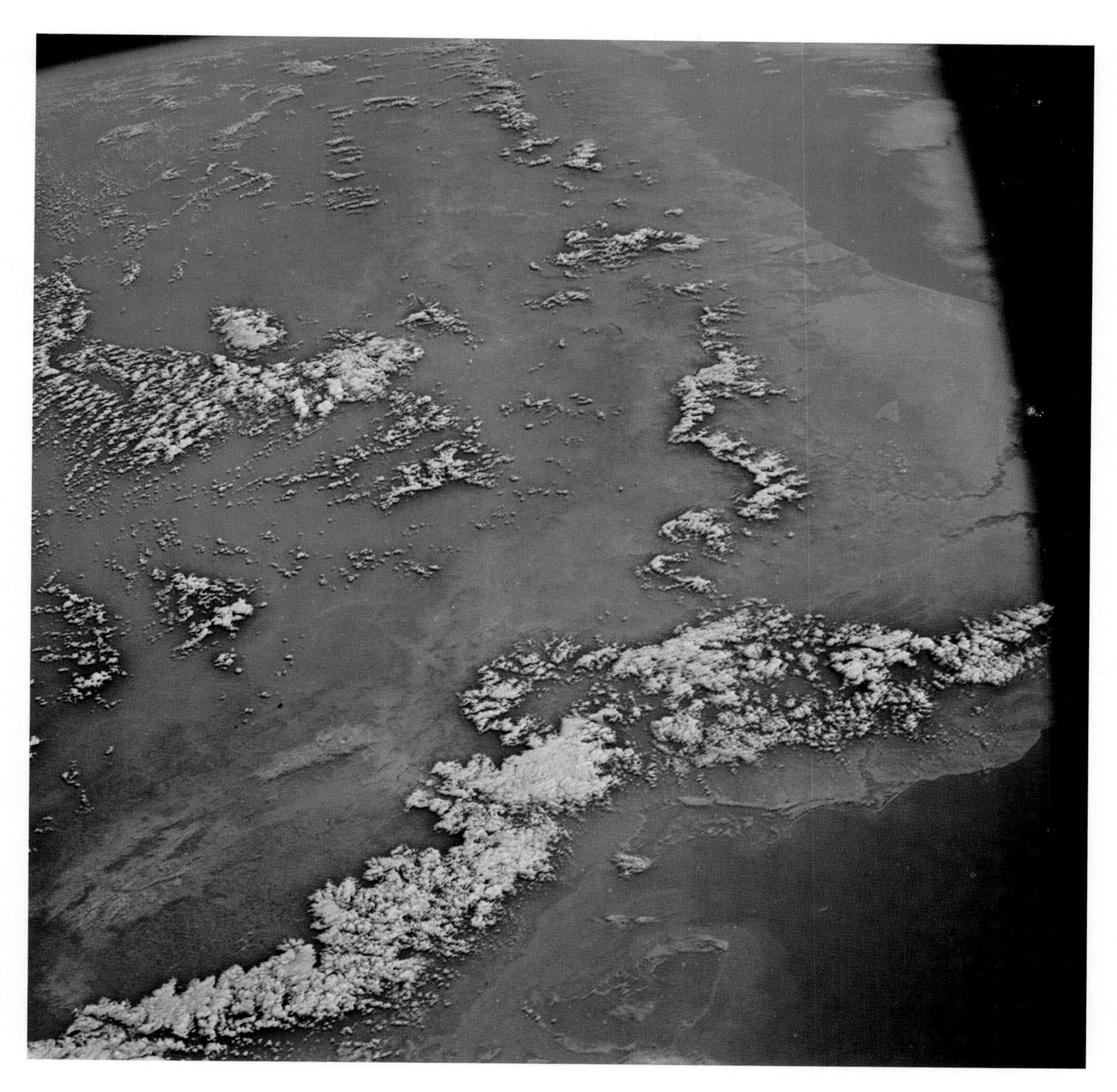

This photo was taken from above the main ridges of the Andes. An irregular band of stratocumulus follows the Western slopes of the mountains a few degrees south of the Equator in Ecuador and Peru. The Amazon Basin begins at the far left, where cumuliform clouds cover the Marañón river's course. The Golfo de Guayaquil is in the foreground, with the Isla de Puna below it. Early in the 1500's, Pizzaro began his search for South America's gold near a point of land formed by a river delta at the lower right. It is now Tumbes, the most northern port of Peru. Another, more southerly, strip of the Peruvian coast is in the upper right corner.

GEMINI IX JUNE 4, 1966 S66–38273

The large curving embayment near the center of this view of western Peru is the Bahía de Sechura, and the narrow coastal plain around it is called the Desierto de Sechura. The results of irrigation along the rivers that cross it are quite apparent. The shoreline shown extends south from Talara about 375 miles to Chimbote. The Pacific waters off the cape at the far left are famous for big-game fishing; black marlin weighing more than half a ton are caught there. The high Andean chain cuts across the upper part of the photo, and snow can be seen on its peaks. South America's enormous Amazon drainage system begins in the upper left corner.

GEMINI IX JUNE 5, 1966 S66–38291

Some parts of the canyon that crosses this picture diagonally are 2 miles deep. These are the mountains of Peru east of the coastal plain shown in the preceding picture. The Rio Marañón, which carries water from them to the Amazon, flows through this canyon. Tropical forests cover the Cordillera Central and the Cordillera Oriental below the scattered cumuliform clouds at the left. Near the right edge, a snow-covered peak of the Cordillera Blanca is quite distinct. This photo includes parts of five northern departments of Peru: Ancash, La Libertad, San Martín, Amazonas, and Cajamarca. This is still a poorly mapped part of the world.

GEMINI IX JUNE 5, 1966 S66-38525

This photograph of nearly 250 miles of Peru's coast suggests how helpful spacecraft may be to surveyors. In the middle of the shoreline shown, a narrow strip of land connects Ferral Peninsula to the mainland near Chimbote. The snowline toward the upper left is more than 16 000 feet above the sea. The Continental Divide follows the Cordillera Blanca across the country there. One of the most prominent snow-covered peaks is the 22 505-foot Huascarán volcano. A thin white line can be seen running down its western slope toward the sea. This is the scar left in 1962 by an avalanche that killed several thousand persons in the Rio Santo Valley.

GEMINI IX JUNE 5, 1966 S66-38298

Another strip of the coast of Peru, south of the area shown on the preceding page, is at the top of this picture of the Andes as they appeared when photographed from the east. The large dark lake in the center here is Lago de Junín. Cerro de Pasco is to the right of it, at an altitude of 17 572 feet. The Cordillera Huayhuash ranges, an important source of minerals, are between the lake and the sea. Snow whitens many of the peaks. The island in the upper right is San Lorenzo. Callao, the port which serves Lima, Peru's capital, is on a small peninsula near that island, over which smoke was floating when this picture was taken.

GEMINI IX   JUNE 5, 1966   S66–38300

Rivers visible between the cumulus clouds at the bottom of this picture flow nearly 4000 miles to mouths on the Atlantic. The Pacific continental shelf is at the top of the photo. The Peruvian coastline shown extends southeastward from Bahia de Caballa to Nevada Coropuna. Inland toward the left one can see the great snowfields on Nevada Coropuna, 21 079 feet high, and Nevada Ampato's twin peaks, 20 702 feet high. The clear zone in the sky may have resulted from the upwelling of cold water and divergence in the atmosphere's friction layer. This divergence is produced when a southeast wind blows over the water adjacent to the arid shoreland.

GEMINI IX JUNE 5, 1966 S66-38303

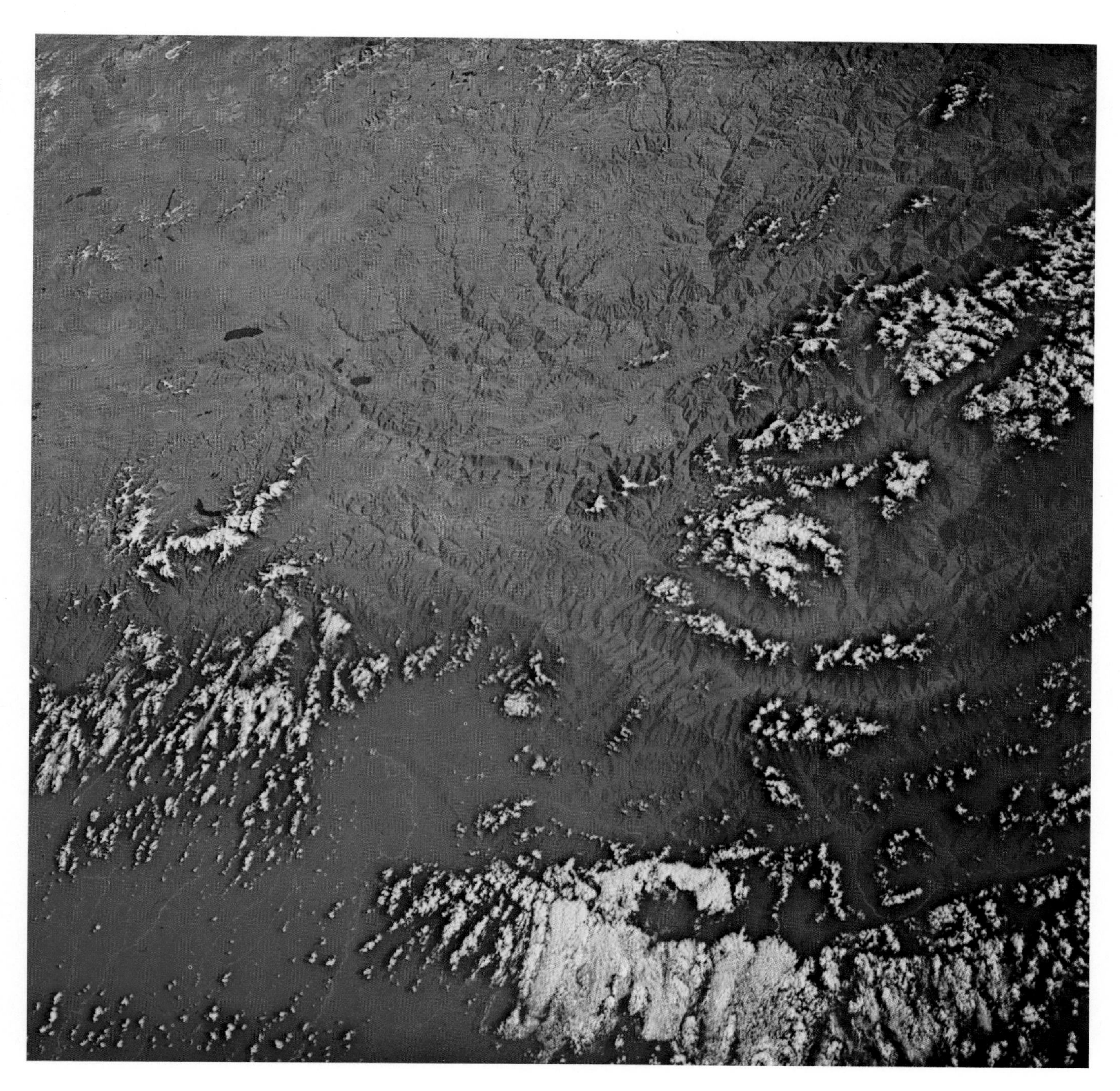

Cusco, once the Inca empire's capital, is nearly in the center of this photo of the towering mountains southeast of Lima, Peru. At the left, where the Cordillera Vilcanota rises 22 000 feet, fields of snow form a white cup around the Laguna Sibanacochas. Below that cup, cumulus clouds and blue haze darken the flat tropical rain forests of the Madre de Dios drainage system. Mile-deep canyons abound along the eastern front of the Andes. The clouds at the right in this view follow the mountains' curving ridges. At the very top of the picture, streaked by snow, is Flor del Mundo. Its northern flank is the source of the Amazon River.

GEMINI IX JUNE 5, 1966 S66-38306

This is the world's highest navigable lake: Titicaca is 12 500 feet above the sea, 700 feet deep, and covers 3200 square miles. La Paz, Bolivia's capital, is tucked against the Cordillera Real southeast of it. Peru shares the shores of Titicaca with Bolivia and in the distance you can see the Chilean-Peruvian desert along the Pacific. The land is arid there despite its nearness to the sea and offshore cloudiness. Two salt flats, Salar de Uyuni and Salar de Coipasa, are near the left edge of the photo. Many volcanoes in the snowcapped Andes exceed 20 000 feet. The snow at the lower right is on the Cordillera Vilcanota.

GEMINI IX JUNE 5, 1966 S66–38312

The bleak, windswept plateau in the lower center of this photo is the Altiplano between Lake Poopo, at the left, and Lake Titicaca, at the right. Lake Poopo is smaller and a few hundred feet lower than Titicaca. West of it enormous salt flats whiten the landscape nearly as much as do the clouds over the Pacific at the upper right. The warm, dry, upper-level air of the trade winds reaches the high elevations of Bolivia and gives this region a desert or steppe climate. Much of the shoreline here is in Chile. The stratus cloudiness over the Pacific is often a persistent feature of the weather along this part of the coast.

GEMINI IX JUNE 5, 1966 S66–38313

The Andean uplift extends along the west coast of South America for 5000 miles. This was the view to the south when the spacecraft crossed it north of Lake Poopo, in the foreground, and the salt flats shown in two previous pictures. Beyond them are the mountains of southern Bolivia, and the volcanoes, lakes, and salt beds of the Puna de Atacama. The view includes northern parts of both Argentina and Chile. At the left the easterly ranges of the Andes drop to the rolling forested region of the Gran Chaco. At the right near the horizon is a deck of stratus clouds that extends far down the long Pacific coast of Chile.

GEMINI IX JUNE 5, 1966 S66–38315

Low stratus clouds extended inland possibly 5 miles and cumuliform clouds covered the Andes 100 miles from the sea when this photo was taken of the mountains around Arequipa, Peru's second largest city. The Río Majes canyon in the center is a mile deep. The city is in the lower part of this view's center, at an altitude of 7500 feet. Northeast of it, three volcanos, Misti, Chachani, and Ampato rise, respectively, 19 098, 19 931, and 20 702 feet. Snow is found on the high peaks, but Arequipa is famous for its flower gardens. Ruins of a civilization believed to have preceded that of the Incas have been found near it.

GEMINI XI SEPTEMBER 14, 1966 S66–54832

The setting Sun's rays gave a golden tint to the thick edges of cirrostratus clouds, and the Cordillera de Los Andes threw long shadows eastward, when the astronauts obtained this picture of southwestern Brazil, northern Argentina, and Chile. Two salt flats and two small lakes, the Laguna Pastos Grandes and the Salina Olaroz, can be distinguished in the foreground when one studies this photo with a map of the area in hand. South America's Andean spine includes many of the Western Hemisphere's highest peaks. Here, however, the convective towers protruding upward in the clouds are more prominent than the mountains for which the area is noted.

GEMINI VII DECEMBER 12, 1965 S65–63780

There were four layers of clouds below the spacecraft the day this picture was taken over equatorial northwest Brazil. When viewed stereoscopically, by using this and an adjacent frame (not reproduced here), each layer is distinct. Two are high-level layers of cirrus, beneath which there is a middle layer of altocumulus, and a lower layer of cumulus. The cumulus-cloud pattern reflects the underlying cool surface of a large river containing islands. It probably is the Río Negros near Barcelos, a town in the State of Amazonas. The Río Negros is a broad stream that crosses the Equator to flow southeast into the Amazon River.

GEMINI X JULY 21, 1966 S66–46047

Brazil's northernmost State, Río Branco, is in the foreground, Venezuela in the left, and Guyana in the right of this photo. The dark, forested areas under cumulus-cloud patterns around the basin in the center are plateaus of sandstones and lava flows, resting on the Precambrian granites and gneisses that constitute the cloud-free basin. The rain forest yields valuable wood and wood products, and the crystalline rocks contain much mineral wealth, including gold and diamonds, but the vegetation has hampered exploration. The large looping river in the lower center is the Río Tacutu, which joins another stream to form the Río Branco.

GEMINI X JULY 21, 1966 S66-46050

The Pakarima Mountains are in the lower right here, and Brazil, Venezuela, and Guyana meet beneath a heavy cloud patch over Mount Roraima near the center. Beyond Mount Roraima is the Gran Sabana, Venezuela's portion of the Guyana highlands. Although these high, flat-topped mesas occupy nearly half of Venezuela, less than 3 percent of the people live on them. The complex pattern of cumulus clouds here is shaped by the topography and by light winds of a weak pressure gradient. Near the coastal region in the upper part of the picture, these clouds trend east-west. There is some cirrus cloudiness in the lower left.

GEMINI X JULY 21, 1966 S66–46051

This picture overlaps the preceding one and includes the northern coast of South America from Caracas, Venezuela, at the left, to Georgetown, Guyana, at the right. Landward, a narrow coastal plane separates the great Guyana plateau from the sea. The massive delta of the Orinoco River is in the upper center and the mouth of the Essequibo River is at the right. The larger tributaries of the Essequibo River system are remarkably outlined in the cumulus-cloud pattern. Sedimentation has discolored the Atlantic waters at the river mouths and along the shore. Scattered over the sea offshore are trade-wind cumuli.

GEMINI X JULY 21, 1966 S66–46052

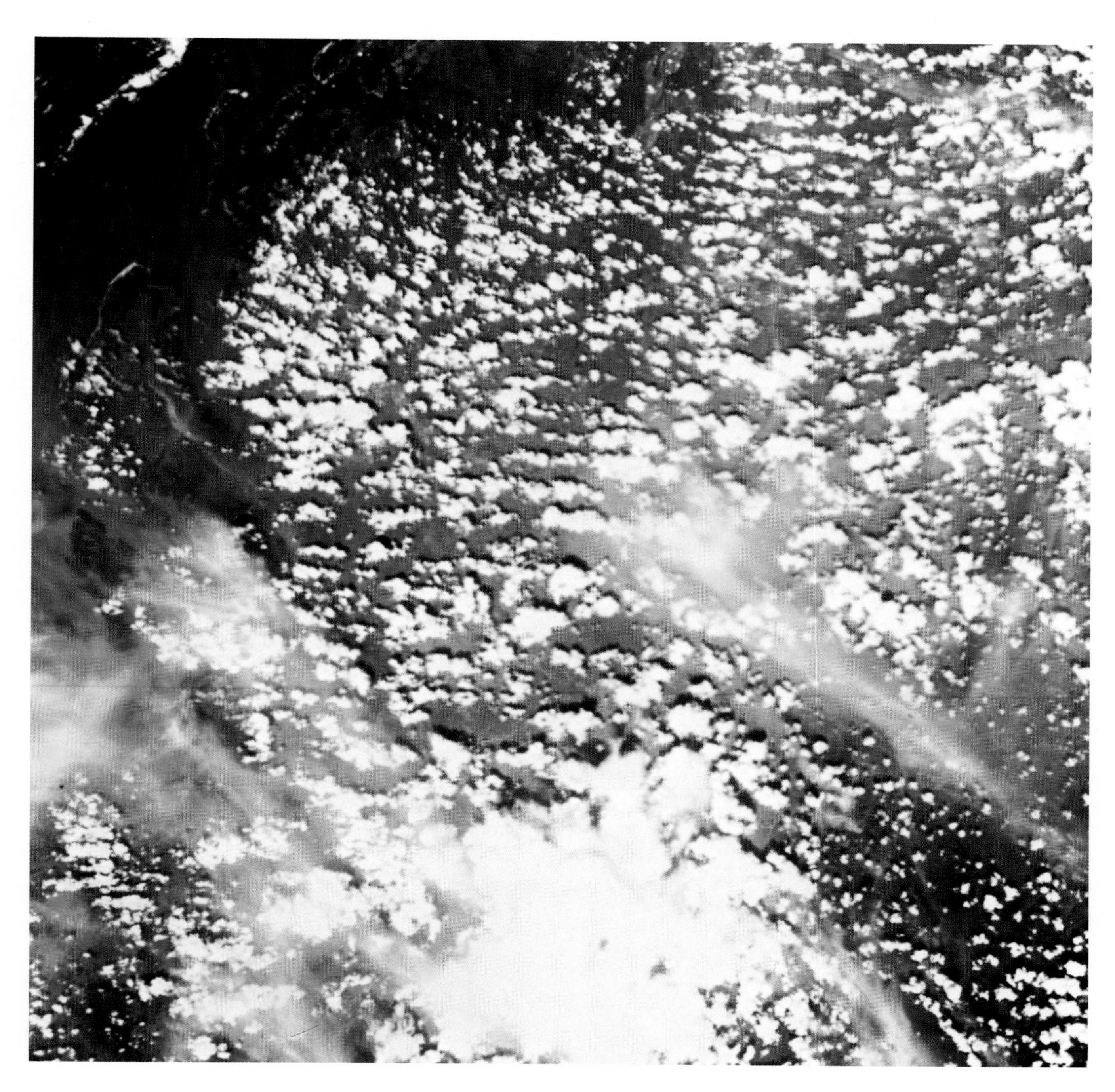

This and the next two photos were taken on color infrared film. They show Brazil's Atlantic coast from the Baía de São Marcos, in the upper left here, eastward around the Natal corner and south to João Pessoa. Varying tones of red indicate changes in the green vegetation. Dense growth on coastal lowlands deepens the red near the Baía de São Marcos. Only a few major streams, draining a small part of Brazil's highlands, feed this bay. From it the land rises gradually to more than 400 feet above sea level at the right edge of the photo. The cloud pattern here consists of cumuli in rows, cumuli congesti, and a few wisps of cirrus.

GEMINI VII DECEMBER 17, 1965 S65–64069

One can trace rivers in the foreground of this infrared photo of the Brazilian coastline from Ponta Redonda east nearly to Natal. The city of Fortaleza is under the clouds over the prominent cape in the center. The shore on both sides of it and inland, where there are mountains, is tinted by dense vegetation. Lowlands surround the Serra da Uruburetama in the lower center. A sea breeze had kept miles of the sandy beach free from clouds. Near the horizon the clouds are distinct because the intervening atmosphere does not scatter as much light at near-infrared wavelengths as it does at the shorter wavelengths used in most photography.

GEMINI VII DECEMBER 17, 1965 S65–64073

This photo partly overlaps the preceding one. It shows Brazil's coast as far east as Ponta Jericoacoaroa, the cape at the very top. Parnaíba is several miles inland from the cape in the center, and Camocim is in a small bay above it. The white splashes are quartz sand, carried down from highlands by rivers, strewn by coastal currents, and whipped into dunes by offshore winds. Cumulus clouds laced above by cirrus begin inland, beyond the cooling effect of the sea breeze. The terrain's redness shows how heavily it is cloaked by vegetation. The land rises to more than 2500 feet at the upper right, where the Serra da Ibiapaba ends.

GEMINI VII DECEMBER 17, 1965 S65–64070

The strip of Brazil's northeast coast in the foreground here begins near Carutapera and continues to the Amazon River's mouth at the right. The many rows of convective clouds, ranging from tiny cumuli to towering cumulonimbi, extend far inland. Near the center they part over the long Baía de Marajó by which ships approach Belém. The Ilha de Marajó is to the right, separated from two other islands, Ilha Mexiana and Caviana (at the right edge), by the Canal do Sul, one of the Amazon's main channels. The sea is discolored beyond them by suspended sediments for distances up to 50 miles.

GEMINI IX JUNE 4, 1966 S66-38191

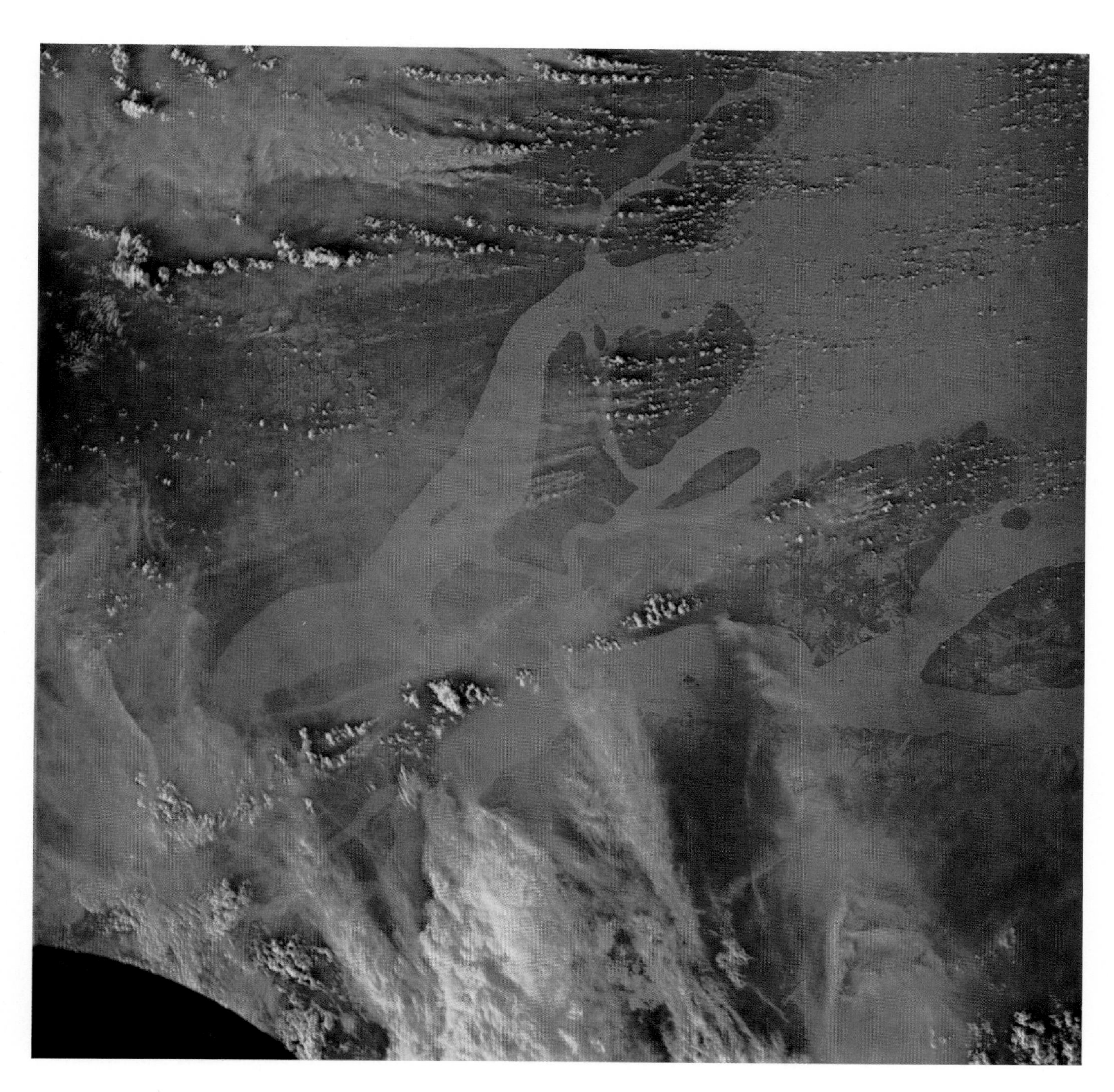

A late-afternoon Sun penetrated the parallel rows of cumulus clouds in the foreground of this nearly vertical picture enough to expose the large islands in the broad, brown Amazon River's mouth. Alongside the cirrus clouds at the top of the photo, thick smoke from burning forests obscured the view. The Amazon's main channels are Canal do Sul, below center, and Canal do Norte, above it. The great river's mouth is dirtied by the vast quantities of mud and silt that it carries far into the Atlantic currents off Brazil's northern shore. Here the water flows through a low, swampy, thinly populated tidewater area covered by forests.

GEMINI VII DECEMBER 12, 1965 S65–64001

When one looks closely at South America's coast here, one sees four rivers adding silt to the coastal currents off Guyana and Surinam. From the left they are the Courantyne, Berbice, Demerara, and Essequibo. Dikes have converted areas slightly below sea level into valuable plantation land along this Atlantic coast. Its sedimentary strata are shales, clays, sands, and lignites, built up largely from the muds brought northward from the Amazon's mouth. Georgetown, Guyana's capital, is at the Demerara's mouth. Convective cloudiness dominates this region throughout the year, and in this photo thunderstorms are also visible inland.

GEMINI VII DECEMBER 13, 1965 S65–64029

"We stole some time from our sleep period to get this picture," Astronaut Michael Collins recalls. "Even from space it appeared as some of the most forbidding jungle territory in the world. This is as close as I ever hope to get to it." The Orinoco River mouth is at the left, and the Essequibo's mouth is near the center of this view. Both rivers were pouring silt and mud into the Atlantic for coastal currents to carry along and build up deposits of shale, clay, and lignites. The morning Sun was heating the land, and complex patterns of cumulus clouds were being built up over it. Broad parts of this coastal land are a few feet below sea level.

GEMINI X JULY 21, 1966 S66-46054

This photograph of the northern coast of Surinam shows low-level cloud convergences that do not appear on the usual synoptic weather map. The cloud lines are readily associated with the boundaries of turbid water. Seeing the distribution of suspended sediment, and the variations in the resulting turbidity of the water, as one can here, is extremely helpful in oceanographic research. The current shears were parallel to the coast on the day this picture was taken, and tons of sediment brought from the continent's interior by the rivers were being spread far to the west. There is no cool season in the Guyanas.

GEMINI X JULY 21, 1966 S66–46056

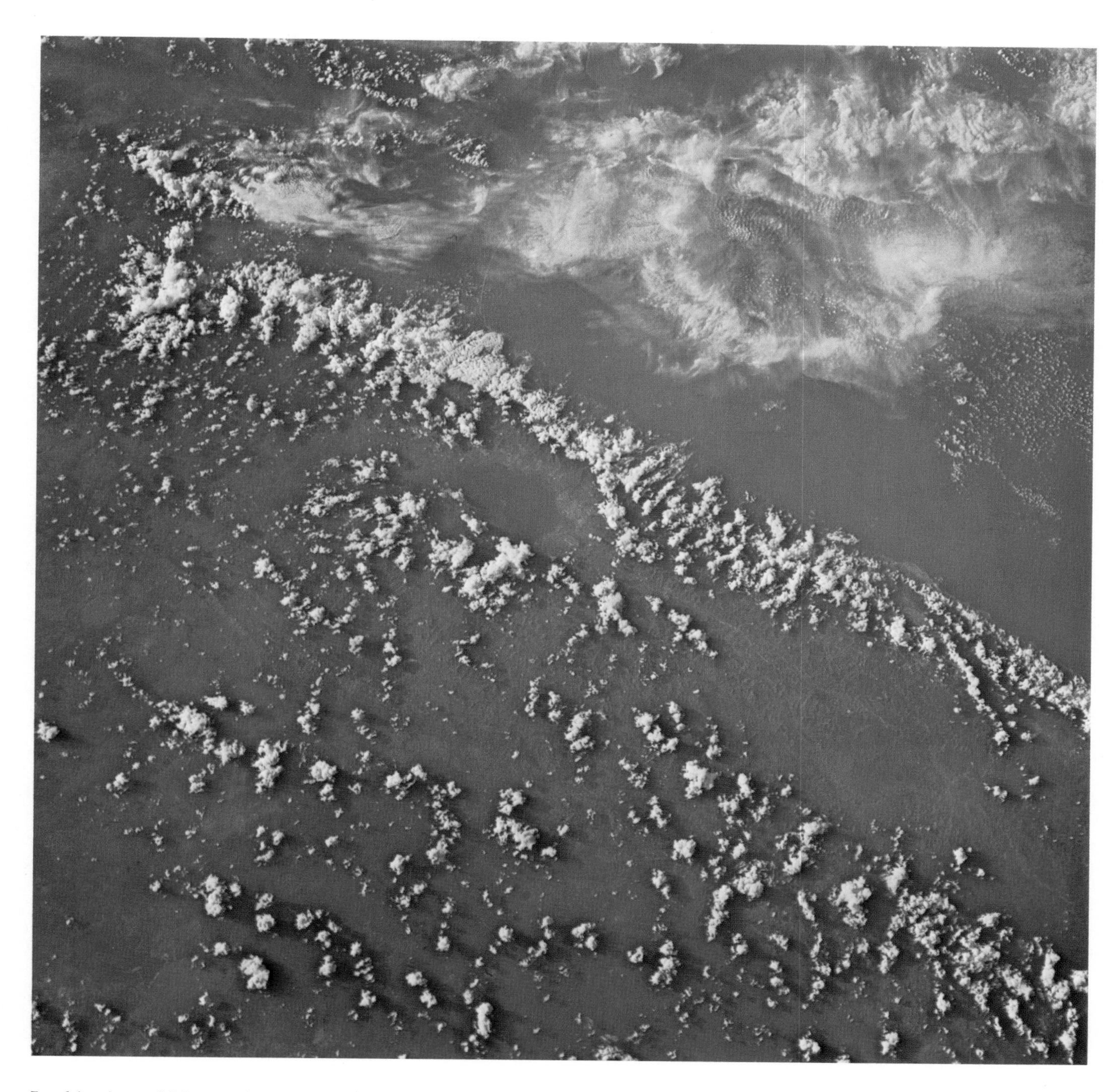

In this view of Venezuela, cumulus clouds dot the land and cirrus veils the Caribbean Sea. The coastline included runs from Tocuyo de la Costa, near the center at the top, to Naiguatá. Lago de Valencia is in the cloud-free area in the center, and the Río Tuy is to the right of it. Caracas, the capital, is about halfway between the river and the coast. The Andes in this area are composed of Mesozoic igneous and metamorphic strata. The vast featureless plain at the lower left is the Orinoco basin. A large reservoir on the Río Guarico is barely discernible there, but the Río Tuy's tributaries stand out clearly in the lower right of the photo.

GEMINI VII DECEMBER 12, 1965 S65-63995

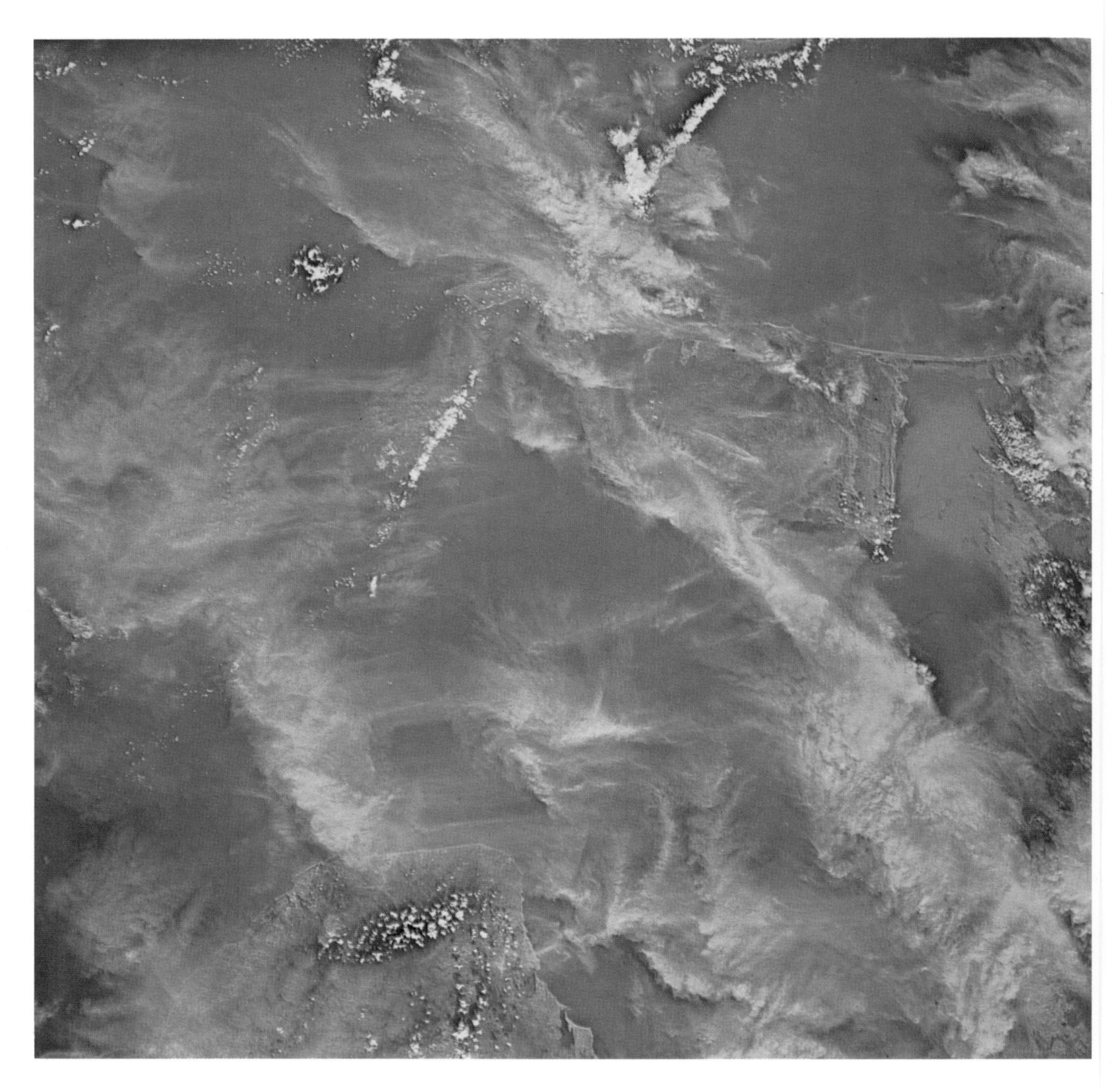

The bright line of cumulus clouds in the upper center runs downward from Curaçao to Aruba. A peninsula of Colombia and the 60-mile-wide entry to the Golfo de Venezuela are under the cirrus clouds in the foreground. At the right, below a narrow strip of land between the Península de Paraguana and the mainland, is the rectangular Golfete de Coro, darkened by the sediment carried seaward by South American streams. Faults between the Andean spurs outline the Golfo de Venezuela, and a surface deposit of Quaternary alluvium is found on the Cretaceous and Tertiary beds in this fault basin.

GEMINI VII DECEMBER 12, 1965 S65–63993

From over the Caribbean Sea, the camera was pointed southwest toward South America to obtain this picture. The semiarid islands of the Lesser Antilles cross it near the center. From the left they are the Isla Orchila, Islas Los Roques, Ilas de Aves, Bonaire, Curaçao, and Aruba. The Venezuelan shore above them extends from Barcelona at the left to the country's reddish, northernmost tip, the Península de Paraguana, at the right. This part of the world has been photographed from several spacecraft, but clouds usually have obscured the surface. Even here convective and cirriform cloudiness conceals much of the landscape.

GEMINI IX JUNE 4, 1966 S66-38189

# Part IX. Mexico

MEXICO is between 14° and 33° north of the Equator and the orbits of the Gemini flights gave the astronauts many opportunities to photograph it. The central plateau is bounded on the west by the Sierra Madre Occidental, and on the east by the Sierra Madre Oriental. Between these high ranges, other mountains partition the land into a maze bedecked by volcanoes, lakes, and deserts. These photos show the land through which the Spaniards advanced into the southwestern part of the United States.

The Gemini astronauts approached it from the Pacific rather than from the Atlantic and often crossed Baja California, which extends down the western coast of North America for 800 miles, before they soared over the mainland. Joseph Wood Krutch has called Baja California "the forgotten peninsula" for reasons quite apparent in these photos.

Below the long Gulf of California, the continent curves east around the Gulf of Mexico. The Yucatan Peninsula extends to the north from this part of Mexico nearly to Cuba's western tip. When one recalls the known history of this land, and the civilizations that flourished there before the Spaniards arrived, the pictures in this section become especially fascinating. Some of the views here extend northward into the United States for many miles.

This and the next few photos, taken from spacecraft as they approached Mexico, show how greatly its appearance varied on different occasions. The thick, high, cirrostratus cloud here concealed all but a few bits of Baja California, at the left and toward the lower right corner. A number of thunderstorms formed this great circular body. Several convective cells appeared to have gained sufficient momentum to penetrate its thick layer, and the rippled surface of the cirrostratus suggests that diverging updrafts from other convective cells have reached their maximum stage of development and begun to dissipate.

GEMINI VII DECEMBER 7, 1965 S65–63834

On one occasion the camera recorded bands of cirrus clouds that extended for 300 miles in southwesterly winds between the mountains in Sonora and Baja California. This photo includes the Pinacate volcanic field at the left, on the border between the United States and Mexico. Baja California has changed less than most parts of the New World since the Spanish built missions there in the 17th century. Here the birds and other native creatures have gone their way virtually undisturbed. So, too, have many of this peninsula's distinctive plants.

GEMINI XII NOVEMBER 14, 1966 S66–63015

This picture, taken on the next revolution after the one on which the previous photo was taken, shows some of Baja California and the North American mainland under different lighting. Dark patches in the Sun glitter on the Pacific are regions of smooth water. Patches of stratocumulus clouds are near the top of the photo. Clouds such as that long, conspicuous band of cirrus that arcs along the right side of the picture usually indicate the existence of a subtropical jetstream nearby. The jetstream winds are encountered in this region when an upper air trough is located over the eastern Pacific Ocean.

GEMINI XII NOVEMBER 14, 1966 S66-63054

From over the Pacific, you are looking southeast now at Baja California. In the foreground long fingers of cirrus reach toward Punta Eugenia. The large oval at the left is Bahía Sebastián Vizcaíno, and the lagoon is Ojo de Liebre, where gray whales breed. The dry air evaporates sea water to form white salt flats south of this lagoon. The mountains in the center of the cape are underlain by Cretaceous metamorphic, igneous, and sedimentary rock. This part of North America's shore is characterized by abundant Tertiary and Quaternary vulcanism. Beyond the Gulf of California, which extends across the upper half of the photo, is Sonora.

GEMINI VII DECEMBER 5, 1965 S65–63822

Astronaut Eugene A. Cernan took this maplike picture of the Pacific coast of Mexico alongside Gemini IX's nose while the hatch was open. The Sierra Madre Occidental extends along the left shore of the Gulf of California in the center. The Sierra La Giganta is in the foreground, and the southern end of Baja California is spread before you at the right. The State capital, La Paz, is at the far end of the large bay in the narrow neck near the long peninsula's tip. The irregular dark topography is typical of a surface underlain mainly by igneous and metamorphic rock. The clouds on the horizon are south of the Tropic of Cancer.

GEMINI IX JUNE 5, 1966 S66-38070

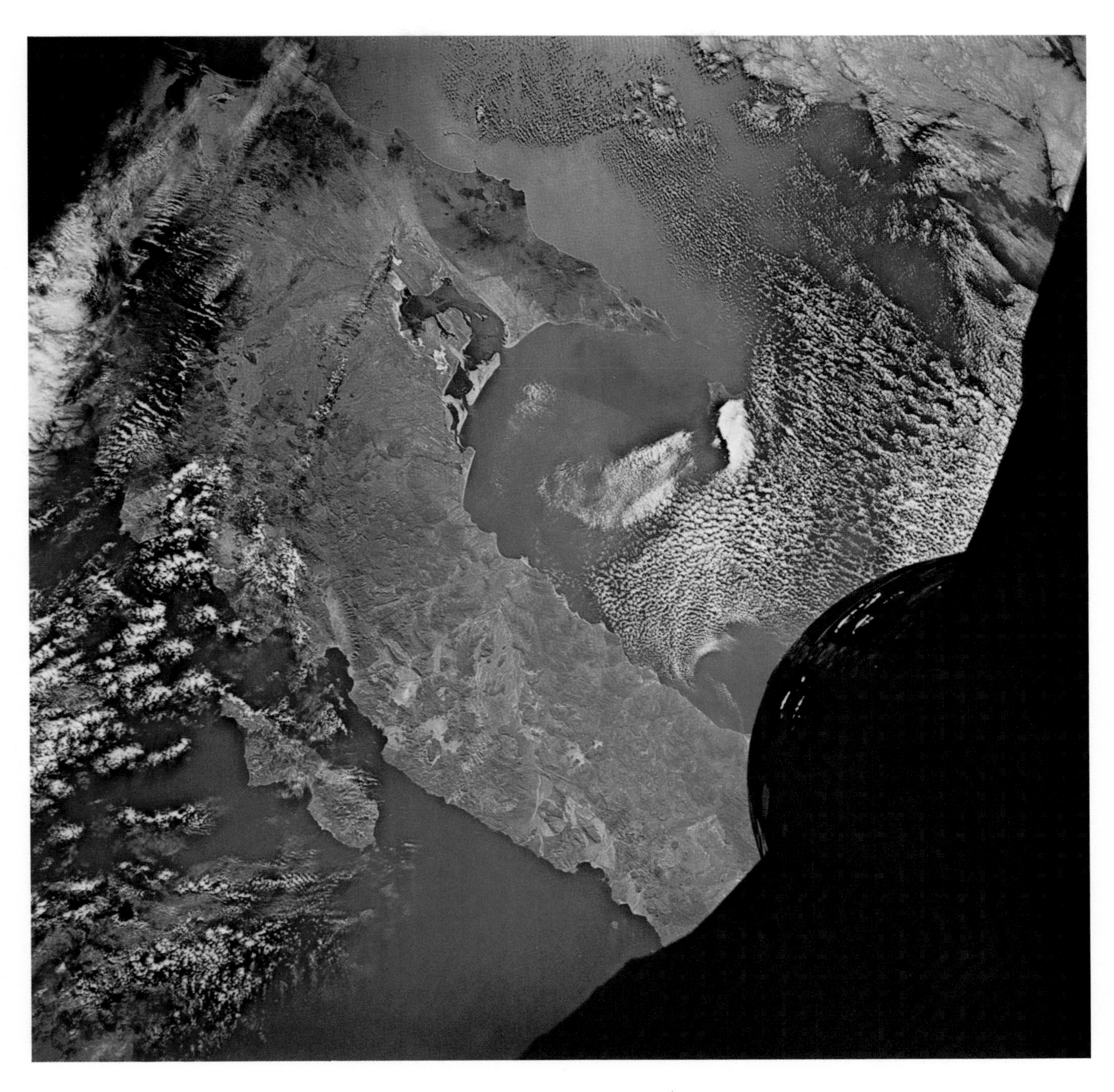

The spacecraft's nose was pointed at the central part of Baja California when this photo was taken. Angel de La Guarda Island in the Gulf of California was visible at the lower left below the cloud system over the gulf. Bahía Sebastián Vizcaíno is in the upper center of this view and beyond it to the south are Punta Abreojos, Laguna San Ignacio, and Bahía Ballenas. The current in the Pacific was sweeping strongly from north to south and relatively cool. Punta Abreojos projected into the main stream of this current, and caused the series of turbulent eddies visible in the slick pattern of the Sun's reflection in the upper center of the picture.

GEMINI XII NOVEMBER 14, 1966 S66-63044

Cabo Corrientes is above Gemini XII's nose in this open-hatch photo, taken by Astronaut Edwin E. Aldrin, Jr., south of Baja California. At the left are dark, dissected ranges of the Sierra Madre Occidental, an extensive plateau of Tertiary volcanics. Beyond the cape, around Lago de Chapala, is the Neo-Volcanic plateau, a band of Tertiary, Quaternary, and Recent volcanics that extends eastward to the Gulf of Mexico. To the south is the Sierra Madre del Sur, a complex mountainous area of older rocks. A spiral is visible in the cumulus-cloud streets near the cape where the coastal configuration induced an eddy in the northerly airflow.

GEMINI XII NOVEMBER 12, 1966 S66–62883

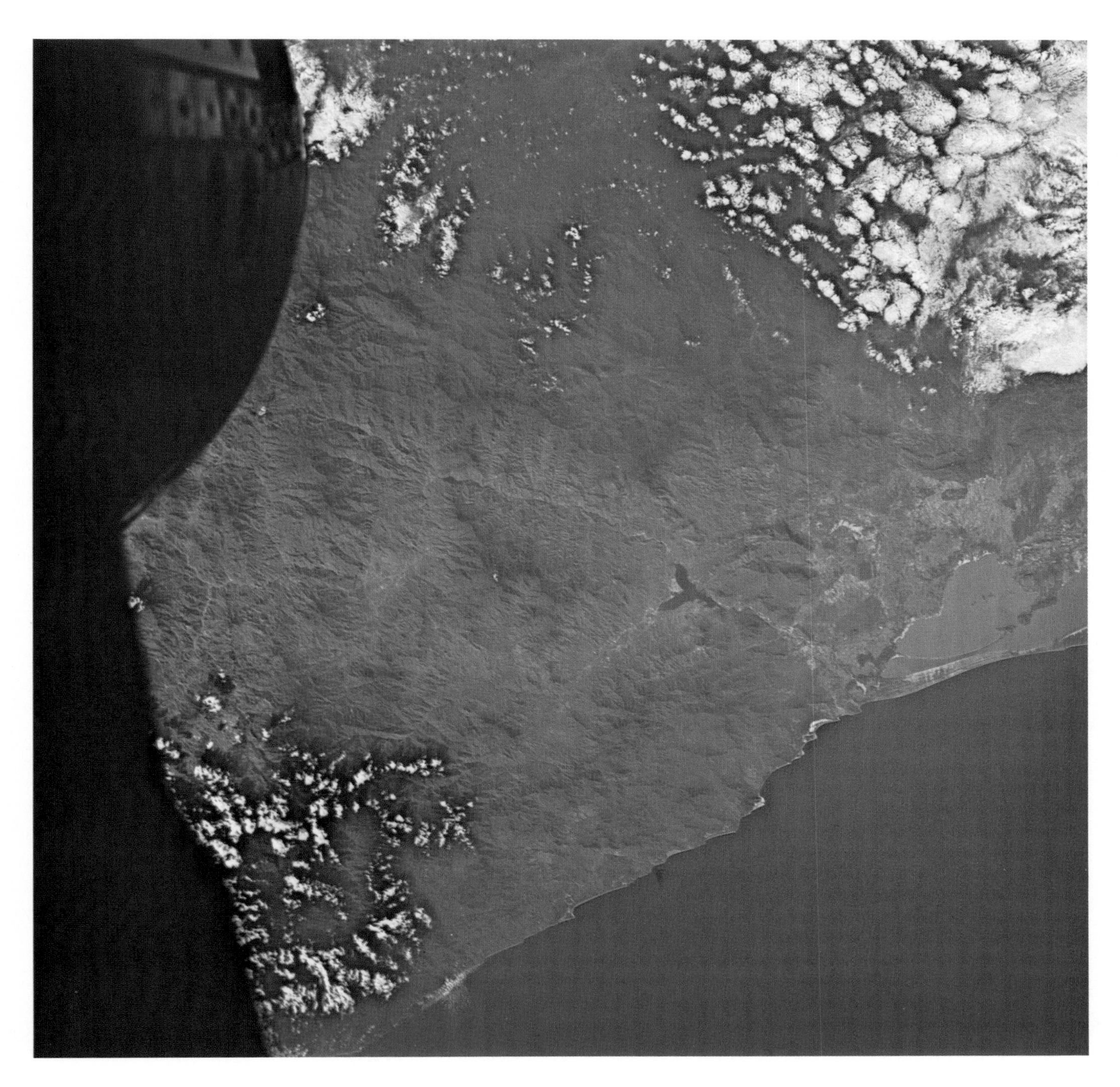

The Gulf of Tehuantepec is in the right foreground now. It is about 1000 miles south at the same longitude as Houston. The **Y**-shaped reservoir is near the Pacific Coastal Plain of Mexico. From it the Río Tehuantepec flows past the city of Tehuantepec. At Laguna Superior, you see a long sand bar. Laguna Inferior is farther right. The Sierra Madre del Sur's southern and eastern edges are in the upper left of this photo. The Gulf Coastal Plain begins below the cellular stratocumulus clouds in the upper right corner. The Sierra Travesada, marking the edge of the Chiapas-Guatemala Uplands, begins just above the lagoons.

GEMINI VII DECEMBER 11, 1965 S65–63760

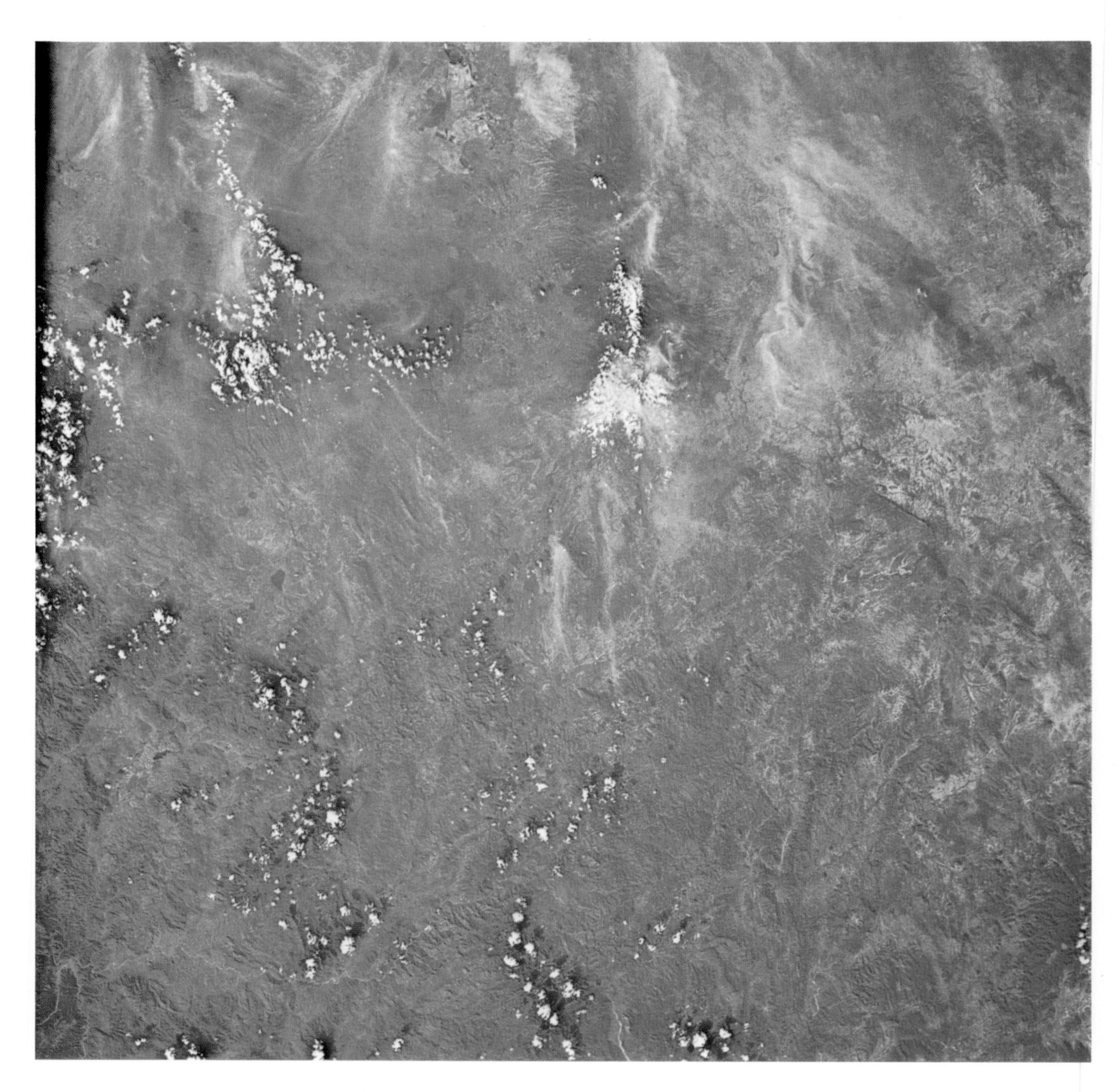

Mexico City is a white patch distinct from the cirrus clouds at the top here. You are looking north and the city of Puebla is in the broad valley toward the upper right. The Neo-Volcanic Plateau in the top half of the photo averages 8000 feet in height. Three volcanic cones—Serro Tláloc, Iztaccíhuatl, and Popocatépetl—extend south from the top center. The latter rises 17 887 feet. In the foreground is part of the Sierra Madre del Sur system. This complex area of Paleozoic metasediments has fewer volcanoes, but pyroclastics cover large areas. The rivers that drain this lower region flow into the Pacific.

GEMINI VII DECEMBER 11, 1965 S65–63757

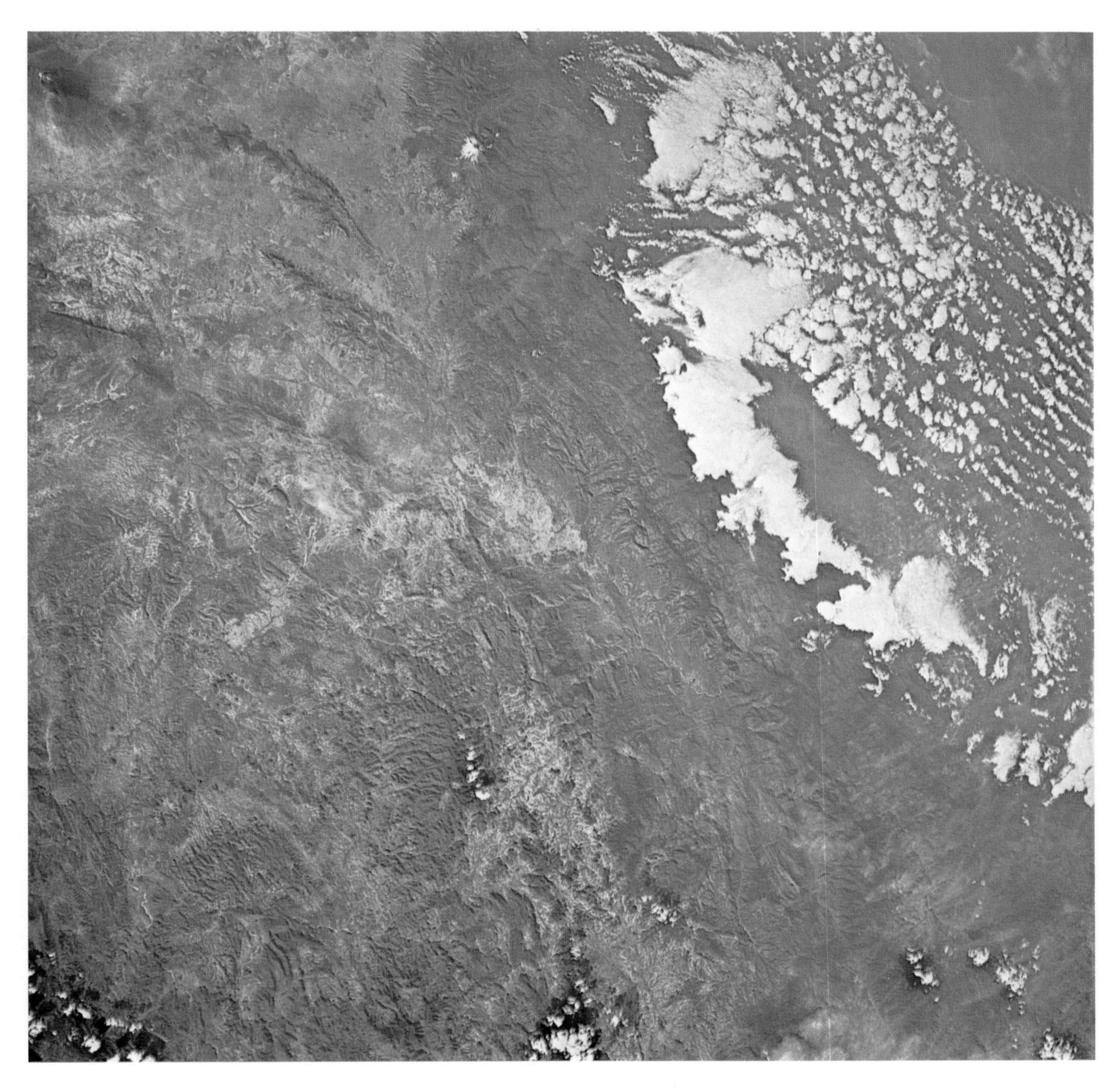

The mountains here are east of those in the preceding picture and the Gulf of Mexico south of Veracruz is in the upper right. An upland of the Madre del Sur system is at the lower left, and the Valle de Oaxaca, bordered by sharply dissected rims on the north and east, is in the foreground. The snow-covered volcano in the upper center is Citlaltépec, 18 701 feet high. Stratocumulus clouds were pushed toward it from the gulf. Through the largest gap in them, Miguel Alemán, a large reservoir, is visible. Radiosonde data at Veracruz showed that the cloud tops were about 3500 feet high when the photo was taken.

GEMINI VII DECEMBER 11, 1965 S65–63758

This view to the southeast over Mexico extends to the Yucatan Peninsula. Mexico City is just north of a forested region from which smoke is rising near the center. The large brown lake in the foreground is Lago de Cuitzeo. The dark spots are areas of volcanic rock. This plateau's thousands of volcanoes are mostly Quaternary and Tertiary. Rocks that span the geologic column from Precambrian to Quaternary time are found in the Madre del Sur Mountains at the right. The rows of cumuli in the foreground are in a light easterly wind. The clouds over Mexico's eastern coast and Central America in the distance are mostly cumuliform.

GEMINI XII NOVEMBER 12, 1966 S66–62887

The tiny, cloud-free area above the spacecraft's open hatch in this view of southern Mexico is a basin near Puebla. Cumulus clouds have formed lines with the wind at many places, and high cirriform clouds are scattered over the Gulf of Mexico and the Yucatan Peninsula at the upper left. The indentation in the clouds on Yucatan's north shore is west of Laguna de Terminos. Surface temperatures are likely to be lower in the marshy land there. Mexico's part of the Yucatan Peninsula is mostly a coastal plain, but south of it in Guatemala there are many complex mountains, bordered by older ranges near the Pacific.

GEMINI XII NOVEMBER 12, 1966 S66–62891

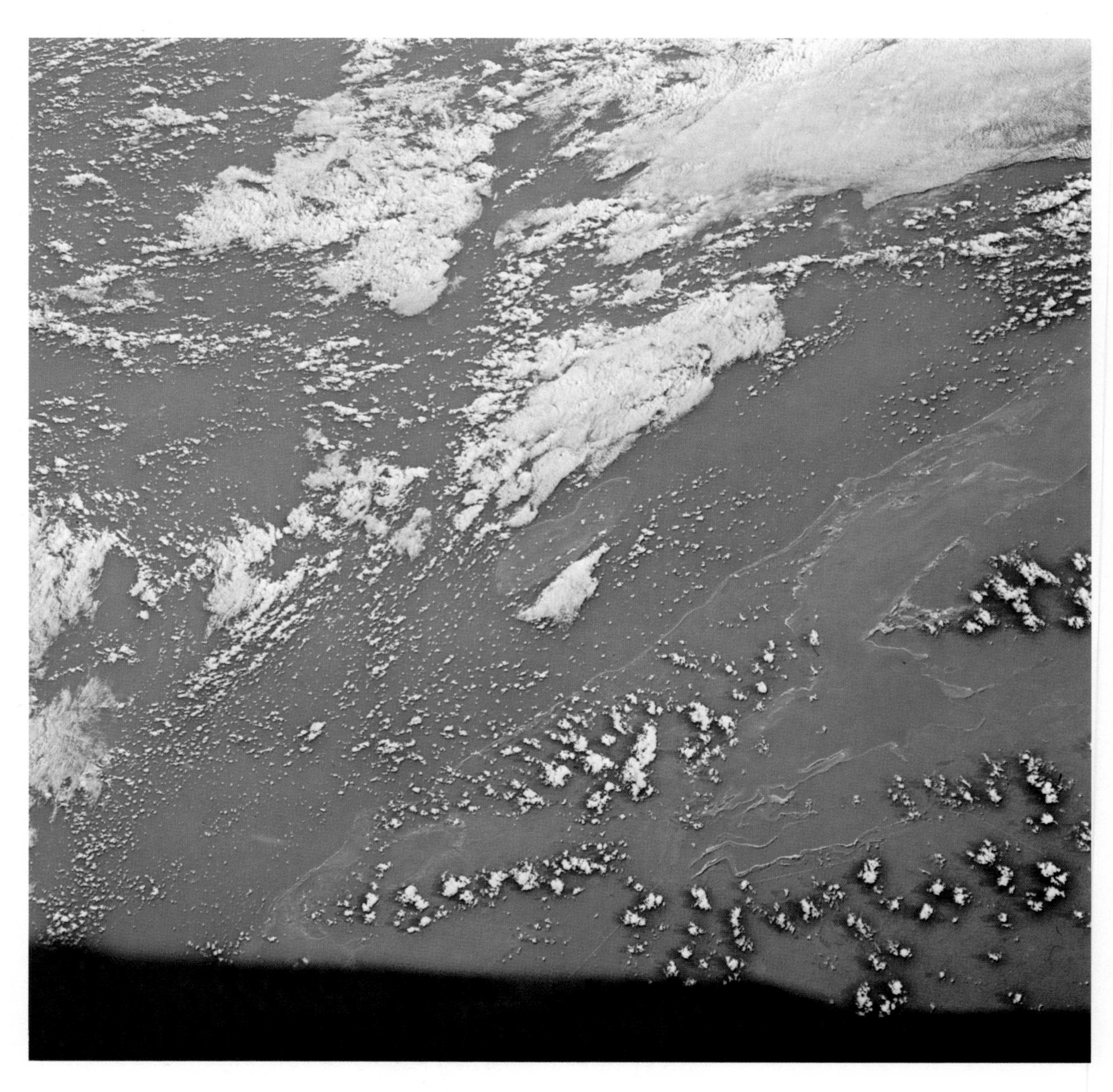

The eastern coast of the Yucatan Peninsula is in the foreground of this photo. Trade-wind cumuli lie beneath a higher stratiform cloud layer. Bahía de la Ascensíon on the Caribbean Sea at the lower left is in Quintana Roo, Mexico, and Ambergris Cay, at the right edge, is in British Honduras. Offshore there are numerous cays and reefs, amidst which Banco Chinchorro stands out near the center. Around Bahía de Chetumal at the lower right, the land is low, flat, and swampy. Dense vegetation obscures its topography. This part of Central America is still emerging geologically and is composed mostly of Tertiary limestones.

GEMINI VII DECEMBER 10, 1965 S65–63741

All three shores of the Yucatan Peninsula can be seen at the left in this northwesterly view from over the Caribbean. This is where Spanish explorers found the remnants of the Mayan civilization. Western Cuba projects from the foreground into the center of this picture. White towers of cumuli reached upward into the moist atmosphere over the Gulf of Mexico the day this photo was taken, and small cumuli dotted Yucatan except where cumulonimbi had developed at its eastern end. Cirrus cloudiness generated by thunderstorms is prevalent in the Caribbean region in the lower left quadrant of the photo.

GEMINI X JULY 19, 1966 S66–45688

Now the view is to the north through central Mexico. The Sierra Madre Occidental is in the lower left and the Sierra Madre Oriental's dark ridges cross this photo above its center. Composed of folded Cretaceous sediments, these mountains form a long chain from the Big Bend country to the Neo-Volcanic plateau. Left of the center, the light-colored, sandy Bolson de Coahuila separates the mountainous Coahuila upland and the westward swing of the cross ranges. Several layers of cumuliform and cirriform clouds are along Mexico's east coast. The cloud deck near the horizon is connected with a cold front moving south from Texas.

GEMINI XII NOVEMBER 12, 1966 S66–62889

North of Mexico City, the Mexican plateau is actually a basin surrounded by higher terrain. This picture of it was obtained with the camera pointed northeast, and includes parts of four States: Aguascalientes, Zacatecas, San Luis Potosí, and Guanajuato. This is a hilly area, composed mostly of dissected volcanics, and the drainage is into shallow lakes. These are usually salty and sometimes dry. The top of this photo is blurred because of a residue on the window of Gemini VII, but a few widely scattered cumulus clouds and some cirrus can be seen. The dark patch at lower left is an area of volcanic rock.

GEMINI VII DECEMBER 6, 1965 S65–63814

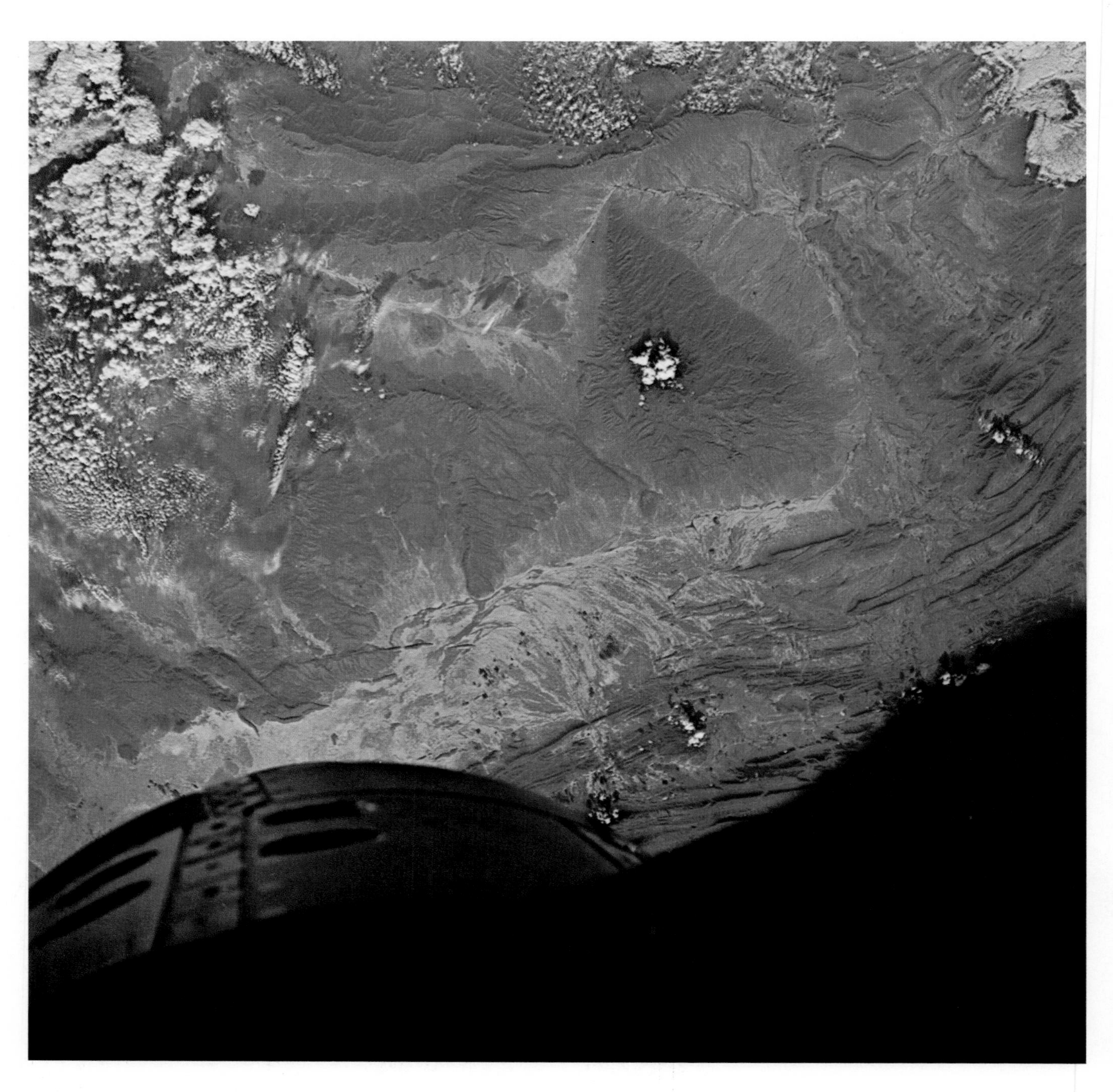

Small cumulus clouds hung like a tiny crown atop the Sierra de la Palma, in the upper center, to adorn this photo of the mainland's eastern mountains. The Sierra de la Palma is a roughly triangular, isolated mass of uplifted Cretaceous rocks at the eastern end of Antefosa de Parras in the Sierra Madre Oriental. Erosion of folded sedimentary rocks formed the zigzag pattern to the right of this peak; these folds plunge eastward so that the uplift is essentially across the direction of the main folds. When Hernán Cortes was asked for a relief map of Mexico after his conquest of it, he simply crumpled a piece of parchment.

GEMINI VII DECEMBER 9, 1965 S65–63888

The stratocumulus cloud deck with cells and billows shown here stretched across eastern Mexico. The high ranges in the foreground are south of Monterrey. These intensely folded Cretaceous sedimentary rocks mark both the front of the Sierra Madre Oriental and a bend in the mountain range. No one knows why the range bends about 60° toward the west here, but some geologists suspect that a major wrench fault going through the Antefosa de Parras dragged the mountains around in this way. The city of Saltillo is in the valley just above the nose of the spacecraft, and parts of two States, Coahuila and Nuevo León, are visible.

GEMINI VII DECEMBER 9, 1965 S65–63889

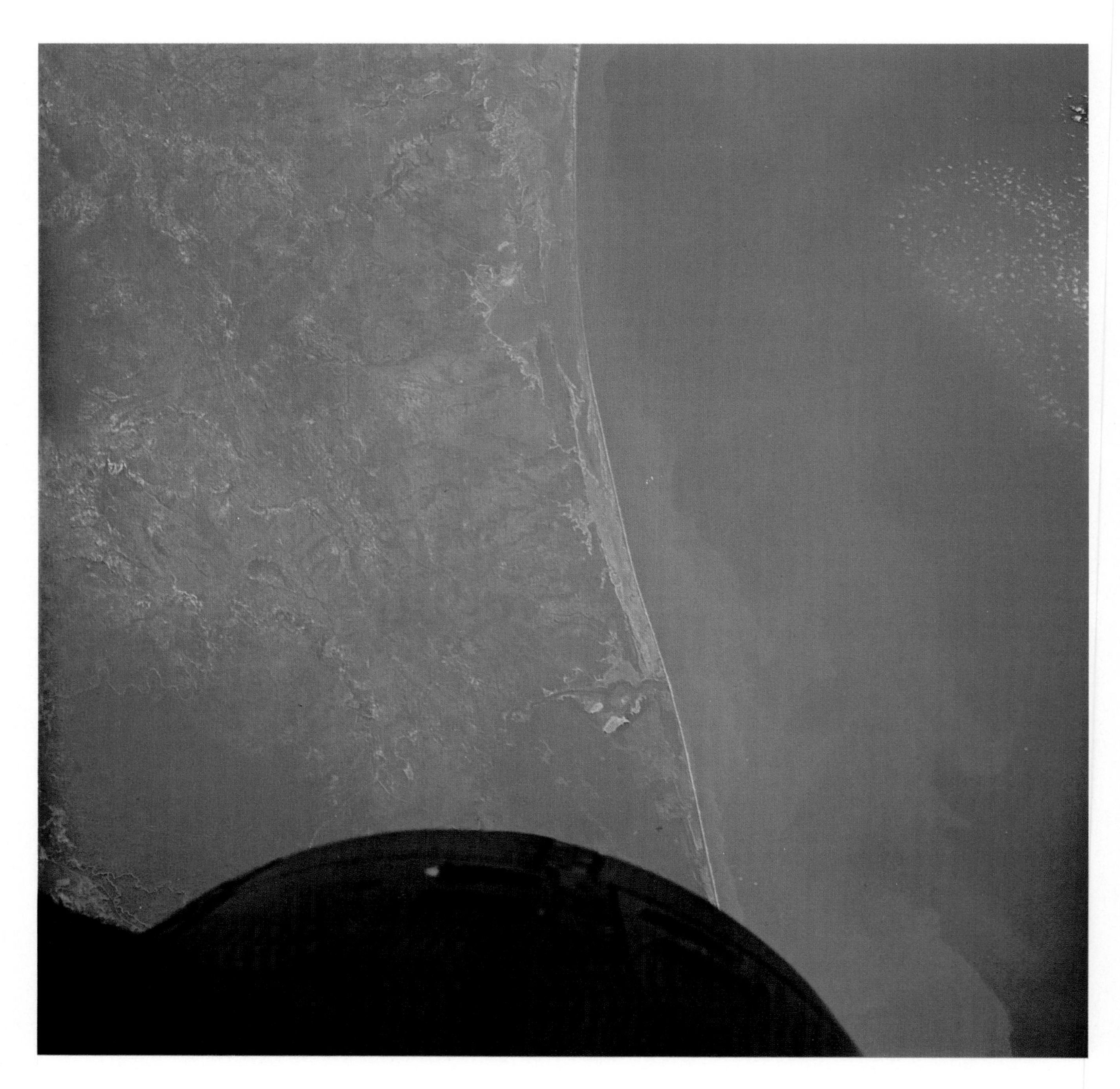

The waters off Tamaulipas, south of Brownsville, Tex., are usually clear, but the high surf the day this photo was taken stirred sediment into suspension, and tidal movements caused the swirls you see in the sediment pattern. The coastal strip shown extends south for 150 miles from Boca de Sandoval to the Tropic of Cancer. Behind the offshore bar is Laguna Madre. At the lower left the Río Purificacíon meanders out of the Sierra de Tamaulipas and across the narrow plain to the gulf.

GEMINI VII DECEMBER 6, 1965 S65–63810

For this picture the camera was pointed east over the Sierra Madre Oriental toward the Gulf of Mexico. Some of the interior highland can be seen in the foreground. Those long dark ridges, visible despite the cirrus-cloud cover, are in the vicinity of Monterrey. The largest deflection in the trend of the Sierra Madre Oriental is found there. In the background, heavy, moist air from the gulf veils the view. The high mountains along the coast barricade the interior land from such humid air.

GEMINI IX JUNE 3, 1966 S66-37907

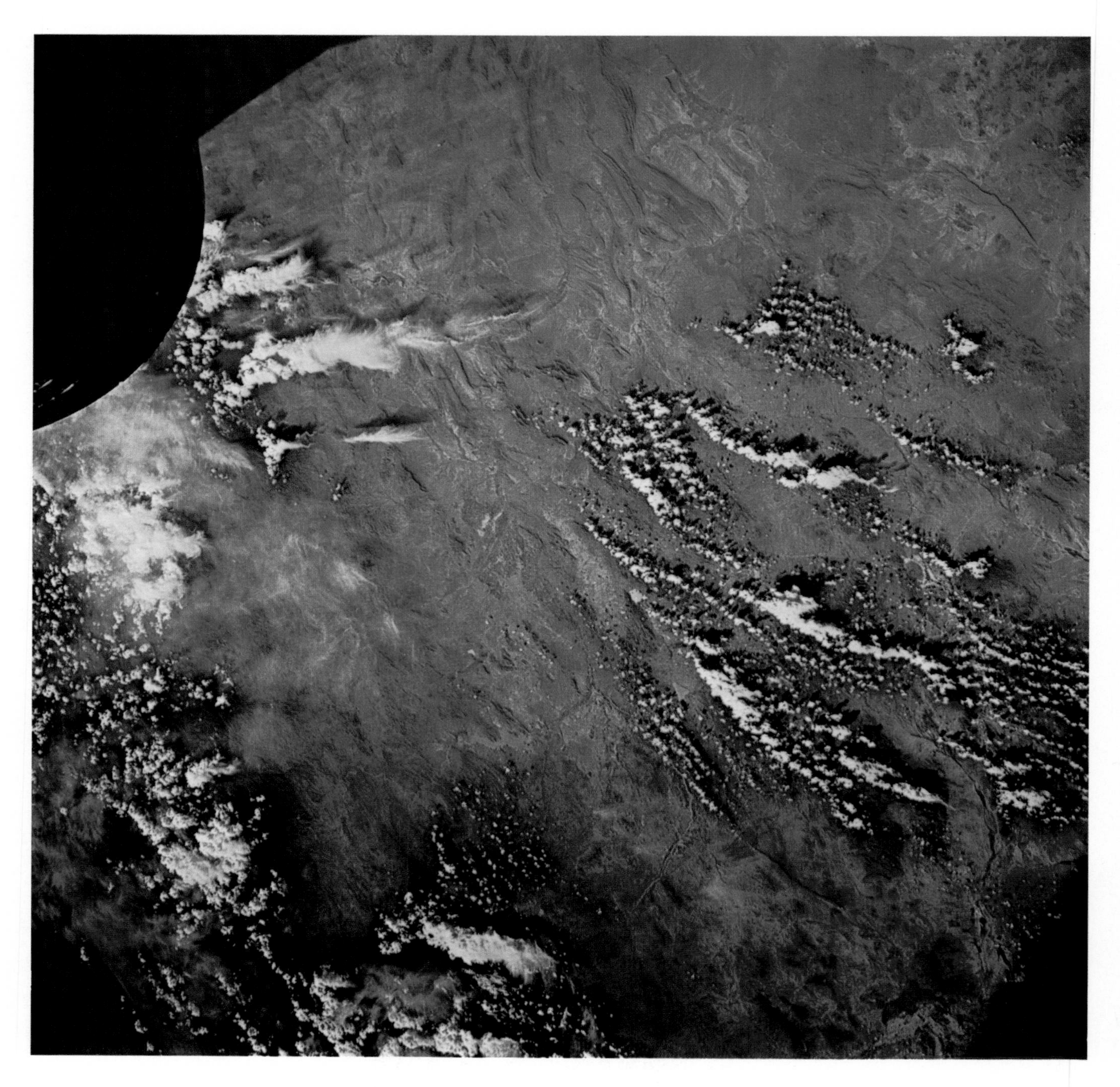

The Sierra Madre Occidental is in the lower left corner of this view and the city of Chihuahua is just below a featherlike cirrus cloud in the upper left center. Rows of cumuli at the right are over a part of the Sierra Madre Oriental. This is an area of relatively low relief but high elevation. Mountain ranges are widely spaced here and intermontane basins are filled with Quaternary alluvium. The Rio Grande flows through the region at the upper right. North of it is El Solitario, a 3-mile-wide dome over a laccolith that brings lower Paleozoic and Cretaceous sediments to the surface along with Tertiary rocks.

GEMINI XII NOVEMBER 14, 1966 S66–63055

This view of northeastern Mexico extends into Texas. The mouth of the Rio Grande is in the upper right, and Nuevo León and Coahuila are in the foreground. The color reveals these States' desertlike climate. The cloud lines over the coastal lowlands show that the airflow in the lower troposphere is from the east. The leeward, western slopes of some ranges of the Sierra Madre Oriental are free of clouds. Notice, too, how the cloud lines conform to the curvature of the ranges near Monterrey at the right. The immense folded mountain chain in the foreground runs southeast from Chihuahua nearly to the gulf.

GEMINI X JULY 20, 1966 S66–45762

The horizon here is more than 1000 miles away. Part of Chihuahua, Mexico, is in the foreground. The Sierra Madre Occidental is at the left and the Sierra Madre Oriental is at the right. The view is directly north up the Rio Grande valley and includes most of the southern Rocky Mountains. Eastern Arizona is on the horizon at the far left, and central Oklahoma and Kansas at the right. Near the center of the picture, the white patch to the right of the Rio Grande is the White Sands National Monument. North of it is the distinct, black, ribbonlike shape of the Malpais, a recent lava flow north of Alamogordo, N. Mex.

GEMINI XII NOVEMBER 14, 1966 S66–63018

# Part X. The United States

Some parts of the United States were shown in pictures that precede this group. Since the girdle that the Gemini program threw around the world did not extend as far north as south of Cape Kennedy, the photographs that follow are predominantly views of the southern coast of the United States around the Gulf of Mexico.

This is not a "forgotten" area such as Baja California. Nor is it a barren land. It differs markedly from many of the regions shown previously. This is a region in which people have been quick to develop the resources available to them, and parts of it are now highly industrialized. Even so, when seen from space its beauty still rivals that of many undeveloped regions.

By enabling us to see the scheme of things entire, space photography can help men both exploit an undeveloped region's natural resources and monitor the skies, seashores, and forests to prevent pollution and degradation of them.

This was the astronauts' homeland and they photographed the city of Houston many times. Along the gulf shore they used infrared along with other color film to obtain more information than one can with the naked eye. Above Florida's east coast they saw their starting point again, and sped east again and again to see more of the world.

"We have achieved the ability to see and contemplate ourselves from afar," Dr. Floyd L. Thompson wrote shortly before he retired as Director of the Langley Research Center, "and thus in a measure to accomplish the wish expressed by Robert Burns: 'To see oursels as ithers see us.' "

North America's Pacific coast, from Los Angeles, near the left edge, to Baja California is slightly above the stratocumulus clouds in the foreground. San Diego is nearly in the center. The massive mountain range at the extreme left is the south end of the Sierra Nevada. Above Los Angeles is the large, bare Mojave Desert. The San Andreas fault runs southeast from it between mountain ranges to the Salton Sea, right of center. The clouds on the horizon hide most of the Colorado Plateau. In the clouds at the lower right, the photo shows a remarkable set of waves, probably induced by irregularity in the terrain along the coast.

GEMINI X JULY 19, 1966 S66–45658

A wide-angle lens used during extravehicular activity produced this colorful view of the United States from the Gulf of California, at lower right, to the Colorado Plateau. The Salton Sea is above the red dot on the spacecraft. Farms outline California's Imperial Valley and the Colorado River's delta in northern Mexico. This part of the Great Basin shows typical basin-and-range topography. The distant clouds were scattered over California and western Arizona. The dark elliptical area above the gulf is the Pinacate volcanic field, and the light smoke plume above it was rising from the forested region northeast of Phoeniz, Ariz.

GEMINI IX JUNE 5, 1966 S66–38068

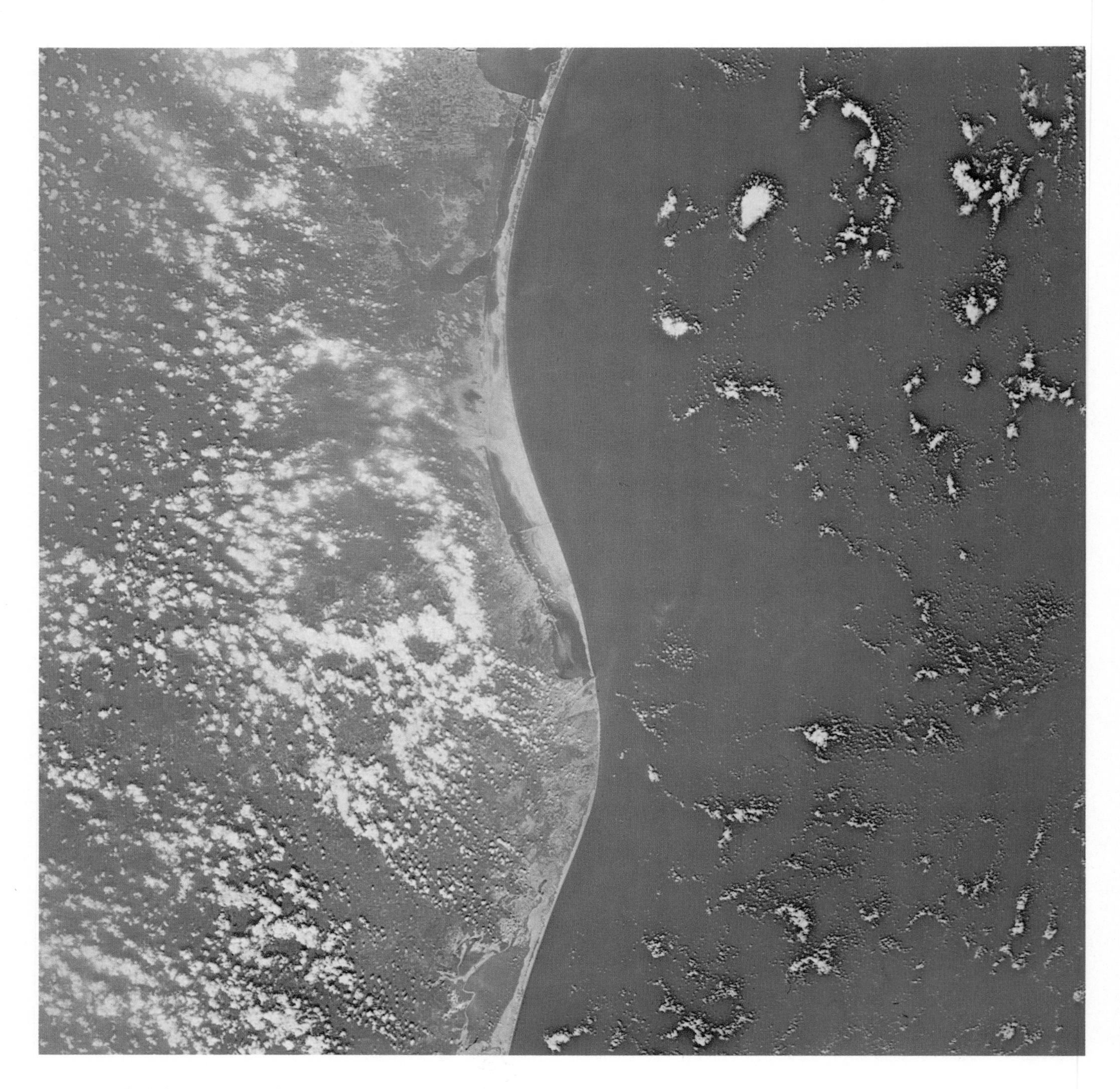

Corpus Christi Bay is at the top and Mexico's Laguna Madre at the bottom of this nearly vertical view of the Rio Grande's deltaic plain. The international boundary is in the lower half of the photo. The long curving beach is Padre Island. It is typical of barriers that rim the Gulf of Mexico on the west, and has been studied as a possible clue to the formation of oil traps. The Intracoastal Waterway can be seen in the shallow Laguna Madre and a belt of grassland begins inland from the sand bars. Cumuli had formed inland while a cool sea breeze restricted cloud development along the coast.

GEMINI X JULY 20, 1966 S66-45764

San Antonio is in the light area left of the center. Austin is above and to the right of it on the Texas Colorado River. The cities are along the fault-controlled Balcones Escarpment that is the east edge of the Edwards Plateau. Differences in the shale and sand content of the Tertiary units cause variations in soil color, topographic expression, and vegetation. In the upper left, the Llano Uplift brings a complex dome of Precambrian rocks to the surface. Lower Paleozoic carbonates and sandstone surround it. The stratocumulus clouds at the right are on the north side of a cold front.

GEMINI XII NOVEMBER 12, 1966 S66–63428

Austin is now above Gemini XII's nose and San Antonio is in the lower center. Near Austin one can see Buchanan, Lyndon B. Johnson, Travis, and Canyon Lakes. The curving Balcones Escarpment is above these cities, and cuestas on the coastal plain are visible from north of San Antonio to the vicinity of Waco. In the upper left, the Red River flood plain crosses dense pine forests of Louisiana. The Mississippi River's mouth is between the stratocumulus and cirrus clouds near the horizon. Suspended alluvial sediments show the currents off the Texas shore in the Gulf of Mexico between the Mississippi and Aransas Pass at the right.

GEMINI XII NOVEMBER 14, 1966 S66–63024

Taken only seconds after the previous photo, this one has Houston's metropolitan area in the center. The Balcones Escarpment is now just above the spacecraft nose. The Houston ship channel and spoil banks in Galveston Bay can be seen at the right, where the ancient Pleistocene shoreline stands out as the present northwest shore of Matagorda and Espirito Santo Bays. Matagorda, Galveston, and other islands are raised offshore bars. Such bars extend along the Texas coast eastward to Sabine Pass. Northerly winds along the Louisiana coast were carrying smoke plumes toward the stratocumulus-cloud field over the Gulf of Mexico.

GEMINI XII NOVEMBER 14, 1966 S66–63025

This picture overlaps the two photos that have preceded it in this volume, and shows the dense pine forest in east Texas that is known as "The Big Thicket" more clearly. The Sam Rayburn Reservoir can be seen in that thicket. Along the shore, suspended sediments can be traced as they are carried out into the Gulf of Mexico. Note especially the upper part of this photo, where wavy patterns in the clouds are quite distinct, and smoke from fires near oil and gas wells in the Vermillion Bay area is being blown out over the gulf. The next picture in this sequence was taken about 90 minutes later and shows interesting changes in the sky.

GEMINI XII NOVEMBER 14, 1966 S66–63031

After circling the Earth, the Gemini astronauts took this picture of the same area shown in the preceding one. The patch of stratiform clouds over Louisiana, in the upper part of the photo, had shrunk in size, and some dissipation of the stratocumulus clouds over the water along the coast had occurred. Smoke from the shoreline still drifted southward, and sediment patterns still discolored the water. The Red River Valley cuts a swath across the dark forest lands in the left center. North of the Red River are ridges of the Ouachita and Wichita Mountains of Oklahoma.

GEMINI XII NOVEMBER 14, 1966 S66–63062

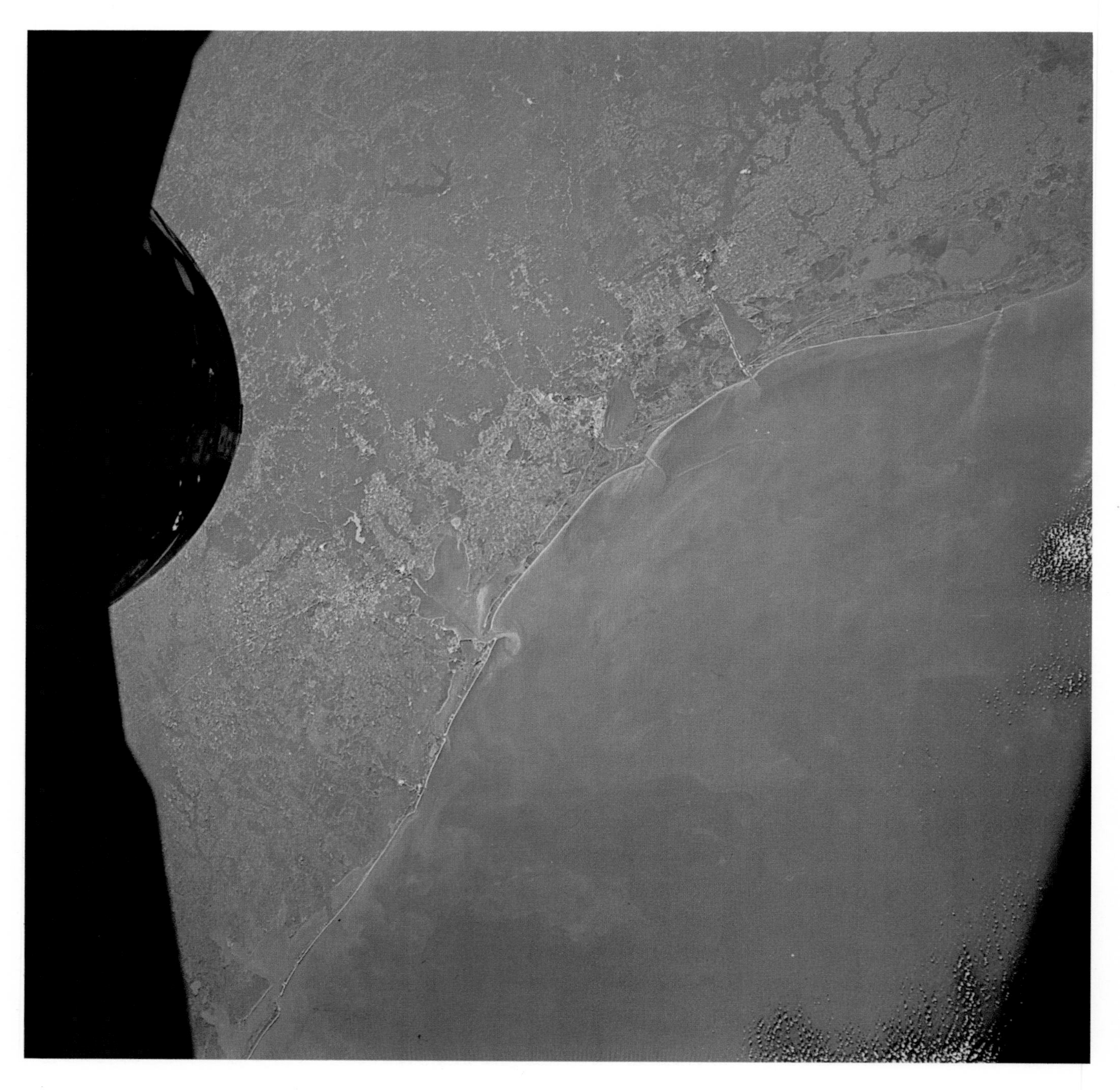

Here is the city of Houston as seen from an altitude of about 175 miles. The city is directly below "The Big Thicket" in this photo. The big Harris County domed stadium in the southwest part of the city is only a white dot. The dark-blue line across Galveston Bay is the Houston ship channel. Turbid waters extend into the Gulf of Mexico from several outlets. A marsh fire sent up the stream of smoke in the upper right. NASA's Manned Spacecraft Center is 20 miles southeast of Houston.

GEMINI XII NOVEMBER 14, 1966 S66–63034

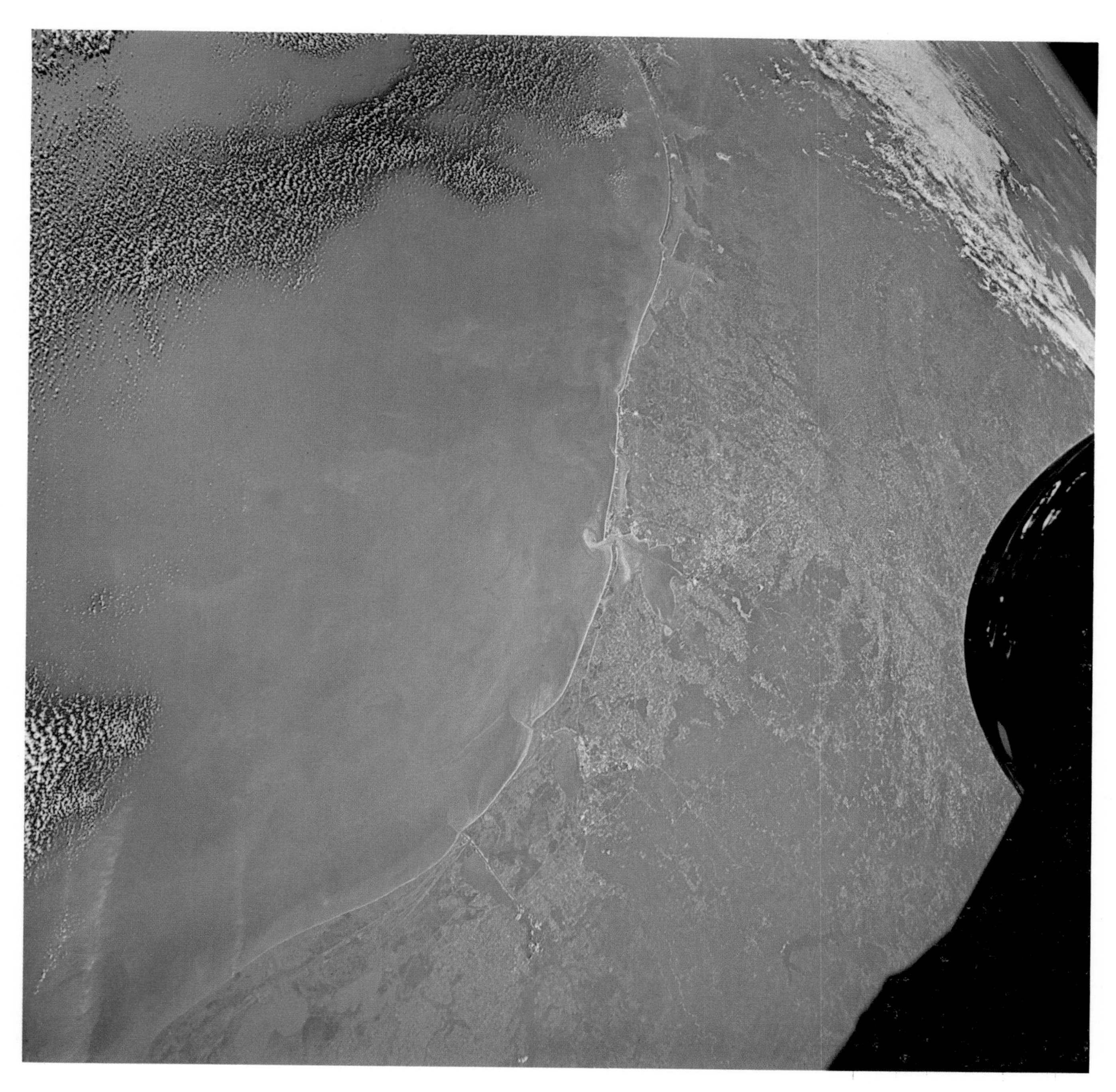

From east of Galveston Bay, Astronaut James A. Lovell, Jr., looked back to photograph it again. To the right is the Beaumont-Port Arthur and Lake Charles industrial complex. The coastal sky was clear from Vermillion Bay to Baffin Bay, and the Intracoastal Waterway can be traced from Orange on the Sabine River east to Grand Lake in this photo. A cold front had crossed the coast 2 days earlier and the winds still were from the northeast. They were thrusting water into the gulf from the lagoons and estuaries. An interference eddy had formed west of the Galveston jetties, and frictional eddies were visible farther seaward.

GEMINI XII NOVEMBER 14, 1966 S66-63035

This southwesterly view of the gulf coast includes many of the same features as the preceding pictures, but extends from Marsh Island in the foreground to south of Brownsville. The cell-like patterns in the stratocumulus clouds over the gulf appear when water warms the lower part of the atmosphere. Drizzle was reported in northeastern Mexico from the clouds near the top center here. Below them one can see the Balcones Escarpment. Some of the world's most important shrimp fisheries are in the coastal waters shown, and photos such as this can be used to improve predictions of currents that affect shrimp migration paths and rates.

GEMINI XII NOVEMBER 14, 1966 S66–63038

Here one sees again some of the same area shown in pictures that have preceded this one. Nueces Bay and Corpus Christi are now above the vehicle's nose, and the rivers flowing into the gulf and the ship channel from Aransas Pass are distinctly shown. Small cumulus clouds dot the area of the mouth and valley of the Rio Grande, and the cumuli ranging inland can be seen to have increased somewhat since the photo that immediately preceded this one was taken, about 90 minutes earlier. From an orbiting spacecraft, a given area can be observed repeatedly at regular intervals, as well as seen from a variety of angles helpful to students.

GEMINI XII NOVEMBER 14, 1966 S66–63060

The gulf coast from Port Arthur, Tex., at the lower left, to Florida, on the horizon, is shown here. From Vicksburg, Miss., near the upper left edge, to the Gulf, the Mississippi River is visible. Between the altostratus clouds in the foreground and rows of cumulus over Louisiana and Mississippi, you see Atchafalaya Bay and the continental shelf offshore that has been tapped for oil. An anticyclone was centered over North Carolina and an upper air trough was over the Mississippi Valley the day of this photo. West of the river, the winds at an altitude of 18 000 feet were from the northwest; east of it, they were from the southwest.

GEMINI IX JUNE 3, 1966 S66–37909

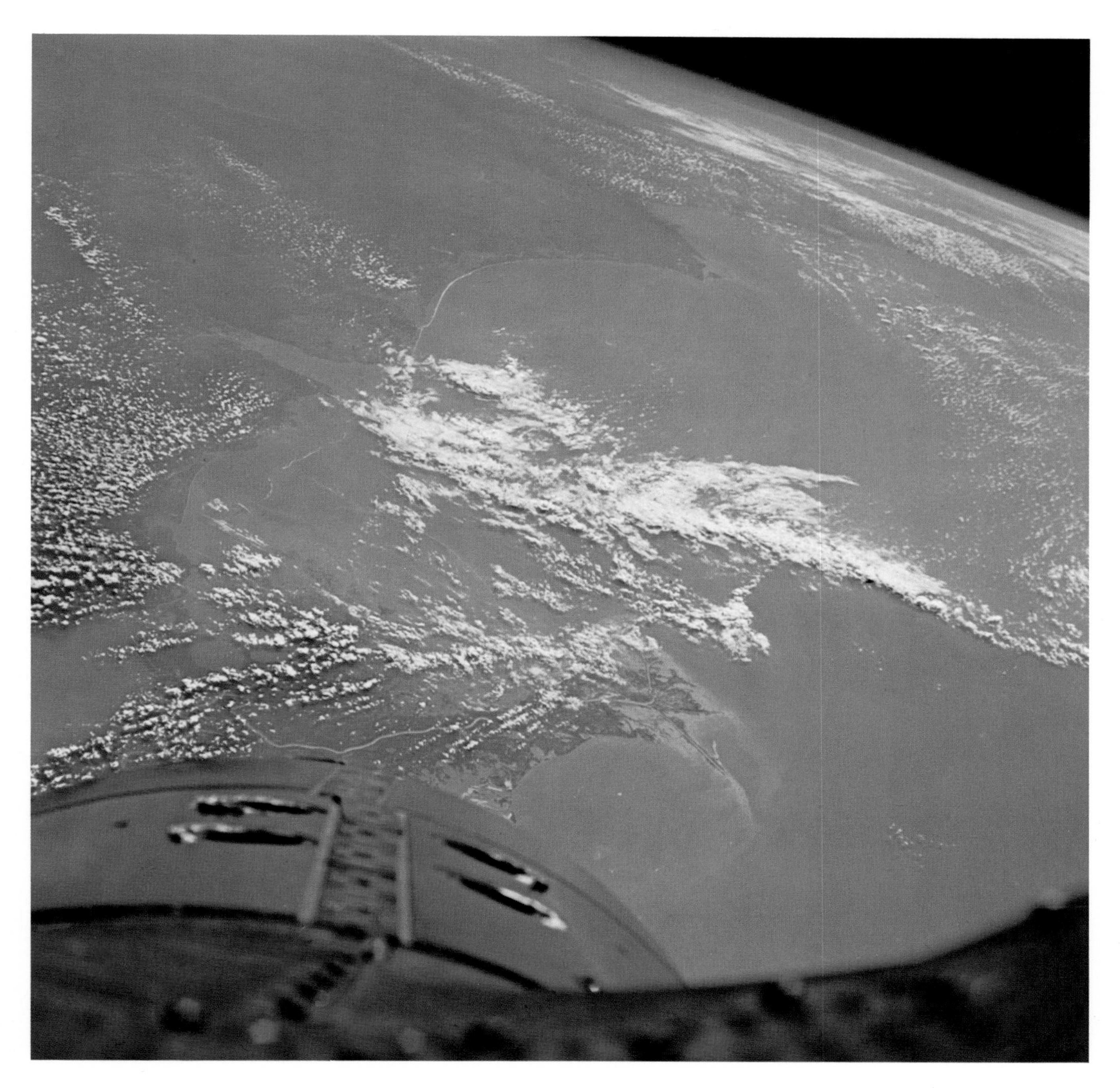

The "bird's foot" in the lower center here is the Mississippi River delta. Lake Pontchartrain is left of it. Rows of cumulus clouds obscure New Orleans and much of southern Mississippi. The long embayment is Mobile Bay, and the Florida peninsula is near the horizon. Offshore bars from Gulfport, Miss., to Apalachicola, Fla., are prominent depositional features. The Mississippi pours great quantities of fine sediment into the gulf. Changes in the color of sediment-laden water off the delta show that the longshore currents were westerly, and light spots reveal the wakes formed around offshore drilling rigs.

GEMINI IX JUNE 3, 1966 S66–37910

Thunderstorms were imbedded in the cloudiness over northern Texas at the upper left in this photo ahead of a cold front advancing southward. The gulf south of Louisiana reflected early-morning sunlight. The contrail from a jetliner near Shreveport left a thin line near the center, and ground fog in valleys of eastern Louisiana and Mississippi produced other bright, irregular lines. A line of cumulus clouds lay parallel to the shore, and smoke plumes showed that winds north of it were northerly. This picture shows how vividly pollution can be seen in photos taken from high altitudes.

GEMINI XI SEPTEMBER 14, 1966 S66–54560

Color infrared film was used for this and the next photo, and coastal sands brighten the shoreline. Pensacola is at the lower left here, Birmingham near the top, the Chattahoochee River in the upper right, and St. Andrew's Bay in the lower right. Tyndall Air Force Base is a light rectangle on the peninsula below the bay. A residue on the spacecraft window degraded this photo's center. Light bands in the upper left are Upper Cretaceous coastal plain clastic sediments overlapping the edge of the Appalachians north of Selma and Montgomery. Sinkholes north of St. Andrew's Bay mark the location of Miocene and Pliocene limestones.

GEMINI VII DECEMBER 7, 1965 S65-64052

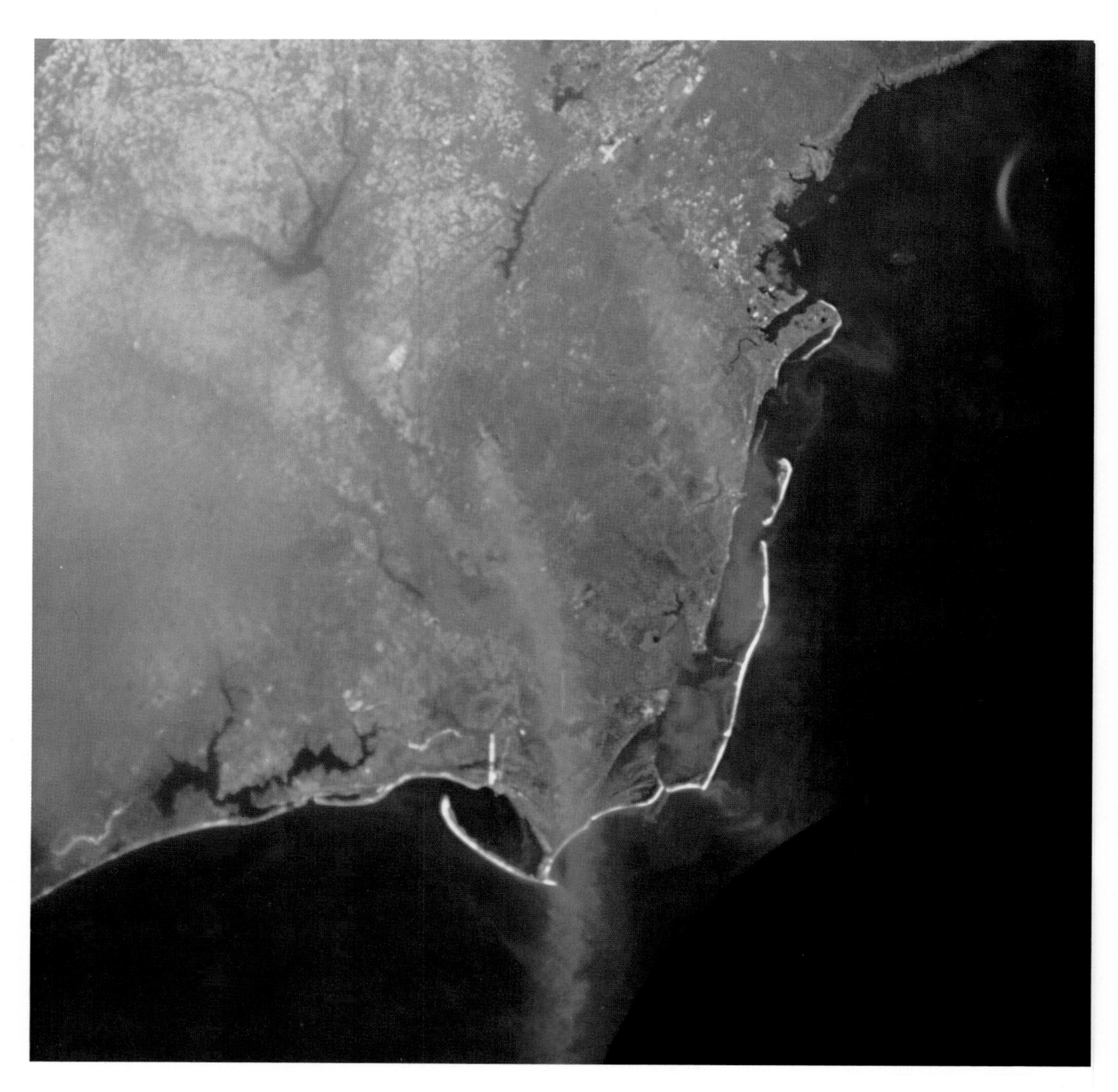

Those long blue plumes in this infrared photo are the smoke from forest fires southwest of Tallahassee, Fla. They are drifting over the Gulf of Mexico. The hook-shaped sand bar in the foreground encloses St. Joseph Bay. Panama City is to the left. From Lake Seminole in the upper left, the Apalachicola River flows south to the bay above the hook. The long blue line to the right of the reservoir is Lake Talquin and you can see the Tallahassee airport runways near its upper end. The vegetation on the swampy tidal flats is reddish in this picture and a narrow band of gray marks the extent of this coastal land.

GEMINI VII DECEMBER 7, 1965 S65–64053

Cumuliform clouds frame Florida's tip and 150 miles of the keys off it in this picture. The Dry Tortugas are at the far left, Key West near the center, and Key Largo near the top. Sediment-laden water is streaming across the bays and a turbid tongue is visible in the channel that separates the Dry Tortugas from the calcareous platform of the Florida and Marquesas Keys. Islands dot the reef between the Marquesas and Key West. Southeast of Key Largo, part of the long, submerged coral reef has been reserved as an underwater park. Sediments formed the southern edge of the mainland, and there is a band of mangrove swamps between it and the Everglades.

GEMINI VII DECEMBER 13, 1965 S65–64024

The day the astronauts took this and the next four pictures, cumulus clouds covered the southern half of Florida in an organized manner and a cold front was along the U.S. Atlantic coast on the horizon here. There were openings in the cumulus over Lake Okeechobee, Tampa Bay, and Charlotte Harbor, because such clouds usually form over land. Tampa was reporting southwest winds at 10 knots and Miami had southeast winds at 5 knots. A long, narrow band of cirrus clouds near the jetstream lay over the frontal zone in the distance. The spacecraft was docked with its Agena target vehicle and approaching Florida from the west.

GEMINI XII NOVEMBER 12, 1966 S66–62897

Strong surface winds were creating turbulence in the shallow waters off southwest Florida as the spacecraft neared the peninsula and the astronauts recorded the view eastward toward the Little Bahama Bank. Tampa Bay is at the left and the Florida Keys are in the lower right. The turbulence was bringing fine, white, calcareous muds into suspension, and muddy water from the coast spread across the western Florida shelf. Layers of stratocumulus covered Cape Kennedy on the eastern coast, and a cloud line bordering the edge of the Gulf Stream extended northeast over the Atlantic. Such a cloud line is frequently seen in this area.

GEMINI XII NOVEMBER 12, 1966 S66-62900

In this photo the puffy cumuliform clouds to which the spacecraft door points are over southern Florida, and the clouds to the left overlay the Gulf Stream. There the northern portion of the Great Bahama Bank and the Little Bahama Bank off the east coast of Florida are clearly defined. This and the next photo are especially interesting to the marine geologist and the cartographer because of the clarity with which they show the relationship of shallow calcareous sandbars in the Bahama Banks. Andros Island is in the upper center here. Bimini Island is on the near edge of a light-blue area below Andros Island, and other islands are left of it.

GEMINI XII NOVEMBER 12, 1966 S66–62903

This and the next picture are additional views of the cold-front cloudiness along the eastern coast of the United States that was first photographed while Gemini XII was over the Gulf of Mexico. The hatch was open and Astronaut Edwin E. Aldrin, Jr., was engaged in extravehicular activity when this one was taken. Florida's Atlantic coast from Cape Kennedy to Fort Pierce is visible. So, too, at the right edge is the northeast part of the Little Bahama Bank. Offshore the line of cumulus is near the Gulf Stream. In the frontal zone the low-level cumulus streets are parallel to the winds. Note how a ropelike band of cirrus follows the cold front.

GEMINI XII NOVEMBER 12, 1966 S66–62905

The astronauts had crossed Florida and were out over the Atlantic again when they looked northward at the southeastern coast of the United States and photographed the cold front there again. This front was a boundary region between the cool, dry air near the left horizon and the warm, moist air located to the right of the large cloudy zone. Stratiform and cumuliform clouds in layers are likely to produce rain showers in the neighborhood of such a front. The Gemini flights ended in 1966, but weather satellites have continued to assist meteorologists studying the global movements of clouds such as these.

GEMINI XII NOVEMBER 12, 1966 S66–62911

Many details of the Atlantic coast of northern Florida and southern Georgia can be seen and related in the left half of this photo. The broad, dark, sinuous line starting at the lower left and continuing northward is the St. John River, which turns toward the sea at Jacksonville. Above this prominent stream is the St. Marys, the boundary between the two States. Below the mouth of the St. John is the inlet to St. Augustine. Many small lakes are clearly visible inland just above the nose of the spacecraft. Photographs such as this can help students understand the patterns of land use, highways, and the water resources available to the increasing population.

GEMINI VII DECEMBER 5, 1965 S65–63824

This picture, taken with a Zeiss Sonnar 250-mm lens from an altitude of 140 miles, shows about 55 miles of the Atlantic coast of Florida, from Flagler Beach south to Allenhurst. The Intracoastal Waterway can be traced in it by small white dots. They are spoil heaps left by its dredgers. The break in the barrier beach, in the center of the picture, is Ponce de Leon inlet. The city of Daytona Beach is on the mainland to the left of it, and New Smyrna Beach is at the right. Thin cirrus clouds make parts of this photo look foggy, but highways, lakes, and other features familiar to Floridians are conspicuous.

GEMINI VII DECEMBER 6, 1965 S65-63808

Cape Kennedy is on the tip of land slightly above the center here. The Florida Keys are a thin curving line at the lower left; Lake Okeechobee is below an oblong hole in fine clouds. The light bands in the center of the State apparently follow outcrops of Bone Valley and Alachua formations. They are Pliocene alluvial formations. Hues are similar to the west where Miocene Tampa limestone is found. A weak cold front extended across Florida when this photo was taken. Cumulus clouds hung between it and the Great Bahama Bank at the right, and were photographed again from the same spacecraft about 90 minutes later.

GEMINI XII NOVEMBER 14, 1966 S66-63013

When this picture was taken, on the next revolution after the preceding photo, cumulus clouds had begun to form rows over Cape Kennedy in a northwesterly wind. Offshore the cumulus in a diagonal line through the center of this view had grown. Open cellular patterns persisted in the cloud field seaward of that line, and tufts of cirrus crossed Florida's eastern coast north of Cape Kennedy. The bands of stratocumulus in the upper left were in the cooler air behind the cold front that lay across the peninsula's southern tip. Cape Kennedy was the starting point of the Gemini flights but not the terminus.

GEMINI XII NOVEMBER 14, 1966 S66–63040

It was late afternoon when this photo was taken, about 90 minutes after the preceding one, and the spacecraft was again near its starting point but proceeding around the world again. The Florida Keys are visible in the lower center. The wide zone of cumuliform clouds passing diagonally through this picture marked the location of the weak cold front that had been photographed during the two preceding revolutions. It was moving off the mainland. The Gemini astronauts obtained many more photos of the Earth than it was possible to include in this volume. All of them are now available for scientific use.

GEMINI XII NOVEMBER 14, 1966 S66-63063

# APPENDIX A

## The Gemini Flight Crews

THE photography presented in this volume and its companion volume, *Earth Photographs from Gemini III, IV, and V,* was made possible by the men who flew the spacecraft. These men were not professional photographers, but they were professional observers, recorders, and interpreters of scientific phenomena, as well as human beings appreciative of natural beauty. Thus, these photographs represent a combination of scientific and esthetic interests. Each of the flight crews was selected for a particular mission several months before the flight and underwent rigorous specific-mission training during the period between selection and launch. The training included not only instruction and practice in the use of the cameras and film but also briefings on the scientific background and purpose of the photographic experiments planned for that particular flight, in addition to the engineering and pilot training required for the mission.

The photographic coverage obtained on each flight was determined by a combination of flight objectives and flight duration, and, to a large degree, by the weather conditions and cloud coverage. On nearly all of the flights, excellent coverage was obtained of various desert areas. Only once or twice, however, was the weather suitable for photography of the surface of some areas such as the Texas gulf coast region. Nearly all of the flights were at altitudes ranging from 100 to 200 statute miles. The exceptions were those of Gemini X and XI, during which excursions were made to 475 and 850 miles (741.5 nautical miles), respectively, using the Agena propulsion system. The higher altitudes reached permitted increased coverage of some areas; and the views obtained of India and Ceylon, in particular, were among the most startling examples of photography that I have seen.

The photography obtained in the Gemini program will stand as a lasting tribute to the flight crews' abilities and interest. The names of these men and the duration of their flights were:

*Gemini III*: Maj. Virgil I. (Gus) Grissom, USAF, and Lt. Comdr. John W. Young, USN; 3 revolutions; 4 hours 53 minutes. Orbit approximately 100 miles by 140 miles.

*Gemini IV:* Maj. James A. (Jim) McDivitt, USAF, and Maj. Edward H. (Ed) White II, USAF; 62 revolutions; 97 hours 56 minutes. Orbit approximately 100 miles by 175 miles.

*Gemini V:* Lt. Col. L. Gordon (Gordo) Cooper, Jr., USAF, and Lt. Comdr. Charles (Pete) Conrad, Jr., USN; 120 revolutions; 190 hours 56 minutes. Orbit approximately 100 miles by 217 miles.

*Gemini VII:* Lt. Col. Frank Borman, USAF, and Comdr. James A. (Jim) Lovell, Jr., USN; 206 revolutions; 330 hours 35 minutes. Orbit approximately 100 miles by 204 miles.

# GEMINI FLIGHT CREWS

GEMINI III
Virgil I. Grissom — John W. Young

GEMINI IV
Edward H. White II — James A. McDivitt

GEMINI V
Charles Conrad, Jr. — L. Gordon Cooper

GEMINI VI
Thomas P. Stafford — Walter M. Schirra, Jr.

James A. Lovell GEMINI VII Frank Borman

Neil A. Armstrong GEMINI VIII David R. Scott

Thomas P. Stafford GEMINI IX Eugene Cernan

John W. Young GEMINI X Michael Collins

Richard F. Gordon, Jr. GEMINI XI Charles Conrad, Jr.

Edward E. Aldrin, Jr. GEMINI XII James A. Lovell

*Gemini VI*: Capt. Walter M. (Wally) Schirra, Jr., USN, and Maj. Thomas P. (Tom) Stafford, USAF; 16 revolutions; 25 hours 51 minutes. Orbit approximately 100 miles by 161 miles.

*Gemini VIII:* Neil A. Armstrong and Maj. David R. (Dave) Scott, USAF; 7 revolutions; 10 hours 42 minutes. Orbit approximately 100 miles by 169 miles.

*Gemini IX:* Lt. Col. Thomas P. (Tom) Stafford, USAF, and Lt. Comdr. Eugene A. (Gene) Cernan, USN; 45 revolutions; 72 hours 21 minutes. Orbit approximately 99 miles by 166 miles.

*Gemini X:* Comdr. John W. Young, USN, and Maj. Michael (Mike) Collins, USAF; 44 revolutions; 70 hours 46 minutes. Orbit approximately 100 miles by 167 miles, with one excursion to 475 miles.

*Gemini XI:* Comdr. Charles (Pete) Conrad, Jr., USN, and Lt. Comdr. Richard F. (Dick) Gordon, Jr., USN; 44 revolutions; 71 hours 17 minutes. Orbit approximately 100 miles by 177 miles, with two excursions to 850 miles.

*Gemini XII:* Capt. James A. (Jim) Lovell, Jr., USN, and Maj. Edwin E. (Buzz) Aldrin, Jr., USAF; 59 revolutions; 94 hours 34 minutes. Orbit approximately 100 miles by 175 miles.

ROBERT E. GILRUTH, *Director,*
*Manned Spacecraft Center, NASA*

# APPENDIX B

Listings printed in italics appear in this volume. Identifications marked with an asterisk (*) are partially degraded. Photos marked with two asterisks (**) are sufficiently degraded to be considered useless, or nearly so.

## GEMINI VI

### MAGAZINE A

| Frame | NASA/MSC Color No. | NASA/MSC B&W No. | Revolution | Date | GMT | Alt, N. Mi. | Area description |
|---|---|---|---|---|---|---|---|
| 1 | S65–63163 | S65–63544 | 5 | Dec. 15, 1965 | 21:26 | 163 | Rendezvous with Gemini VII, oblique view, pilot side, nose down, range 48 ft. |
| 2 | S65–63164 | S65–63545 | 5 | Dec. 15, 1965 | ....... | ........ | Rendezvous with Gemini VII, nose toward camera, range 40 ft. |
| 3 | S65–63165 | S65–63546 | 5 | Dec. 15, 1965 | ....... | ........ | Rendezvous with Gemini VII, nose toward camera, range 43 ft. |
| 4 | S65–63166 | S65–63547 | 5 | Dec. 15, 1965 | ....... | ........ | Rendezvous with Gemini VII, nose toward camera, range 37 ft. |
| 5 | S65–63167 | S65–63548 | 5 | Dec. 15, 1965 | ....... | ........ | Rendezvous with Gemini VII, nose toward camera, range 36 ft. |
| 6 | S65–63168 | S65–63549 | 5 | Dec. 15, 1965 | ....... | ........ | Rendezvous with Gemini VII, nose toward camera, range 40 ft. |
| 7 | S65–63169 | S65–63550 | 5 | Dec. 15, 1965 | ....... | ........ | Rendezvous with Gemini VII, nose toward camera, range 43 ft. |
| 8 | S65–63170 | S65–63551 | 5 | Dec. 15, 1965 | ....... | ........ | Rendezvous with Gemini VII, nose toward camera, range 45 ft. |
| 9 | S65–63171 | S65–63552 | 5 | Dec. 15, 1965 | ....... | ........ | Rendezvous with Gemini VII, nose toward camera, range 55 ft. |
| 10 | S65–63172 | S65–63553 | 5 | Dec. 15, 1965 | ....... | ........ | Rendezvous with Gemini VII, nose toward camera, range 45 ft. |
| 11 | S65–63173 | S65–63554 | 5 | Dec. 15, 1965 | ....... | ........ | Rendezvous with Gemini VII, nose toward camera, range 53 ft. |
| 12 | S65–63174 | S65–63555 | 5 | Dec. 15, 1965 | ....... | ........ | Rendezvous with Gemini VII, nose toward camera, range 62 ft. |
| 13 | S65–63175 | S65–63556 | 5 | Dec. 15, 1965 | ....... | ........ | Rendezvous with Gemini VII, nose toward camera, range 63 ft. |
| 14 | S65–63176 | S65–63557 | 5 | Dec. 15, 1965 | ....... | ........ | Earth limb, clouds over ocean. |
| 15 | S65–63177 | S65–63558 | 5 | Dec. 15, 1965 | ....... | ........ | Rendezvous with Gemini VII, side view, range 52 ft; clouds. |
| 16 | S65–63178 | S65–63559 | 5 | Dec. 15, 1965 | ....... | ........ | Rendezvous with Gemini VII, side view, range 58 ft; clouds. |
| 17 | S65–63179 | S65–63560 | 5 | Dec. 15, 1965 | ....... | ........ | Rendezvous with Gemini VII, side view, range 68 ft; clouds. |
| 18 | S65–63180 | S65–63561 | 5 | Dec. 15, 1965 | ....... | ........ | Rendezvous with Gemini VII, oblique view, adapter section toward camera, range 87 ft. |
| 19 | S65–63181 | S65–63562 | 5 | Dec. 15, 1965 | ....... | ........ | Rendezvous with Gemini VII, oblique view, adapter section toward camera, range 110 ft. |
| 20 | S65–63182 | S65–63563 | 5 | Dec. 15, 1965 | ....... | ........ | Rendezvous with Gemini VII, oblique view, adapter section toward camera, range 120 ft. |
| 21 | S65–63183 | S65–63564 | 5 | Dec. 15, 1965 | ....... | ........ | Rendezvous with Gemini VII, oblique view, adapter section toward camera, range 120 ft. |
| 22 | S65–63184 | S65–63565 | 5 | Dec. 15, 1965 | ....... | ........ | Rendezvous with Gemini VII, oblique view, adapter section toward camera, range 150 ft. |
| 23 | S65–63185 | S65–63566 | 5 | Dec. 15, 1965 | ....... | ........ | Rendezvous with Gemini VII, side view, range 210 ft; sky background. |

MAGAZINE A Continued

| Frame | NASA/MSC Color No. | NASA/MSC B&W No. | Revolution | Date | GMT | Alt, N. Mi. | Area description |
|---|---|---|---|---|---|---|---|
| 24 | S65–63186 | S65–63567 | 5 | Dec. 15, 1965 | ...... | ........ | Rendezvous with Gemini VII, side view, range 220 ft; sky background. |
| 25 | S65–63187 | S65–63568 | 5 | Dec. 15, 1965 | ...... | ........ | Rendezvous with Gemini VII, side view, range 275 ft; sky background. |
| *26* | *S65–63188* | *S65–63569* | *5* | *Dec. 15, 1965* | ...... | ........ | *Rendezvous with Gemini VII, oblique nose view, range 50 ft.* |
| 27 | S65–63189 | S65–63570 | 5 | Dec. 15, 1965 | ...... | ........ | Rendezvous with Gemini VII, oblique nose view, range 35 ft; perfect stereo with No. 28. |
| 28 | S65–63190 | S65–63571 | 5 | Dec. 15, 1965 | ...... | ........ | Rendezvous with Gemini VII, oblique nose view, range 35 ft; perfect stereo with No. 27. |
| 29 | S65–63191 | S65–63572 | 5 | Dec. 15, 1965 | ...... | ........ | Rendezvous with Gemini VII, oblique nose view, range 33 ft. |
| 30 | S65–63192 | S65–63573 | 5 | Dec. 15, 1965 | ...... | ........ | Rendezvous with Gemini VII, side view, nose hidden by Gemini VI nose, range 24 ft. |
| 31 | S65–63193 | S65–63574 | 5 | Dec. 15, 1965 | ...... | ........ | Rendezvous with Gemini VII, side view, part of adapter hidden by nose of Gemini VI, range 22 ft. |
| 32 | S65–63194 | S65–63575 | 5 | Dec. 15, 1965 | ...... | ........ | Rendezvous with Gemini VII, side view, part of adapter hidden by nose of Gemini VI, range 35 ft. |
| 33 | S65–63195 | S65–63576 | 5 | Dec. 15, 1965 | ...... | ........ | Rendezvous with Gemini VII, side view turning nose away from camera, range 38 ft. |
| 34 | S65–63196 | S65–63577 | 5 | Dec. 15, 1965 | ...... | ........ | Rendezvous with Gemini VII, oblique view, turning nose away from camera, range 40 ft. |
| 35 | S65–63197 | S65–63578 | 5 | Dec. 15, 1965 | ...... | ........ | Rendezvous with Gemini VII, oblique view, dark shadows on adapter section, range 42 ft. |
| 36 | S65–63198 | S65–63579 | 5 | Dec. 15, 1965 | ...... | ........ | Rendezvous with Gemini VII, adapter section in deep shadow, range 47 ft. |
| 37 | S65–63199 | S65–63580 | 5 | Dec. 15, 1965 | ...... | ........ | Rendezvous with Gemini VII, adapter side, range 25 ft; Sun in lens, ruins picture quality. |
| 38 | S65–63200 | S65–63581 | 5 | Dec. 15, 1965 | ...... | ........ | Rendezvous with Gemini VII, side view, range 30 ft; Sun in lens, ruins picture quality. |
| 39 | S65–63201 | S65–63582 | 5 | Dec. 15, 1965 | 21:47 | 163 | Rendezvous with Gemini VII, side view, range 65 ft; Sun in lens, ruins picture quality. |
| 40 | S65–63202 | S65–63583 | 6 | Dec. 15, 1965 | 22:46 | 161 | Rendezvous with Gemini VII, side-view adapter section, range 30 ft. |
| 41 | S65–63203 | S65–63584 | 6 | Dec. 15, 1965 | ...... | ........ | Rendezvous with Gemini VII, side-view adapter section, range 32 ft. |
| *42* | *S65–63204* | *S65–63585* | *6* | *Dec. 15, 1965* | ...... | ........ | *Rendezvous with Gemini VII, side view, turning adapter section toward camera, range 40 ft.* |
| 43 | S65–63205 | S65–63586 | 6 | Dec. 15, 1965 | ...... | ........ | Rendezvous with Gemini VII, side view, turning adapter section toward camera, range 45 ft. |
| 44 | S65–63206 | S65–63587 | 6 | Dec. 15, 1965 | ...... | ........ | Rendezvous with Gemini VII, oblique view, turning adapter section toward camera, range 50 ft. |
| 45 | S65–63207 | S65–63588 | 6 | Dec. 15, 1965 | ...... | ........ | Rendezvous with Gemini VII, oblique view, turning adapter section toward camera, range 65 ft. |
| 46 | S65–63208 | S65–63589 | 6 | Dec. 15, 1965 | ...... | ........ | Rendezvous with Gemini VII, oblique view, turning adapter section toward camera, range 75 ft. |
| 47 | S65–63209 | S65–63590 | 6 | Dec. 15, 1965 | ...... | ........ | Rendezvous with Gemini VII, side view, range 130 ft; clouds, sea background. |
| 48 | S65–63210 | S65–63591 | 6 | Dec. 15, 1965 | ...... | ........ | Rendezvous with Gemini VII, side view, range 130 ft; clouds, sea background. |
| 49 | S65–63211 | S65–63592 | 6 | Dec. 15, 1965 | ...... | ........ | Rendezvous with Gemini VII, side view, range 125 ft; clouds, sea background. |

MAGAZINE A Continued

| Frame | NASA/MSC Color No. | NASA/MSC B&W No. | Revolution | Date | GMT | Alt, N. Mi. | Area description |
|---|---|---|---|---|---|---|---|
| 50 | S65–63212 | S65–63593 | 6 | Dec. 15, 1965 | ....... | ........ | Rendezvous with Gemini VII, oblique view, adapter toward camera, range 100 ft; clouds, ocean. |
| 51 | S65–63213 | S65–63594 | 6 | Dec. 15, 1965 | ....... | ........ | Rendezvous with Gemini VII, oblique view, adapter toward camera, range 90 ft. |
| 52 | S65–63214 | S65–63595 | 6 | Dec. 15, 1965 | ....... | ........ | Rendezvous with Gemini VII, oblique view, adapter toward camera, range 75 ft. |
| 53 | S65–63215 | S65–63596 | 6 | Dec. 15. 1965 | ....... | ........ | Rendezvous with Gemini VII, oblique view, adapter toward camera, range 65 ft. |
| 54 | S65–63216 | S65–63597 | 6 | Dec. 15, 1965 | ....... | ........ | Rendezvous with Gemini VII, side view, range 50 ft; clouds, sea background. |
| 55 | S65–63217 | S65–63598 | 6 | Dec. 15, 1965 | ....... | ........ | Rendezvous with Gemini VII, side view, range 48 ft; clouds, sea background. |
| 56 | S65–63218 | S65–63599 | 6 | Dec. 15. 1965 | ....... | ........ | Rendezvous with Gemini VII, side view, range 45 ft; clouds, sea background. |
| 57 | S65–63219 | S65–63600 | 6 | Dec. 15, 1965 | ....... | ........ | Rendezvous with Gemini VII, oblique view, turning adapter toward camera, range 40 ft. |
| 58 | S65–63220 | S65–63601 | 6 | Dec. 15, 1965 | ....... | ........ | Rendezvous with Gemini VII, oblique view, turning adapter toward camera, range 37 ft. |
| 59 | S65–63221 | S65–63602 | 6 | Dec. 15, 1965 | ....... | ........ | Rendezvous with Gemini VII, oblique view, turning adapter toward camera, range 37 ft. |
| 60 | S65–63222 | S65–63603 | 6 | Dec. 15, 1965 | ....... | ........ | Rendezvous with Gemini VII, adapter end, range 42 ft. |
| 61 | S65–63223 | S65–63604 | 6 | Dec. 15, 1965 | ....... | ........ | Rendezvous with Gemini VII, adapter end, range 42 ft. |
| 62 | S65–63224 | S65–63605 | 6 | Dec. 15, 1965 | 23:14 | 166 | Rendezvous with Gemini VII, adapter end, range 42 ft; partial frame. |

MAGAZINE B

| Frame | NASA/MSC Color No. | NASA/MSC B&W No. | Revolution | Date | GMT | Alt, N. Mi. | Area description |
|---|---|---|---|---|---|---|---|
| 1 | S65–63101 | S65–64887 | 7 | Dec. 15, 1965 | 23:54 | 157 | Rendezvous with Gemini VII, side view, range 50 ft; off west coast of India. |
| 2 | S65–63102 | S65–64888 | 7 | Dec. 15, 1965 | ....... | ........ | Rendezvous with Gemini VII, side view, range 58 ft; off west coast of India. |
| 3 | S65–63103 | S65–64889 | 7 | Dec. 15, 1965 | ....... | ........ | Rendezvous with Gemini VII, side view, range 60 ft; off west coast of India. |
| 4 | S65–63104 | S65–64890 | 7 | Dec. 15, 1965 | ....... | ........ | Rendezvous with Gemini VII, side view; double exposure. |
| 5 | S65–63105 | S65–64891 | 7 | Dec. 15, 1965 | ....... | ........ | Rendezvous with Gemini VII, side view, range 150 ft; rotation sequence. |
| 6 | S65–63106 | S65–64892 | 7 | Dec. 15, 1965 | ....... | ........ | Rendezvous with Gemini VII, side view, range 150 ft. |
| 7 | S65–63107 | S65–64893 | 7 | Dec. 15, 1965 | ....... | ........ | Rendezvous with Gemini VII, side view, range 150 ft. |
| 8 | S65–63108 | S65–64894 | 7 | Dec. 15, 1965 | ....... | ........ | Rendezvous with Gemini VII, side view, range 160 ft. |
| 9 | S65–63109 | S65–64895 | 7 | Dec. 15, 1965 | ....... | ........ | Rendezvous with Gemini VII, side view, range 180 ft. |
| 10 | S65–63110 | S65–64896 | 7 | Dec. 15, 1965 | ....... | ........ | Rendezvous with Gemini VII, side view, range 160 ft. |
| 11 | S65–63111 | S65–64897 | 7 | Dec. 15, 1965 | ....... | ........ | Rendezvous with Gemini VII, side view, range 170 ft. |
| 12 | S65–63112 | S65–64898 | 7 | Dec. 15, 1965 | ....... | ........ | Rendezvous with Gemini VII, side view, range 180 ft. |
| 13 | S65–63113 | S65–64899 | 7 | Dec. 15, 1965 | ....... | ........ | Rendezvous with Gemini VII, side view, range 150 ft. |

MAGAZINE B Continued

| Frame | NASA/MSC | | Revolution | Date | GMT | Alt, N. Mi. | Area description |
|---|---|---|---|---|---|---|---|
| | Color No. | B&W No. | | | | | |
| 14 | S65–63114 | S65–64900 | 7 | Dec. 15, 1965 | ...... | ........ | Rendezvous with Gemini VII, side view, range 150 ft. |
| 15 | S65–63115 | S65–64901 | 7 | Dec. 15, 1965 | ...... | ........ | Rendezvous with Gemini VII, side view, range 140 ft. |
| 16 | S65–63116 | S65–64902 | 7 | Dec. 15, 1965 | ...... | ........ | Rendezvous with Gemini VII, side view, range 125 ft. |
| 17 | S65–63117 | S65–64903 | 7 | Dec. 15, 1965 | ...... | ........ | Rendezvous with Gemini VII, side view, range 125 ft. |
| 18 | S65–63118 | S65–64904 | 7 | Dec. 15, 1965 | ...... | ........ | Rendezvous with Gemini VII, side view, range 90 ft. |
| 19 | S65–63119 | S65–64905 | 7 | Dec. 15, 1965 | ...... | ........ | Rendezvous with Gemini VII, side view, range 120 ft. |
| 20 | S65–63120 | S65–64906 | 7 | Dec. 15, 1965 | ...... | ........ | Rendezvous with Gemini VII, side view, range 100 ft. |
| 21 | S65–63121 | S65–64907 | 7 | Dec. 15, 1965 | ...... | ........ | Rendezvous with Gemini VII, side view, range 70 ft. |
| 22 | S65–63122 | S65–64908 | 7 | Dec. 15, 1965 | ...... | ........ | Rendezvous with Gemini VII, side view, range 37 ft. |
| 23 | S65–63123 | S65–64909 | 7 | Dec. 15, 1965 | ...... | ........ | Rendezvous with Gemini VII, side view, range 45 ft. |
| 24 | S65–63124 | S65–64910 | 7 | Dec. 15, 1965 | ...... | ........ | Rendezvous with Gemini VII, side view, range 47 ft. |
| 25 | S65–63125 | S65–64911 | 7 | Dec. 15, 1965 | ...... | ........ | Rendezvous with Gemini VII, side view, range 50 ft. |
| 26 | S65–63126 | S65–64912 | 7 | Dec. 15, 1965 | ...... | ........ | Rendezvous with Gemini VII, nose view, range 75 ft; stereo with No. 27. |
| 27 | S65–63127 | S65–64913 | 7 | Dec. 16, 1965 | 00:07 | 159 | Rendezvous with Gemini VII, nose view, range 75 ft; stereo with No. 26. |
| *28* | *S65–63128* | *S65–64914* | *9* | *Dec. 16, 1965* | *03:10* | *155* | *India, Nepal: Bareilly, Rampur; Ganges plain, Himalaya front, east of Delhi.* |
| 29 | S65–63129 | S65–64915 | ............ | Dec. 16, 1965 | ...... | ........ | Urine drops in sunlight. |
| *30* | *S65–63130* | *S65–64916* | *13* | *Dec. 16, 1965* | *09:28* | *159* | *Somali Republic: Ras Hafun, Wadi Giael.* |
| *31* | *S65–63131* | *S65–64917* | *13* | *Dec. 16, 1965* | *09:28* | *159* | *Somali Republic: Ras Hafun, Wadi Giael.* |
| *32* | *S65–63132* | *S65–64918* | *13* | *Dec. 16, 1965* | *09:28* | *159* | *Somali Republic: Ras Hafun, Wadi Giael.* |
| 33 | S65–63133 | S65–64919 | 13 | Dec. 16, 1965 | 09:28 | 159 | Somali Republic: Wadi Giael. |
| 34 | S65–63134 | S65–64920 | 13 | Dec. 16, 1965 | 09:30 | 160 | Socotra Island, extreme east tip, Arabian Sea. |
| *35* | *S65–63135* | *S65–64921* | *13* | *Dec. 16, 1965* | *09:45* | *167* | *Western Australia: Lake McLeod.* |
| *36* | *S65–63136* | *S65–64922* | *13* | *Dec. 16, 1965* | *09:45* | *167* | *Western Australia: Shark Bay, Denham Sound, Carnarvon Tracking Station.* |
| 37 | S65–63137 | S65–64923 | 13 | Dec. 16, 1965 | 09:45 | 167 | Western Australia: Kennedy Range and plateau to the southeast. |
| 38 | S65–63138 | S65–64924 | 14 | Dec. 16, 1965 | 10:34 | 154 | Cumulus clouds over western Atlantic. |
| 39 | S65–63139 | S65–64925 | 14 | Dec. 16, 1965 | 10:34 | 154 | Cumulus clouds over western Atlantic. |
| 40 | S65–63140 | S65–64926 | 14 | Dec. 16, 1965 | 10:34 | 154 | Cumulus clouds over western Atlantic. |
| 41 | S65–63141 | S65–64927 | 14 | Dec. 16, 1965 | 10:42 | 155 | Large disturbance over central Atlantic, 1000 miles west of Canary Islands. |
| 42 | S65–63142 | S65–64928 | 14 | Dec. 16, 1965 | 10:42 | 155 | Large disturbance over central Atlantic, 1000 miles west of Canary Islands. |
| *43* | *S65–63143* | *S65–64929* | *14* | *Dec. 16, 1965* | *10:43* | *155* | *Large disturbance over central Atlantic, 1000 miles west of Canary Islands.* |
| 44 | S65–63144 | S65–64930 | 14 | Dec. 16, 1965 | 10:43 | 155 | Large disturbance over central Atlantic, 1000 miles west of Canary Islands. |
| 45 | S65–63145 | S65–64931 | 14 | Dec. 16, 1965 | 10:43 | 155 | Large disturbance over central Atlantic, 1000 miles west of Canary Islands. |
| *46* | *S65–63146* | *S65–64932* | *14* | *Dec. 16, 1965* | *10:45* | *156* | *Cellular cloud formations west of Canary Islands.* |
| 47 | S65–63147 | S65–64933 | 14 | Dec. 16, 1965 | 10:45 | 156 | Cellular cloud formations west of Canary Islands. |

MAGAZINE B Continued

| Frame | NASA/MSC Color No. | NASA/MSC B&W No. | Revolution | Date | GMT | Alt, N. Mi. | Area description |
|---|---|---|---|---|---|---|---|
| *48* | *S65–63148* | *S65–64934* | *14* | *Dec. 16, 1965* | *10:45* | *156* | *Eddies in stratocumulus near Gomera, La Palma, and Hierro Islands.* |
| *49* | *S65–63149* | *S65–64935* | *14* | *Dec. 16, 1965* | *10:46* | *156* | *Eddies in stratocumulus near Tenerife and Gomera Islands.* |
| *50* | *S65–63150* | *S65–64936* | *14* | *Dec. 16, 1965* | *10:46* | *156* | *Eddies in stratocumulus near Tenerife, Gomera, and Gran Canaria Islands.* |
| *51* | *S65–63151* | *S65–64937* | *14* | *Dec. 16, 1965* | *10:46* | *156* | *Eddies in stratocumulus near Tenerife and Gran Canaria Islands.* |
| 52 | S65–63152 | S65–64938 | 14 | Dec. 16, 1965 | 10:46 | 156 | Eddies in stratocumulus near Gran Canaria and Fuerteventura Islands. |
| 53 | S65–63153 | S65–64939 | 14 | Dec. 16, 1965 | 10:47 | 157 | Morocco, Algeria, Mauritania, Spanish Sahara: Hamada du Dra area. |
| 54 | S65–63154 | S65–64940 | 14 | Dec. 16, 1965 | 10:48 | 157 | Algeria, Mauritania: Erg Iguidi. |
| *55* | *S65–63155* | *S65–64941* | *14* | *Dec. 16, 1965* | *10:48* | *157* | *Algeria, Mauritania: Erg Iguidi.* |
| 56 | S65–63156 | S65–64942 | 14 | Dec. 16, 1965 | 10:49 | 157 | Southern Algeria: Tanezrouft Desert of Sahara. |
| *57* | *S65–63157* | *S65–64943* | *14* | *Dec. 16, 1965* | *10:51* | *158* | *Southeast Algeria: Fort Lapperine; Ahaggar Mountains.* |
| *58* | *S65–63158* | *S65–64944* | *14* | *Dec. 16, 1965* | *10:52* | *158* | *Niger Republic: Air ou Azbine.* |
| *59* | *S65–63159* | *S65–64945* | *14* | *Dec. 16, 1965* | *10:56* | *159* | *Sudan: Darfur Province; Jebel Gurgei.* |
| *60* | *S65–63160* | *S65–64946* | *14* | *Dec. 16, 1965* | *10:56* | *159* | *Sudan: Darfur Province; Jebel Marva.* |
| *61* | *S65–63161* | *S65–64947* | *14* | *Dec. 16, 1965* | *10:58* | *160* | *Sudan: Upper Nile Province; the Sudd, large swamp in White Nile.* |
| *62* | *S65–63162* | *S65–64948* | *14* | *Dec. 16, 1965* | *11:00* | *161* | *Ethiopia: Lakes Zwai, Langana, and Shala; Koka Dam south of Addis Ababa—partial frame.* |

MAGAZINE C

| Frame | NASA/MSC Color No. | NASA/MSC B&W No. | Revolution | Date | GMT | Alt, N. Mi. | Area description |
|---|---|---|---|---|---|---|---|
| *1* | *S65–63280* | *S65–63293* | *14* | *Dec. 16, 1965* | *11:12* | *166* | *Clouds over southeast Indian Ocean.* |
| *2* | *S65–63279* | *S65–63294* | *14* | *Dec. 16, 1965* | *11:12* | *166* | *Clouds over southeast Indian Ocean.* |
| *3* | *S65–63278* | *S65–63295* | *14* | *Dec. 16, 1965* | *11:13* | *166* | *Clouds over southeast Indian Ocean.* |
| 4 | S65–63277 | S65–63296 | 14 | Dec. 16, 1965 | 11:13 | 166 | Clouds over southeast Indian Ocean. |
| 5 | S65–63276 | S65–63297 | 14 | Dec. 16, 1965 | 11:14 | 167 | Clouds over southeast Indian Ocean. |
| 6 | S65–63275 | S65–63298 | 14 | Dec. 16, 1965 | 11:14 | 167 | Clouds over southeast Indian Ocean. |
| 7 | S65–63274 | S65–63299 | 14 | Dec. 16, 1965 | 11:14 | 167 | Clouds over southeast Indian Ocean. |
| 8 | S65–63273 | S65–63300 | 14 | Dec. 16, 1965 | 11:14 | 167 | Clouds over southeast Indian Ocean. |
| 9 | S65–63272 | S65–63301 | 14 | Dec. 16, 1965 | 11:14 | 167 | Clouds over southeast Indian Ocean. |
| 10 | S65–63271 | S65–63302 | 14 | Dec. 16, 1965 | 11:15 | 167 | Clouds over southeast Indian Ocean. |
| 11 | S65–63270 | S65–63303 | 14 | Dec. 16, 1965 | 11:15 | 167 | Clouds over southeast Indian Ocean. |
| 12 | S65–63269 | S65–63304 | 14 | Dec. 16, 1965 | 11:47 | 156 | Sunset. |
| 13 | S65–63268 | S65–63305 | 14 | Dec. 16, 1965 | 11:47 | 156 | Sunset. |
| 14 | S65–63267 | S65–63306 | 14 | Dec. 16, 1965 | 11:47 | 156 | Sunset. |
| 15 | S65–63266 | S65–63307 | 14 | Dec. 16, 1965 | 11:47 | 156 | Sunset. |
| 16 | S65–63265 | S65–63308 | 14 | Dec. 16, 1965 | 11:47 | 156 | Sunset. |
| 17 | .......... | .......... | .......... | .............. | ...... | ....... | Blank. |
| *18* | *S65–63264* | *S65–63309* | *15* | *Dec. 16, 1965* | *12:21* | *158* | *Lines of cumulus clouds southwest of Canary Islands.* |
| 19 | S65–63263 | S65–63310 | 15 | Dec. 16, 1965 | 12:21 | 158 | Lines of cumulus clouds southwest of Canary Islands. |
| 20 | S65–63262 | S65–63311 | 15 | Dec. 16, 1965 | 12:21 | 158 | Lines of cumulus clouds southwest of Canary Islands. |
| 21 | S65–63261 | S65–63312 | 15 | Dec. 16, 1965 | 12:21 | 158 | Lines of cumulus clouds southwest of Canary Islands. |
| 22 | S65–63260 | S65–63313 | 15 | Dec. 16, 1965 | 12:22 | 158 | Lines of cumulus clouds southwest of Canary Islands. |
| 23 | S65–63259 | S65–63314 | 15 | Dec. 16, 1965 | 12:22 | 158 | Lines of cumulus clouds southwest of Canary Islands. |
| 24 | S65–63258 | S65–63315 | 15 | Dec. 16, 1965 | 12:22 | 158 | Lines of cumulus clouds southwest of Canary Islands. |

MAGAZINE C Continued

| Frame | NASA/MSC Color No. | NASA/MSC B&W No. | Revolution | Date | GMT | Alt, N. Mi. | Area description |
|---|---|---|---|---|---|---|---|
| 25 | S65–63257 | S65–63316 | 15 | Dec. 16, 1965 | 12:23 | 158 | Spanish Sahara, Mauritania: Port Etienne; Cap Blanc, Levrier Bay. |
| 26 | S65–63256 | S65–63317 | 15 | Dec. 16, 1965 | 12:23 | 158 | Spanish Sahara, Mauritania: Cap Blanc, Levrier Bay. |
| *27* | *S65–63255* | *S65–63318* | *15* | *Dec. 16, 1965* | *12:24* | *158* | *Spanish Sahara, Mauritania: Cap Blanc, Levrier Bay.* |
| 28 | S65–63254 | S65–63319 | 15 | Dec. 16, 1965 | 12:24 | 159 | Mauritania, Senegal: Dakar, Noaukchott; Senegal River. |
| 29 | S65–63253 | S65–63320 | 15 | Dec. 16, 1965 | 12:24 | 159 | Mauritania, Senegal: Gambia, Guinea, Portuguese Guinea: Aouker Basin. |
| 30 | S65–63252 | S65–63321 | 15 | Dec. 16, 1965 | 12:24 | 159 | Mauritania, Senegal: Gambia, Guinea, Portuguese Guinea: Aouker Basin. |
| *31* | *S65–63251* | *S65–63322* | *15* | *Dec. 16, 1965* | *12:24* | *159* | *Mauritania, Senegal: Gambia, Guinea, Portuguese Guinea: Aouker Basin.* |
| 32 | S65–63250 | S65–63323 | 15 | Dec. 16, 1965 | 12:24 | 159 | Mauritania, Senegal: Gambia, Guinea, Portuguese Guinea. |
| 33 | S65–63249 | S65–63324 | 15 | Dec. 16, 1965 | 12:24 | 159 | Mauritania, Senegal, Mali: Aouker Basin. |
| 34 | S65–63248 | S65–63325 | 15 | Dec. 16, 1965 | 12:25 | 159 | Mauritania, Senegal, Spanish Sahara. |
| *35* | *S65–63247* | *S65–63326* | *15* | *Dec. 16, 1965* | *12:26* | *159* | *Mauritania, Mali: Timbuktu; Niger River marshes.* |
| 36 | S65–63246 | S65–63327 | 15 | Dec. 16, 1965 | 12:26 | 159 | Mauritania, Mali: Timbuktu; Niger River marshes. |
| 37 | S65–63245 | S65–63328 | 15 | Dec. 16, 1965 | 12:26 | 159 | Mauritania, Mali, Upper Volta: Timbuktu, Niger River marshes. |
| 38 | S65–63244 | S65–63329 | 15 | Dec. 16, 1965 | 12:27 | 159 | Mali, Upper Volta, Niger: Niger River Basin, Sahara. |
| 39 | S65–63243 | S65–63330 | 15 | Dec. 16, 1965 | 12:29 | 160 | Cirrus puff over Nigeria, Niger, Mali. |
| 40 | S65–63242 | S65–63331 | 15 | Dec. 16, 1965 | 12:29 | 160 | Cirrus puffs over Nigeria, Niger, Mali, Upper Volta, Dahomey. |
| 41 | S65–63241 | S65–63332 | 15 | Dec. 16, 1965 | 12:29 | 160 | Cirrus puffs over Nigeria, Niger, Mali, Upper Volta, Dahomey. |
| *42* | *S65–63240* | *S65–63333* | *15* | *Dec. 16, 1965* | *12:30* | *160* | *Cirrus puffs over Nigeria, Niger, Mali, Upper Volta, Dahomey.* |
| 43 | S65–63239 | S65–63334 | 15 | Dec. 16, 1965 | 12:30 | 160 | Cirrus puffs over Nigeria, Niger, Mali, Upper Volta, Dahomey. |
| 44 | S65–63238 | S65–63335 | 15 | Dec. 16, 1965 | 12:30 | 160 | Cirrus puffs over Nigeria, Niger, Mali, Upper Volta, Dahomey. |
| 45 | S65–63237 | S65–63336 | 15 | Dec. 16, 1965 | ...... | ........ | Sky, horizon. |
| *46* | *S65–63236* | *S65–63337* | *15* | *Dec. 16, 1965* | ...... | ........ | *Heavy haze, cellular cumulus clouds over Cameroon, Central African Republic.* |
| 47 | S65–63235 | S65–63338 | 15 | Dec. 16, 1965 | ...... | ........ | Heavy haze, cellular cumulus clouds over Cameroon, Central African Republic. |
| 48 | S65–63234 | S65–63339 | 15 | Dec. 16, 1965 | ...... | ........ | Very heavy haze, clouds over Republic of the Congo. |
| 49 | S65–63233 | S65–63340 | 15 | Dec. 16, 1965 | 12:36 | 163 | Uganda: Lake Victoria, Sese Islands; cumulus clouds. |
| *50* | *S65–63232* | *S65–63341* | *15* | *Dec. 16, 1965* | *12:37* | *163* | *Tanzania: Lake Victoria, Speke Gulf; cumulus clouds.* |
| 51 | S65–63231 | S65–63342 | 15 | Dec. 16, 1965 | 12:37 | 163 | Tanzania: Lake Victoria, Speke Gulf; cumulus clouds. |
| 52 | S65–63230 | S65–63343 | 15 | Dec. 16, 1965 | 12:38 | 164 | Tanzania coast, islands of Zanzibar and Pemba; cumulus clouds. |
| 53 | S65–63229 | S65–63344 | 15 | Dec. 16, 1965 | 12:38 | 164 | Tanzania coast, south of Dar es Salaam. |
| *54* | *S65–63228* | *S65–63345* | *15* | *Dec. 16, 1965* | *12:40* | *165* | *Tanzania, Mozambique coast: Indian Ocean; clouds.* |
| *55* | *S65–63227* | *S65–63346* | *15* | *Dec. 16, 1965* | *12:41* | *165* | *Comoro Islands: Ile Moheli, Ile d'Anjouan, Gran Comore Island, Ile de Mayotte.* |
| 56 | S65–63226 | S65–63347 | 15 | Dec. 16, 1965 | 12:41 | 165 | Comoro Islands: Ile Moheli, Ile d'Anjouan, Gran Comore Island, Ile de Mayotte. |
| 57 | S65–63225 | S65–63348 | 15 | Dec. 16, 1965 | 12:41 | 165 | Comoro Islands: Ile de Mayotte. |

## MAGAZINE D

| Frame | NASA/MSC Color No. | NASA/MSC B&W No. | Revolution | Date | GMT | Alt, N. Mi. | Area description |
|---|---|---|---|---|---|---|---|
| 1 | S65–63281 | S65–63700 | 15 | Dec. 16, 1965 | 12:43 | 167 | Northeast of Madagascar Island, Malagasy Republic in background. |
| 2 | S65–63282 | S65–63701 | 15 | Dec. 16, 1965 | 12:43 | 167 | Northeast of Madagascar Island, Malagasy Republic in background. |
| *3* | *S65–63283* | *S65–63702* | *15* | *Dec. 16, 1965* | *12:44* | *167* | *Mascarene Islands: La Réunion, Madagascar in background.* |
| *4* | *S65–63284* | *S65–63703* | *15* | *Dec. 16, 1965* | *12:44* | *167* | *Mascarene Islands: La Reunion and Mauritius.* |
| 5 | S65–63285 | S65–63704 | 15 | Dec. 16, 1965 | 12:44 | 167 | Mascarene Islands: La Réunion and Mauritius. |
| 6 | S65–63286 | S65–63705 | 15 | Dec. 16, 1965 | 13:39 | 154 | Cumulus puffs over Gulf of Mexico. |
| 7 | S65–63287 | S65–63706 | 15 | Dec. 16, 1965 | 13:39 | 154 | Cumulus puffs over Gulf of Mexico. |
| 8 | S65–63288 | S65–63707 | 15 | Dec. 16, 1965 | 13:40 | 154 | Cumulus puffs over Gulf of Mexico. |
| 9 | S65–63289 | S65–63708 | 15 | Dec. 16, 1965 | 13:40 | 154 | Cumulus puffs over Gulf of Mexico. |
| 10 | S65–63290 | S65–63709 | 16 | Dec. 16, 1965 | ....... | ....... | Nose of Gemini VI showing insulation extrusion on thruster ports. |
| 11 | S65–63291 | S65–63710 | 16 | Dec. 16, 1965 | ....... | ....... | Nose of Gemini VI showing insulation extrusion on thruster ports. |
| 12 | S65–63292 | S65–63711 | 16 | Dec. 16, 1965 | ....... | ....... | Nose of Gemini VI out of focus. |

# GEMINI VII

## MAGAZINE 22

| Frame | NASA/MSC Color No. | NASA/MSC B&W No. | Revolution | Date | GMT | Alt, N. Mi. | Area description |
|---|---|---|---|---|---|---|---|
| 1 | S65–63832 | S65–64949 | 11 | Dec. 5, 1965 | 16:33 | 120 | Saudi Arabia: Ar Riyad; Jabal Tuwayiq |
| 2 | S65–63831 | S65–64950 | ............ | Dec. 5, 1965 | ....... | ....... | Algeria: Erg Iquidi, good display of sand dunes (250-mm lens). |
| *3* | *S65–63830* | *S65–64951* | *13* | *Dec. 5, 1965* | *19:32* | *121* | *Algeria: Oued Saoura, south of Bechar, rain runoff in normally dry lake bed (250-mm); see frames 46, 47.* |
| 4 | S65–63829 | S65–64952 | 13 | Dec. 5, 1965 | 19:34 | 121 | Algeria: south of Fort Flatters, Tifernine dunes, 1000 ft. high (250-mm lens). |
| 5 | S65–63828 | S65–64953 | 13 | Dec. 5, 1965 | 19:36 | 121 | Algeria, Libya: Looking across Idehan Marzuq, toward Tibesti Mountains. |
| *6* | *S65–63827* | *S65–64954* | *13* | *Dec. 5, 1965* | *20:38* | *164* | *Tuamotu Archipelago: atolls of Tikehua, Rangiroa, Arutua, Apataki, Kaukura, Toau, Niau, Fakarava.* |
| *7* | *S65–63826* | *S65–64955* | *14* | *Dec. 5, 1965* | *20:50* | *129* | *Cuba: Oriente Province, Guantanamo Bay, Santiago de Cuba.* |
| *8* | *S65–63825* | *S65–64956* | *15* | *Dec. 5, 1965* | *17:54* | *124* | *Bahama Islands: Andros, New Providence, Berry Islands.* |
| *9* | *S65–63824* | *S65–64957* | *15* | *Dec. 5, 1965* | *19:28* | *121* | *Florida-Georgia; Atlantic Coast, Jacksonville; St. Johns River.* |
| 10 | S65–63823 | S65–64958 | 16 | Dec. 5, 1965 | 20:54 | 124 | Mexico, California, Arizona: Baja California, Sonora area. |
| *11* | *S65–63822* | *S65–64959* | *16* | *Dec. 5, 1965* | *20:55* | *123* | *Mexico: Baja California, Punta Eugenia.* |
| 12 | S65–63821 | S65–64960 | 17 | Dec. 5, 1965 | 22:01 | 159 | Australia: Northern Territory, east coast of Joseph Bonaparte Gulf, west of Darwin. |
| 13 | S65–63820 | S65–64961 | 17 | Dec. 5, 1965 | 22:30 | 120 | Mexico, California, Arizona; Baja California; Moon near full. |
| 14 | S65–63819 | S65–64962 | 19 | Dec. 6, 1965 | ....... | ....... | Double exposure over Mexico. |
| 15 | S65–63818 | S65–64963 | 19 | Dec. 6, 1965 | 01:10 | 146 | Stratocumulus cells over Indian Ocean. |
| 16 | S65–63817 | S65–64964 | 19 | Dec. 6, 1965 | 01:10 | 146 | Stratocumulus cells over Indian Ocean. |
| 17 | S65–63816 | S65–64965 | 19 | Dec. 6, 1965 | ....... | ....... | Clouds, Moon near full. |
| 18 | S65–63815 | S65–64966 | 29 | Dec. 6, 1965 | 17:46 | 131 | *Central Mexico: Aguascalientes-Zacatecas area. |
| *19* | *S65–63814* | *S65–64967* | *29* | *Dec. 6, 1965* | *17:47* | *131* | **Central Mexico: San Luis Potosí area.* |
| 20 | S65–63813 | S65–64968 | 29 | Dec. 6, 1965 | 17:47 | 130 | *Eastern Mexico: San Luis Potosí-Matehuela area. |
| 21 | S65–63812 | S65–64969 | 29 | Dec. 6, 1965 | 17:47 | 129 | *Eastern Mexico: Ciudad Victoria area. |

MAGAZINE 22 Continued

| Frame | NASA/MSC Color No. | NASA/MSC B&W No. | Revolution | Date | GMT | Alt, N. Mi. | Area description |
|---|---|---|---|---|---|---|---|
| 22 | S65–63811 | S65–64970 | 29 | Dec. 6, 1965 | 17:48 | 129 | *Eastern Mexico: Ciudad Victoria-gulf coast. |
| *23* | *S65–63810* | *S65–64971* | *29* | *Dec. 6, 1965* | *17:48* | *129* | *Eastern Mexico: Gulf coast at La Pesca.* |
| 24 | S65–63809 | S65–64972 | 30 | Dec. 6, 1965 | 19:25 | 121 | Florida: east coast, St. Augustine to Fort Pierce, Kennedy Space Center. |
| *25* | *S65–63808* | *S65–64973* | *30* | *Dec. 6, 1965* | *19:25* | *121* | *Florida: east coast, Titusville to north of Daytona Beach (250-mm lens).* |
| *26* | *S65–63807* | *S65–64974* | *30* | *Dec. 6, 1965* | *19:25* | *121* | *Florida: east coast, Kennedy Space Center, Merritt Island Complex (250-mm lens).* |
| 27 | S65–63806 | S65–64975 | 31 | Dec. 6, 1965 | 19:25 | 121 | Florida: Kennedy Space Center, Merritt Island to Daytona Beach (250-mm lens). |
| 28 | S65–63805 | S65–64976 | 31 | Dec. 6, 1965 | ...... | ........ | Moonrise out of focus. |
| 29 | S65–63804 | S65–64977 | 31 | Dec. 6, 1965 | 20:57 | 120 | Gulf coast: Texas, Galveston Bay to central Louisiana, very hazy. |
| 30 | S65–63803 | S65–64978 | 31 | Dec. 6, 1965 | 20:57 | 120 | Gulf coast: Texas, Galveston Bay to central Louisiana, very hazy. |
| 31 | S65–63802 | S65–64979 | 31 | Dec. 6, 1965 | 20:57 | 120 | Texas; Houston, Beaumont; Jetero Airport, very hazy. |
| 32 | S65–63801 | S65–64980 | 31 | Dec. 6, 1965 | 20:57 | 120 | East Texas, west Louisiana: Sam Rayburn Reservoir, very hazy. |
| 33 | S65–63800 | S65–64981 | 32 | Dec. 6, 1965 | 21:01 | 120 | Ocean off Florida. |
| 34 | S65–63799 | S65–64982 | 32 | Dec. 6, 1965 | 21:01 | 120 | Ocean off Florida. |
| 35 | S65–63798 | S65–64983 | 32 | Dec. 6, 1965 | 21:01 | 120 | Polaris underwater launch, missile and trail off Florida. |
| 36 | S65–63797 | S65–64984 | 32 | Dec. 6, 1965 | 21:01 | 120 | Polaris underwater launch, missile and trail off Florida. |
| 37 | S65–63796 | S65–64985 | 32 | Dec. 6, 1965 | 21:01 | 120 | Polaris underwater launch, missile and trail off Florida. |
| 38 | S65–63795 | S65–64986 | ........... | .............. | ...... | ........ | *Clouds, underexposed. |
| 39 | S65–63794 | S65–64987 | 32 | Dec. 6, 1965 | 21:02 | 120 | *Bahama Islands: south end of Andros Island. |
| 40 | S65–63793 | S65–64988 | 32 | Dec. 6, 1965 | 21:02 | 120 | *Bahama Islands: Great Exuma Island, Long Island. |
| 41 | S65–63792 | S65–64989 | 32 | Dec. 6, 1965 | 21:02 | 120 | *Bahama Islands: Crooked Island, Acklins Island. |
| 42 | S65–63791 | S65–64990 | ........... | .............. | ...... | ........ | Double exposure, limb plus sunset or sunrise. |
| 43 | S65–63790 | S65–64991 | 32 | Dec. 6, 1965 | 22:31 | 120 | Mexico: Tamaulipas, Tampico; gulf coast, Cape Rojo. |
| 44 | S65–63789 | S65–64992 | 33 | Dec. 6, 1965 | 22:43 | 129 | Limb at sunset. |
| 45 | S65–63788 | S65–64993 | 33 | Dec. 6, 1965 | 22:45 | 131 | Sunset, note cloud layers in red. |
| 46 | S65–63787 | S65–64994 | 43 | Dec. 7, 1965 | 14:55 | 121 | Algeria: Oued Saoura, south of Bechar, rain runoff in normally dry lake bed (see frame 3 for telephoto view). |
| 47 | S65–63786 | S65–64995 | 43 | Dec. 7, 1965 | 14:55 | 121 | Algeria: Oued Saoura, south of Bechar, rain runoff in normally dry lake bed, good display of sand dunes (see frame 3 for telephoto view). |
| 48 | S65–63785 | S65–64996 | 43 | Dec. 7, 1965 | 14:56 | 121 | Algeria: Tidikelt, Ahnet regions, Ahaggar Mountains. |
| *49* | *S65–63784* | *S65–64997* | *43* | *Dec. 7, 1965* | *14:56* | *121* | *Algeria: Tidikelt, Ahnet regions, (good dome structure), Ahaggar Mountains.* |
| 50 | S65–63783 | S65–64998 | ........... | .............. | ...... | ........ | Underexposed. |
| 51 | S65–63782 | S65–64999 | 46 | Dec. 7, 1965 | 20:30 | 155 | Marshall Islands: Namorik Atoll. |
| 52 | S65–63781 | S65–64500 | ........... | .............. | ...... | ........ | Partial frame. |

MAGAZINE 17

| Frame | NASA/MSC Color No. | NASA/MSC B&W No. | Revolution | Date | GMT | Alt, N. Mi. | Area description |
|---|---|---|---|---|---|---|---|
| 1 | S65–63833 | S65–65337 | 47 | Dec. 7, 1965 | 22:24 | 126 | Clouds, tropical storm off Baja California. |
| *2* | *S65–63834* | *S65–65338* | *47* | *Dec. 7, 1965* | *22:25* | *126* | *Clouds, tropical storm off Baja California.* |
| 3 | S65–63835 | S65–65339 | 47 | Dec. 7, 1965 | 22:26 | 126 | Clouds, tropical storm off Baja California. |
| 4 | S65–63836 | S65–65340 | 47 | Dec. 7, 1965 | 22:27 | 126 | *Western Mexico: east of Culiacan. |
| 5 | S65–63837 | S65–65341 | 47 | Dec. 7, 1965 | 22:27 | 126 | *Western Mexico: Laguna de Santiaguillo. |
| 6 | S65–63838 | S65–65342 | 47 | Dec. 7, 1965 | 22:28 | 126 | *Western Mexico: Durango. |
| 7 | S65–63839 | S65–65343 | 47 | Dec. 7, 1965 | 22:28 | 126 | *Western Mexico: Durango. |
| 8 | S65–63840 | S65–65344 | 47 | Dec. 7, 1965 | 22:28 | 126 | *Western Mexico: Sombrerete, Rio Grande, Valparaiso. |
| 9 | S65–63841 | S65–65345 | 47 | Dec. 7, 1965 | 22:28 | 126 | *Central Mexico: Fresnillo Zacatecas. |
| 10 | S65–63842 | S65–65346 | 47 | Dec. 7, 1965 | 22:28 | 126 | *Central Mexico: Zacatecas, Salinas. |
| 11 | S65–63843 | S65–65347 | 47 | Dec. 7, 1965 | 22:28 | 126 | *Central Mexico: Salinas, San Luis Potosí. |
| 12 | S65–63844 | S65–65348 | 47 | Dec. 7, 1965 | 22:29 | 126 | *Central Mexico: San Luis Potosí. |
| 13 | S65–63845 | S65–65349 | ........... | ............... | ....... | ........ | Blank. |
| 14 | S65–63846 | S65–65350 | 48 | Dec. 7, 1965 | 23:23 | 160 | Moon, full. |
| 15 | S65–63847 | S65–65351 | 48 | Dec. 7, 1965 | 23:23 | 160 | Moon, full (warped picture). |
| 16 | ........... | ........... | ........... | ............... | ....... | ........ | Blank. |
| 17 | ........... | ........... | ........... | ............... | ....... | ........ | Blank. |
| 18 | S65–63848 | S65–65352 | 56 | Dec. 8, 1965 | 11:48 | 131 | *Libya; Gulf of Sirte. |
| *19* | *S65–63849* | *S65–65353* | *56* | *Dec. 8, 1965* | *11:52* | *129* | *Israel, Syria, Jordan, Lebanon, Turkey, Cyprus, Iraq: Nile Delta, Sinai Peninsula.* |
| 20 | S65–63850 | S65–65354 | 56 | Dec. 8, 1965 | 11:52 | 128 | *Israel, Jordan, Lebanon, United Arab Republic: Dead Sea. |
| 21 | S65–63851 | S65–65355 | 56 | Dec. 8, 1965 | 11:55 | 127 | Muscat and Oman: Ra's al Hadd. |
| 22 | S65–63852 | S65–65356 | 56 | Dec. 8, 1965 | 12:00 | 130 | Full Moon, cirrus clouds over Indian Ocean, note patterns (see frame 49). |
| 23 | S65–63853 | S65–65357 | 56 | Dec. 8, 1965 | 12:00 | 130 | Clouds, Indian Ocean, note patterns (see frame 49). |
| *24* | *S65–63854* | *S65–65358* | *56* | *Dec. 8, 1965* | *12:56* | *160* | *Galapagos Islands; openings in clouds.* |
| *25* | *S65–63855* | *S65–65359* | *57* | *Dec. 8, 1965* | *13:04* | *149* | *Leeward Islands: Guadeloupe, Antigua, Maria Galante, Montserrat.* |
| 26 | S65–63856 | S65–65360 | 57 | Dec. 8, 1965 | 13:23 | 128 | Libya: basalt flows of Black Haruj. |
| *27* | *S65–63857* | *S65–65361* | *58* | *Dec. 8, 1965* | *14:37* | *145* | *Bahama Islands: Crooked, Acklins, Long and Mayaguana Islands, San Salvador, Plana Cays and Samana Cay.* |
| *28* | *S65–63858* | *S65–65362* | *58* | *Dec. 8, 1965* | *14:37* | *145* | *Bahama Islands: Crooked, Acklins, Mayaguana Islands, Plana Cays, Samana Cay.* |
| 29 | S65–63859 | S65–65363 | ........... | ............... | ....... | ........ | Blank. |
| 30 | S65–63860 | S65–65364 | 58 | Dec. 8, 1965 | 16:10 | 140 | **Florida Keys. |
| 31 | S65–63861 | S65–65365 | 58 | Dec. 8, 1965 | 16:10 | 140 | **Florida: Keys, Whitewater Bay. |
| 32 | S65–63862 | S65–65366 | 58 | Dec. 8, 1965 | 16:10 | 140 | **Florida: Keys, Florida Bay, Everglades. |
| 33 | S65–63863 | S65–65367 | 58 | Dec. 8, 1965 | 16:11 | 140 | **Florida: Keys, Florida Bay, Everglades. |
| 34 | S65–63864 | S65–65368 | 59 | Dec. 8, 1965 | 16:12 | 140 | **Edge of Great Bahama Bank, Straits of Florida. |
| 35 | S65–63865 | S65–65369 | 59 | Dec. 8, 1965 | 16:12 | 140 | **Edge of Great Bahama Bank, Straits of Florida, Andros Island. |
| 36 | S65–63866 | S65–65370 | 59 | Dec. 8, 1965 | 16:12 | 140 | **Bahama Islands: Andros Island area. |
| 37 | S65–63867 | S65–65371 | 59 | Dec. 8, 1965 | 16:13 | 139 | **Bahama Islands: Andros Island area. |
| 38 | S65–63868 | S65–65372 | 61 | Dec. 8, 1965 | 20:45 | 135 | Clouds over eastern Pacific off Mexico (see frames 50–55). |
| 39 | S65–63869 | S65–65373 | 61 | Dec. 8, 1965 | 20:45 | 135 | *Clouds over eastern Pacific off Mexico (see frames 50–55). |
| *40* | *S65–63870* | *S65–65372* | *61* | *Dec. 8, 1965* | *20:47* | *133* | **Guadalupe Island, Pacific Ocean off Baja California, Mexico.* |
| 41 | S65–63871 | S65–65375 | 61 | Dec. 8, 1965 | 20:49 | 132 | *Mexico: Baja California, Punta Eugenia, Cedros Island. |
| *42* | *S65–63872* | *S65–65376* | *63* | *Dec. 8, 1965* | *21:30* | *155* | *Moon, clouds over western Pacific.* |
| 43 | S65–63873 | S65–65377 | 63 | Dec. 8, 1965 | 21:30 | 155 | Moon, clouds over western Pacific. |
| 44 | S65–63874 | S65–65378 | ........... | ............... | ....... | ........ | Blank. |

MAGAZINE 17 Continued

| Frame | NASA/MSC Color No. | NASA/MSC B&W No. | Revolution | Date | GMT | Alt, N. Mi. | Area description |
|---|---|---|---|---|---|---|---|
| 45 | S65–63875 | S65–65379 | 73 | Dec. 9, 1965 | 14:48 | 131 | *Canary Islands: Tenerife and La Palma Islands. |
| 46 | S65–63876 | S65–65380 | 73 | Dec. 9, 1965 | 14:49 | 130 | *Canary Islands: Tenerife, Gomera, Gran Canaria Islands. |
| 47 | S65–63877 | S65–65381 | 73 | Dec. 9, 1965 | 14:49 | 130 | *Canary Islands: Tenerife, Gran Canaria Islands. |
| 48 | S65–63878 | S65–65382 | 74 | Dec. 9, 1965 | 16:26 | 126 | **Mauritania: Dhar Adrar, Richat Structure. |
| 49 | S65–63879 | S65–65383 | 74 | Dec. 9, 1965 | 16:50 | 161 | Clouds, Indian Ocean (see frames 22 and 23) |
| 50 | S65–63880 | S65–65384 | 76 | Dec. 9, 1965 | 20:45 | 161 | Clouds over eastern Pacific off Mexico (see frames 39, 38) |
| 51 | S65–63881 | S65–65385 | 76 | Dec. 9, 1965 | 20:45 | 161 | Clouds over eastern Pacific off Mexico (see frames 38, 39) |
| 52 | S65–63882 | S65–65386 | 76 | Dec. 9, 1965 | 20:46 | 161 | Clouds over eastern Pacific off Mexico (see frames 38, 39) |
| 53 | S65–63883 | S65–65387 | 76 | Dec. 9, 1965 | 20:46 | 161 | Clouds over eastern Pacific off Mexico (see frames 38, 39) |
| 54 | S65–63884 | S65–65388 | 76 | Dec. 9, 1965 | 20:46 | 161 | Clouds over eastern Pacific off Mexico (see frames 38, 39) |
| 55 | S65–63885 | S65–65389 | 76 | Dec. 9, 1965 | 20:47 | 161 | Clouds over Mexico, Sonora. |
| 56 | S65–63886 | S65–65390 | 76 | Dec. 9, 1965 | 20:50 | 161 | Mexico: Torreon, Camargo area. |
| 57 | S65–63887 | S65–65391 | 76 | Dec. 9, 1965 | 20:50 | 161 | Mexico: Torreon area. |
| *58* | *S65–63888* | *S65–65392* | *76* | *Dec. 9, 1965* | *20:50* | *161* | *Mexico: Torreon, Saltillo area.* |
| *59* | *S65–63889* | *S65–65393* | *76* | *Dec. 9, 1965* | *20:51* | *161* | *Mexico: Saltillo, Monterrey area.* |

MAGAZINE 24

| Frame | NASA/MSC Color No. | NASA/MSC B&W No. | Revolution | Date | GMT | Alt, N. Mi. | Area description |
|---|---|---|---|---|---|---|---|
| 1 | S65–63722 | S65–65120 | 77 | Dec. 9, 1965 | 21:51 | 162 | *Clouds at twilight. |
| 2 | S65–63723 | S65–65121 | 77 | Dec. 9, 1965 | 21:52 | 162 | *Clouds. |
| 3 | S65–63724 | S65–65122 | 77 | Dec. 9, 1965 | 21:52 | 162 | *Clouds, western Pacific. |
| 4 | S65–63725 | S65–65123 | 77 | Dec. 9, 1965 | 21:55 | 162 | Clouds, western Pacific. |
| *5* | *S65–63726* | *S65–65124* | *77* | *Dec. 9, 1965* | *22:09* | *162* | *Hawaiian Islands: Pearl and Hermes Reef, Kure Island, Midway Island.* |
| *6* | *S65–63727* | *S65–65125* | *77* | *Dec. 9, 1965* | *22:09* | *162* | *Hawaiian Islands: Pearl and Hermes Reef.* |
| 7 | S65–63728 | S65–65126 | 79 | Dec. 10, 1965 | 01:03 | 161 | China: Kwangtung Province, Hong Kong. |
| 8 | S65–63729 | S65–65127 | 79 | Dec. 10, 1965 | 01:03 | 161 | China: Kwangtung Province, Hong Kong. |
| 9 | S65–63730 | S65–65128 | 79 | Dec. 10, 1965 | 01:08 | 161 | Daito Islands: Kita and Minami. |
| 10 | S65–63731 | S65–65129 | 88 | Dec. 10, 1965 | 15:02 | 160 | *Niger, Nigeria, Chad: Lake Chad. |
| 11 | S65–63732 | S65–65130 | 88 | Dec. 10, 1965 | 15:02 | 160 | *Niger, Nigeria, Chad: Lake Chad. |
| 12 | S65–63733 | S65–65131 | 88 | Dec. 10, 1965 | 15:03 | 160 | *Niger, Nigeria, Chad: Lake Chad. |
| 13 | S65–63734 | S65–65132 | 89 | Dec. 10, 1965 | 16:29 | 161 | **Mauritania, Spanish Sahara; Cap Blanc |
| 14 | S65–63735 | S65–65133 | 89 | Dec. 10, 1965 | 16:31 | 160 | **Mauritania, Spanish Sahara; Cap Blanc |
| 15 | S65–63736 | S65–65134 | 91 | Dec. 10, 1965 | 20:54 | 161 | Clouds, Pacific Ocean off Mexico. |
| 16 | S65–63737 | S65–65135 | 91 | Dec. 10, 1965 | 20:56 | 161 | **West-central Mexico. |
| 17 | S65–63738 | S65–65136 | 91 | Dec. 10, 1965 | 20:57 | 161 | **West-central Mexico. |
| 18 | S65–63739 | S65–65137 | 91 | Dec. 10, 1965 | 20:57 | 161 | **West-central Mexico. |
| 19 | S65–63740 | S65–65138 | 91 | Dec. 10, 1965 | 20:58 | 161 | *Mexico: north of San Luis Potosí. |
| *20* | *S65–63741* | *S65–65139* | *91* | *Dec. 10, 1965* | *21:01* | *161* | *Mexico, British Honduras: Yucatan Peninsula, Quintana Roo.* |
| 21 | S65–63742 | S65–65140 | 91 | Dec. 10, 1965 | 21:01 | 161 | British Honduras: city of Belize, Gulf of Honduras. |
| 22 | ........... | ........... | ........... | ........... | ....... | ....... | Blank. |
| *23* | *S65–63743* | *S65–65141* | *100* | *Dec. 11, 1965* | *10:37* | *160* | *India, Ceylon: Palk Strait, Adam's Bridge.* |
| 24 | S65–63744 | S65–65142 | 100 | Dec. 11, 1965 | 10:38 | 160 | India, Ceylon: Palk Strait, Adam's Bridge. |
| 25 | S65–63745 | S65–65143 | 100 | Dec. 11, 1965 | 10:38 | 160 | India, Ceylon: Palk Strait, Adam's Bridge. |
| 26 | S65–63746 | S65–65144 | 101 | Dec. 11, 1965 | 11:58 | 162 | Libya, Chad, Niger: Tibesti Mountains. |
| 27 | S65–63747 | S65–65145 | 101 | Dec. 11, 1965 | 11:58 | 162 | **Libya, Chad, Nigeria: Tibesti Mountains. |
| 28 | S65–63748 | S65–65146 | 101 | Dec. 11, 1965 | 11:59 | 162 | Eastern Libya: Al Kufrah, Libyan Desert. |
| 29 | S65–63749 | S65–65147 | 101 | Dec. 11, 1965 | 12:01 | 162 | United Arab Republic, Libya: Western and Libyan Deserts |

MAGAZINE 24 Continued

| Frame | NASA/MSC Color No. | NASA/MSC B&W No. | Revolution | Date | GMT | Alt, N. Mi. | Area description |
|---|---|---|---|---|---|---|---|
| 30 | S65-63750 | S65-65148 | 101 | Dec. 11, 1965 | 12:07 | 161 | Somali Republic: Ras Asir, Ras Hafun, Abd al Kuri Island. |
| 31 | S65-63751 | S65-65149 | ............ | Dec. 11, 1965 | ...... | ........ | Clouds, sunlit cumulus tops. |
| 32 | S65-63752 | S65-65150 | 102 | Dec. 11, 1965 | 14:46 | 163 | **Florida: Keys and Miami area. |
| *33* | *S65-63753* | *S65-65151* | *103* | *Dec. 11, 1965* | *14:47* | *163* | *Bahama Islands: Andros, New Providence, Abaco, Eleuthera Islands.* |
| *34* | *S65-63754* | *S65-65152* | *104* | *Dec. 11, 1965* | *16:37* | *160* | *Senegal, Gambia, Portuguese Guinea: Dakar, Cape Vert.* |
| 35 | S65-63755 | S65-65153 | 106 | Dec. 11, 1965 | 19:38 | 160 | *Venezuela: Peninsula de Araya, Isla de Margarita. |
| 36 | S65-63756 | S65-65154 | 106 | Dec. 11, 1965 | 21:05 | 161 | Mexico: Federal District, Morelos, Puebla, Tlaxcala, Guerrero. |
| *37* | *S65-63757* | *S65-65155* | *106* | *Dec. 11, 1965* | *21:05* | *161* | *Mexico: Federal District, Morelos, Puebla, Tlaxcala, Guerrero, Oaxaco, Veracruz.* |
| *38* | *S65-63758* | *S65-65156* | *106* | *Dec. 11, 1965* | *21:05* | *161* | *Mexico: Puebla, Veracruz, Tlaxcala, Oaxaco.* |
| 39 | S65-63759 | S65-65157 | 106 | Dec. 11, 1965 | 21:06 | 161 | Mexico: Veracruz, Oaxaco. |
| *40* | *S65-63760* | *S65-65158* | *106* | *Dec. 11, 1965* | *21:06* | *161* | *Mexico: Veracruz, Oaxaco; Golfo and Istmo de Tehuantepec.* |
| 41 | S65-63761 | S65-65159 | ............ | .............. | ...... | ........ | *Clouds. |
| 42 | S65-63762 | S65-65160 | 109 | Dec. 12, 1965 | 01:16 | 161 | China: Kweichow-Kwangsi Provinces. |
| 43 | S65-63763 | S65-65161 | 109 | Dec. 12, 1965 | 01:17 | 161 | China: Kwangtung Province, looking toward Canton and Hong Kong. |
| 44 | S65-63764 | S65-65162 | 109 | Dec. 12, 1965 | 01:17 | 161 | China: coastline of Formosa Strait. |
| 45 | S65-63765 | S65-65163 | 116 | Dec. 12, 1965 | 12:12 | 160 | Somali Republic: Ras Asir, Ras Hafun. |
| 46 | S65-63766 | S65-65164 | 116 | Dec. 12, 1965 | 12:13 | 160 | Somali Republic: Ras Asir, Ras Hafun, Socotra Island. |
| 47 | S65-63767 | S65-65165 | 116 | Dec. 12, 1965 | 12:13 | 160 | Aden, Somali Republic; Gulf of Aden, Ras Asir. |
| 48 | S65-63768 | S65-65166 | ............ | .............. | ...... | ........ | *Clouds. |
| 49 | S65-63769 | S65-65167 | 117 | Dec. 12, 1965 | 14:52 | 161 | *Florida: Kennedy Space Center, Gemini VI abort. |
| 50 | S65-63770 | S65-65168 | 117 | Dec. 12, 1965 | 14:52 | 161 | *Florida: Kennedy Space Center, Gemini VI abort. |
| 51 | S65-63771 | S65-65169 | 117 | Dec. 12, 1965 | 14:52 | 161 | *Florida: Kennedy Space Center, Gemini VI abort. |
| 52 | S65-63772 | S65-65170 | 118 | Dec. 12, 1965 | 14:53 | 161 | *Florida: Kennedy Space Center, Gemini VI abort. |
| 53 | S65-63773 | S65-65171 | ............ | .............. | ...... | ........ | Clouds over ocean. |
| 54 | S65-63774 | S65-65172 | ............ | .............. | ...... | ........ | Clouds over ocean. |
| 55 | S65-63775 | S65-65173 | ............ | .............. | ...... | ........ | Clouds over ocean. |
| 56 | S65-63776 | S65-65174 | ............ | .............. | ...... | ........ | Clouds over ocean. |
| 57 | S65-63777 | S65-65175 | ............ | .............. | ...... | ........ | Clouds over ocean, contrails. |
| 58 | S65-63778 | S65-65176 | ............ | .............. | ...... | ........ | Clouds over ocean. |
| 59 | S65-63779 | S65-65177 | 119 | Dec. 12, 1965 | 16:55 | 160 | *Clouds. |
| *60* | *S65-63780* | *S65-65178* | *123* | *Dec. 12, 1965* | *22:59* | *161* | *Bolivia, Chile, Argentina: cloud over Andes, Salar de Uyuni.* |
| 61 | S65-63781 | ........... | ............ | .............. | ...... | ........ | Partial frame. |

MAGAZINE 25

| Frame | NASA/MSC Color No. | NASA/MSC B&W No. | Revolution | Date | GMT | Alt, N. Mi. | Area description |
|---|---|---|---|---|---|---|---|
| 1 | S65-63991 | S65-65061 | 120 | Dec. 12, 1965 | 19:39 | 161 | *Honduras, El Salvador, Nicaragua: Carribbean in foreground, Pacific in background. |
| 2 | S65-63992 | S65-65062 | 121 | Dec. 12, 1965 | 19:43 | 160 | Colombia, Venezuela: Peninsula de la Guajira, Peninsula de Paraguana. |
| *3* | *S65-63993* | *S65-65063* | *121* | *Dec. 12, 1965* | *19:43* | *160* | *Colombia, Venezuela: Peninsula de la Guajira, Peninsula de Paraguana.* |
| 4 | S65-63994 | S65-65064 | 121 | Dec. 12, 1965 | ...... | 160 | Venezuela: Partial frame. |
| *5* | *S65-63995* | *S65-65065* | *121* | *Dec. 12, 1965* | *19:44* | *160* | *Venezuela: Caracas, Lago de Valencia.* |

MAGAZINE 25 Continued

| Frame | NASA/MSC | | Revolution | Date | GMT | Alt, N. Mi. | Area description |
|---|---|---|---|---|---|---|---|
| | Color No. | B&W No. | | | | | |
| 6 | S65–63996 | S65–65066 | 121 | Dec. 12, 1965 | ....... | 160 | Clouds off Guyana coast. |
| 7 | S65–63997 | S65–65067 | 121 | Dec. 12, 1965 | 19:49 | 160 | Brazil: Mouth of Amazon River. |
| 8 | S65–63998 | S65–65068 | 121 | Dec. 12, 1965 | 19:49 | 160 | Brazil: Mouth of Amazon River. |
| 9 | S65–63999 | S65–65069 | 121 | Dec. 12, 1965 | 19:50 | 160 | Brazil: Mouth of Amazon River, Baia de Marajo. |
| 10 | S65–64000 | S65–65070 | 121 | Dec. 12, 1965 | 19:50 | 160 | Brazil: Mouth of Amazon River, Baia de Marajo. |
| *11* | *S65–64001* | *S65–65071* | *121* | *Dec. 12, 1965* | *19:50* | *160* | *Brazil: Mouth of Amazon River.* |
| 12 | S65–64002 | S65–65072 | 121 | Dec. 12, 1965 | 19:50 | 160 | Brazil: Mouth of Amazon River, Baia de Marajo. |
| 13 | S65–64003 | S65–65073 | 121 | Dec. 12, 1965 | 19:50 | 160 | Brazil: Mouth of Amazon River, Baia de Marajo. |
| 14 | S65–64004 | S65–65074 | ........... | .............. | ...... | ........ | Double exposure. |
| 15 | S65–64005 | S65–65075 | 130 | Dec. 13, 1965 | 10:42 | 161 | Saudi Arabia, Sudan, Ethiopia: Red Sea. |
| *16* | *S65–64006* | *S65–65076* | *130* | *Dec. 13, 1965* | *10:42* | *161* | *Saudi Arabia, Sudan, Ethiopia, United Arab Republic: Red Sea.* |
| *17* | *S65–64007* | *S65–65077* | *130* | *Dec. 13, 1965* | *10:43* | *161* | *Saudi Arabia, Yemen, Ethiopia: Red Sea.* |
| 18 | S65–64008 | S65–65078 | 130 | Dec. 13, 1965 | 10:43 | 161 | Yemen: Southwest corner of Empty Quarter. |
| 19 | S65–64009 | S65–65079 | 130 | Dec. 13, 1965 | 10:43 | 161 | Aden Protectorate: Hadramawt Plateau, Wadi Hadramawt. |
| *20* | *S65–64010* | *S65–65080* | *130* | *Dec. 13, 1965* | *10:43* | *161* | *Aden Protectorate: Hadramawt Plateau, Wadi Hadramawt, Al Mukalla, Gulf of Aden.* |
| *21* | *S65–64011* | *S65–65081* | *130* | *Dec. 13, 1965* | *10:44* | *160* | *Aden Protectorate: Mouth of Wadi Hadramawt, Gulf of Aden.* |
| 22 | S65–64012 | S65–65082 | 130 | Dec. 13, 1965 | 10:45 | 160 | Somali Republic: Ras Asir, Ras Hafun. |
| *23* | *S65–64013* | *S65–65083* | *130* | *Dec. 13, 1965* | *10:45* | *160* | *Socotra Island, Abd al Kuri Island, The Brothers Islands.* |
| *24* | *S65–64014* | *S65–65084* | *131* | *Dec. 13, 1965* | *12:17* | *160* | *Ethiopia: Lake Tana, Blue Nile.* |
| 25 | S65–64015 | S65–65085 | 131 | Dec. 13, 1965 | 12:17 | 160 | Ethiopia: Harar, Bale Provinces. |
| 26 | S65–64016 | S65–65086 | 131 | Dec. 13, 1965 | 12:17 | 160 | Ethiopia: Harar, Bale Provinces. |
| 27 | S65–64017 | S65–65087 | 131 | Dec. 13, 1965 | 12:18 | 160 | Ethiopia: Harar, Bale Provinces. |
| 28 | S65–64018 | S65–65088 | 131 | Dec. 13, 1965 | 12:18 | 160 | Ethiopia: Harar Province; Somali Republic. |
| 29 | S65–64019 | S65–65089 | 131 | Dec. 13, 1965 | 12:18 | 160 | Ethiopia: Harar Province; Somali Republic. |
| 30 | S65–64020 | S65–65090 | 131 | Dec. 13, 1965 | 12:18 | 160 | Ethiopia: Harar Province; Somali Republic. |
| *31* | *S65–64021* | *S65–65091* | *131* | *Dec. 13, 1965* | *12:18* | *160* | *Somali Republic: Coastline north of Mogadishu.* |
| *32* | *S65–64022* | *S65–65092* | *133* | *Dec. 13, 1965* | *15:25* | *160* | *Congo, Brazzaville; Republic of Congo, Leopoldville: Stanley Pool, Congo River.* |
| 33 | S65–64023 | S65–65093 | 133 | Dec. 13, 1965 | 15:31 | 161 | Mozambique: Mouth of Zambeze River. |
| *34* | *S65–64024* | *S65–65094* | *134* | *Dec. 13, 1965* | *18:11* | *161* | *Florida: Keys, Florida Bay, Cape Sable, underwater detail clearly shown.* |
| *35* | *S65–64025* | *S65–65095* | *135* | *Dec. 13, 1965* | *18:11* | *161* | *Cuba: Camaguey Province; Great Bahama Bank, Tongue of the Ocean.* |
| *36* | *S65–64026* | *S65–65096* | *135* | *Dec. 13, 1965* | *18:11* | *161* | *Cuba: Golfo de Ana Maria, Jardines de la Reina Islands.* |
| *37* | *S65–64027* | *S65–65097* | *135* | *Dec. 13, 1965* | *18:13* | *161* | *Haiti, western Dominican Republic.* |
| *38* | *S65–64028* | *S65–65098* | *135* | *Dec. 13, 1965* | *18:13* | *161* | *Southeastern Haiti, western Dominican Republic.* |
| *39* | *S65–64029* | *S65–65099* | *135* | *Dec. 13, 1965* | *18:14* | *161* | *Guyana: Coastline at Georgetown.* |
| 40 | S65–64030 | S65–65100 | 143 | Dec. 14, 1965 | 07:19 | 158 | *Cape Verde Islands: Sao Nicolau, Sao Vicente. |
| 41 | S65–64031 | S65–65101 | 143 | Dec. 14, 1965 | 07:19 | 158 | **Cape Verde Islands: underexposed. |
| 42 | S65–64032 | S65–65102 | 143 | Dec. 14, 1965 | 07:23 | 159 | *Mauritania: Dhar Adrar, Richat Structure. |
| 43 | S65–64033 | S65–65103 | ........... | .............. | ...... | ........ | **Clouds. |
| 44 | S65–64034 | S65–65104 | 162 | Dec. 15, 1965 | 13:37 | 160 | Florida: Kennedy Space Center, Gemini VI launch, smoke puff at pad 19, clouds, contrails. |
| 45 | S65–64035 | S65–65105 | ........... | .............. | ...... | ........ | **Clouds. |
| 46 | ........... | ........... | ........... | .............. | ...... | ........ | Blank. |
| 47 | ........... | ........... | ........... | .............. | ...... | ........ | Blank. |
| 48 | ........... | ........... | ........... | .............. | ...... | ........ | Blank. |

MAGAZINE 25 Continued

| Frame | NASA/MSC | | Revolution | Date | GMT | Alt, N. Mi. | Area description |
|---|---|---|---|---|---|---|---|
| | Color No. | B&W No. | | | | | |
| 49 | S65-64036 | S65-65106 | 166 | Dec. 15, 1965 | 21:40 | 161 | Rendezvous, with Gemini VI, range 45 ft; underexposed. |
| 50 | S65-64037 | S65-65107 | 166 | Dec. 15, 1965 | ...... | ........ | Rendezvous, with Gemini VI, nose view, range 45 ft. |
| 51 | S65-64038 | S65-65108 | 166 | Dec. 15, 1965 | ...... | ........ | Rendezvous, with Gemini VI, nose view, range 48 ft. |
| 52 | S65-64039 | S65-65109 | 166 | Dec. 15, 1965 | ...... | ........ | Rendezvous, with Gemini VI, nose view, range 38 ft; "Beat Army" sign. |
| 53 | S65-64040 | S65-65110 | 166 | Dec. 15, 1956 | ...... | ........ | Rendezvous, with Gemini VI, nose view, range 38 ft; "Beat Army" sign. |
| 54 | S65-64041 | S65-65111 | 166 | Dec. 15, 1965 | ...... | ........ | Rendezvous, with Gemini VI, nose view, range 55 ft. |
| 55 | S65-64042 | S65-65112 | 166 | Dec. 15, 1965 | ...... | ........ | Rendezvous, with Gemini VI, nose view, range 45 ft. |
| 56 | S65-64043 | S65-65113 | 166 | Dec. 15, 1965 | ...... | ........ | Rendezvous, with Gemini VI, nose view, range 45 ft. |
| 57 | S65-64044 | S65-65114 | 166 | Dec. 15, 1965 | ...... | ........ | Rendezvous, with Gemini VI, nose view, range 270 ft. |
| 58 | S65-64045 | S65-65115 | 166 | Dec. 15, 1965 | ...... | ........ | Rendezvous, with Gemini VI, nose view, range 40 ft. |
| 59 | S65-64046 | S65-65116 | 166 | Dec. 15, 1965 | ...... | ........ | Rendezvous, with Gemini VI, nose view 35 ft. |
| 60 | S65-64047 | S65-65117 | 166 | Dec. 15, 1965 | ...... | ........ | Rendezvous, with Gemini VI, nose view 33 ft. |
| 61 | S65-64048 | S65-65118 | 166 | Dec. 15, 1965 | ...... | ........ | Rendezvous, with Gemini VI, oblique view, range 60 ft. |
| 62 | S65-64049 | S65-65119 | 166 | Dec. 15, 1965 | ...... | ........ | Rendezvous, with Gemini VI, oblique view. range 60 ft. |

MAGAZINE 13

| Frame | NASA/MSC | | Revolution | Date | GMT | Alt, N. Mi. | Area description |
|---|---|---|---|---|---|---|---|
| | Color No. | B&W No. | | | | | |
| 1 | ........... | ........... | ............ | ............. | ...... | ........ | Blank. |
| 2 | S65-63890 | S65-65296 | 166 | Dec. 15, 1965 | ...... | ........ | **Rendezvous with Gemini VI, nose view, range 100 ft. |
| 3 | S65-63891 | S65-65297 | 166 | Dec. 15, 1965 | ...... | ........ | **Rendezvous with Gemini VI, nose view, range 130 ft. |
| 4 | S65-63892 | S65-65298 | 166 | Dec. 15, 1965 | ...... | ........ | **Rendezvous with Gemini VI, nose view, range 145 ft. |
| 5 | S65-63893 | S65-65299 | 166 | Dec. 15, 1965 | ...... | ........ | **Rendezvous with Gemini VI, oblique nose view, range 70 ft. |
| 6 | S65-63894 | S65-65300 | 166 | Dec. 15, 1965 | ...... | ........ | Rendezvous with Gemini VI, oblique nose view, range 43 ft. |
| 7 | S65-63895 | S65-65301 | 166 | Dec. 15, 1965 | ...... | ........ | Rendezvous with Gemini VI, oblique nose view, range 40 ft. |
| 8 | S65-63896 | S65-65302 | 166 | Dec. 15, 1965 | ...... | ........ | **Rendezvous with Gemini VI, oblique nose view, range 40 ft. |
| 9 | S65-63897 | S65-65303 | 166 | Dec. 15, 1965 | ...... | ........ | Rendezvous with Gemini VI, nose view, range 58 ft. |
| 10 | S65-63898 | S65-65304 | 166 | Dec. 15, 1965 | ...... | ........ | Rendezvous with Gemini VI, nose view, range 43 ft. |
| 11 | S65-63899 | S65-65305 | 166 | Dec. 15, 1965 | ...... | ........ | Rendezvous with Gemini VI, nose view, range 43 ft. |
| 12 | S65-63900 | S65-65306 | 166 | Dec. 15, 1965 | ...... | ........ | Rendezvous with Gemini VI, nose view, range 40 ft. |
| 13 | S65-63901 | S65-65307 | 166 | Dec. 15, 1965 | ...... | ........ | Rendezvous with Gemini VI, nose view, range 32 ft. |
| 14 | S65-63902 | S65-65308 | 166 | Dec. 15, 1965 | ...... | ........ | Rendezvous with Gemini VI, nose view; underexposed. |

MAGAZINE 13 Continued

| Frame | NASA/MSC Color No. | NASA/MSC B&W No. | Revolution | Date | GMT | Alt, N. Mi. | Area description |
|---|---|---|---|---|---|---|---|
| 15 | S65–63903 | S65–65309 | 166 | Dec. 15, 1965 | ....... | ........ | Rendezvous with Gemini VI, nose view; underexposed. |
| 16 | S65–63904 | S65–65310 | ............ | .............. | ....... | ........ | **Double exposure, clouds. |
| 17 | S65–63905 | S65–65311 | ............ | .............. | ....... | ........ | Clouds, reflections on window. |
| 18 | S65–63906 | S65–65312 | 178 | Dec. 16, 1965 | 15:45 | 162 | **Southwest Africa: Rocky Point, Cape Fria. |
| 19 | S65–63907 | S65–65313 | 178 | Dec. 16, 1965 | 15:45 | 162 | **Southwest Africa: Rocky Point, Cape Fria. |
| 20 | S65–63908 | S65–65314 | 178 | Dec. 16, 1965 | 15:45 | 162 | **Southwest Africa: Kaoko Veld. |
| 21 | S65–63909 | S65–65315 | 178 | Dec. 16, 1965 | 15:45 | 162 | **Southwest Africa: Kaoko Veld. |
| 22 | S65–63910 | S65–65316 | 178 | Dec. 16, 1965 | 15:45 | 162 | **Southwest Africa: Kaoko Veld, Etosha Pan. |
| 23 | S65–63911 | S65–65317 | 178 | Dec. 16, 1965 | 15:45 | 162 | **Southwest Africa: Etosha Pan. |
| 24 | S65–63912 | S65–65318 | 178 | Dec. 16, 1965 | 15:46 | 162 | **Southwest Africa: Etosha Pan. |
| 25 | S65–63913 | S65–65319 | 178 | Dec. 16, 1965 | 15:46 | 162 | **Southwest Africa: Etosha Pan. |
| 26 | S65–63914 | S65–65320 | 178 | Dec. 16, 1965 | 15:46 | 162 | **Southwest Africa. |
| 27 | S65–63915 | S65–65321 | 178 | Dec. 16, 1965 | 15:46 | 162 | **Southwest Africa. |
| 28 | S65–63916 | S65–65322 | 178 | Dec. 16, 1965 | 15:47 | 162 | **Southwest Africa. |
| 29 | S65–63917 | S65–65323 | 178 | Dec. 16, 1965 | 15:47 | 162 | **Southwest Africa, Bechuanaland. |
| 30 | S65–63918 | S65–65324 | 179 | Dec. 16, 1965 | 16:54 | 160 | **Cuba: Pinar del Rio, La Habana Provinces. |
| 31 | S65–63919 | S65–65325 | 179 | Dec. 16, 1965 | 16:54 | 160 | **Cuba: Matanzas, Las Villas Provinces. |
| 32 | S65–63920 | S65–65326 | 179 | Dec. 16, 1965 | 16:54 | 160 | **Cuba: Las Villas, Camaguey Provinces. |
| 33 | S65–63921 | S65–65327 | 179 | Dec. 16, 1965 | 16:55 | 160 | **Cuba: Camaguey, Oriente Provinces. |
| 34 | S65–63922 | S65–65328 | 179 | Dec. 16, 1965 | 16:55 | 160 | **Cuba: Oriente Province. |
| 35 | S65–63923 | S65–65329 | 179 | Dec. 16, 1965 | 16:56 | 160 | **Cuba: Oriente Province. |
| 36 | S65–63924 | S65–65330 | 179 | Dec. 16, 1965 | 16:56 | 160 | **Cuba: Oriente Province. |
| 37 | S65–63925 | S65–65331 | 179 | Dec. 16, 1965 | 16:56 | 160 | *Haiti, western Dominican Republic. |
| 38 | S65–63926 | S65–65332 | 179 | Dec. 16, 1965 | 16:57 | 160 | *Dominican Republic. |
| 39 | S65–63927 | S65–65333 | 179 | Dec. 16, 1965 | 16:58 | 160 | **Easternmost Dominican Republic, Puerto Rico. |
| 40 | S65–63928 | S65–65334 | 179 | Dec. 16, 1965 | 17:01 | 160 | **Guyana: Mouths of Essequibo and Demerara Rivers. |
| 41 | S65–63929 | S65–65335 | 179 | Dec. 16, 1965 | 17:02 | 161 | **Surinam, Guyana: Coastline, clouds. |
| 42 | S65–63930 | S65–65336 | 179 | Dec. 16, 1965 | 17:03 | 161 | *Brazil: Mouth of Amazon. |

MAGAZINE 23

| Frame | NASA/MSC Color No. | NASA/MSC B&W No. | Revolution | Date | GMT | Alt, N. Mi. | Area description |
|---|---|---|---|---|---|---|---|
| 1 | S65–63990 | S65–65001 | 190 | Dec. 17, 1965 | 10:54 | 160 | **Mauritania, Mali: Erg Iguidi. |
| 2 | S65–63989 | S65–65002 | 190 | Dec. 17, 1965 | 10:55 | 160 | **Mali, Algeria: Erg Chech. |
| 3 | S65–63988 | S65–65003 | 190 | Dec. 17, 1965 | 10:55 | 160 | **Mali, Algeria: Erg Chech. |
| 4 | S65–63987 | S65–65004 | 190 | Dec. 17, 1965 | 10:55 | 160 | **Mali, Algeria: Tanezrouft region. |
| 5 | S65–63986 | S65–65005 | 190 | Dec. 17, 1965 | 10:56 | 160 | **Algeria: Tanezrouft region. |
| 6 | S65–63985 | S65–65006 | 190 | Dec. 17, 1965 | 10:56 | 160 | **Algeria: Tanezrouft region. |
| 7 | S65–63984 | S65–65007 | 190 | Dec. 17, 1965 | 10:56 | 160 | **Algeria: Tanezrouft region. |
| 8 | S65–63983 | S65–65008 | 190 | Dec. 17, 1965 | 10:56 | 160 | **Algeria: Tanezrouft region. |
| 9 | S65–63982 | S65–65009 | 190 | Dec. 17, 1965 | 10:56 | 160 | **Algeria: Tanezrouft region, Assedjrad Escarpment. |
| 10 | S65–63981 | S65–65010 | 190 | Dec. 17, 1965 | 10:57 | 160 | **Algeria: Tanezrouft region, Assedjrad Escarpment. |
| 11 | S65–63980 | S65–65011 | 190 | Dec. 17, 1965 | 10:57 | 160 | **Algeria: Tanezrouft region, Assedjrad Escarpment. |
| 12 | S65–63979 | S65–65012 | 190 | Dec. 17, 1965 | 10:57 | 160 | **Algeria: Tanezrouft region, Assedjrad Escarpment. |
| 13 | S65–63978 | S65–65013 | 190 | Dec. 17, 1965 | 10:58 | 160 | **Algeria, Mali: Adrar des Iforas. |
| 14 | S65–63977 | S65–65014 | 190 | Dec. 17, 1965 | 10:58 | 160 | **Algeria, Mali: Adrar des Iforas. |
| 15 | S65–63976 | S65–65015 | 190 | Dec. 17, 1965 | 10:58 | 160 | **Niger: Northwest corner. |
| 16 | S65–63975 | S65–65016 | 190 | Dec. 17, 1965 | 10:59 | 160 | **Niger: Air ou Azbine. |
| 17 | S65–63974 | S65–65017 | 190 | Dec. 17, 1965 | 10:59 | 160 | **Niger: Air ou Azbine. |
| 18 | S65–63973 | S65–65018 | 190 | Dec. 17, 1965 | 10:59 | 160 | **Niger: Air ou Azbine. |
| 19 | S65–63972 | S65–65019 | 190 | Dec. 17, 1965 | 10:59 | 160 | **Niger: Northwest of Lake Chad. |

MAGAZINE 23 Continued

| Frame | NASA/MSC Color No. | NASA/MSC B&W No. | Revolution | Date | GMT | Alt, N. Mi. | Area description |
|---|---|---|---|---|---|---|---|
| 20 | S65–63971 | S65–65020 | 190 | Dec. 17, 1965 | 11:00 | 160 | **Niger: Lake Chad. |
| 21 | S65–63970 | S65–65021 | 190 | Dec. 17, 1965 | 11:00 | 160 | *Niger, Chad, Nigeria, Cameroon: Lake Chad. |
| *22* | *S65–63969* | *S65–65022* | *190* | *Dec. 17, 1965* | *11:00* | *160* | *Niger, Chad, Nigeria, Cameroon: Lake Chad.* |
| 23 | S65–63968 | S65–65023 | 190 | Dec. 17, 1965 | 11:00 | 160 | Chad: East, central, partial frame. |
| 24 | S65–63967 | S65–65024 | 190 | Dec. 17, 1965 | 11:01 | 160 | Chad: East, central. |
| 25 | S65–63966 | S65–65025 | 190 | Dec. 17, 1965 | 11:01 | 160 | Chad: East, central. |
| 26 | S65–63965 | S65–65026 | 190 | Dec. 17, 1965 | 11:01 | 160 | Chad: East, central. |
| 27 | S65–63964 | S65–65027 | 190 | Dec. 17, 1965 | 11:02 | 161 | Chad: East, central. |
| *28* | *S65–63963* | *S65–65028* | *190* | *Dec. 17, 1965* | *11:02* | *161* | *Chad: East, central* |
| 29 | S65–63962 | S65–65029 | 190 | Dec. 17, 1965 | 11:02 | 161 | Chad: Southeast. |
| 30 | S65–63961 | S65–65030 | 190 | Dec. 17, 1965 | 11:02 | 161 | Chad: Southeast. |
| 31 | S65–63960 | S65–65031 | 190 | Dec. 17, 1965 | 11:03 | 161 | Chad, Central African Republic. |
| 32 | S65–63959 | S65–65032 | 190 | Dec. 17, 1965 | 11:03 | 161 | Chad, Central African Republic, Sudan. |
| 33 | S65–63958 | S65–65033 | 190 | Dec. 17, 1965 | 11:03 | 161 | Central African Republic, Sudan: forest fires. |
| 34 | S65–63957 | S65–65034 | 190 | Dec. 17, 1965 | 11:04 | 161 | Central African Republic, Sudan: forest fires. |
| 35 | S65–63956 | S65–65035 | 190 | Dec. 17, 1965 | 11:04 | 161 | Central African Republic, Sudan: forest fires. |
| 36 | S65–63955 | S65–65036 | 190 | Dec. 17, 1965 | 11:04 | 161 | Central African Republic, Sudan: forest fires. |
| 37 | S65–63954 | S65–65037 | 190 | Dec. 17, 1965 | 11:04 | 161 | Central African Republic, Sudan, Republic of the Congo: forest fires. |
| 38 | S65–63953 | S65–65038 | 190 | Dec. 17, 1965 | 11:05 | 161 | Central African Republic, Sudan, Republic of the Congo: forest fires. |
| 39 | S65–63952 | S65–65039 | 190 | Dec. 17, 1965 | 11:09 | 161 | Somali Republic: Coastline south of Mogadishu. |
| 40 | S65–63951 | S65–65040 | ........... | ........... | ...... | ....... | Out of focus, overexposed. |
| 41 | S65–63950 | S65–65041 | 192 | Dec. 17, 1965 | 14:03 | 161 | Cape Verde Islands: Brava, Fogo, Sao Tiago, Maio, Boa Vista, Sal. |
| 42 | S65–63949 | S65–65042 | 193 | Dec. 17, 1965 | 15:27 | 160 | **Bahama Bank area: Andros, Great Exuma Islands, north coast of Cuba. |
| 43 | S65–63948 | S65–65043 | 193 | Dec. 17, 1965 | 15:27 | 160 | **Bahama Bank area: Andros Island, Tongue of the Ocean. |
| 44 | S65–63947 | S65–65044 | 193 | Dec. 17, 1965 | 15:27 | 160 | **Bahama Bank area: Andros, Great Exuma, Long Islands. |
| 45 | S65–63946 | S65–65045 | 193 | Dec. 17, 1965 | 15:27 | 160 | **Cuba: Oriente Province. |
| 46 | S65–63945 | S65–65046 | 193 | Dec. 17, 1965 | 15:27 | 160 | **Cuba: Las Villas, Camaguey, Oriente Provinces. |
| 47 | S65–63944 | S65–65047 | 193 | Dec. 17, 1965 | 15:27 | 160 | **Cuba: Oriente Province. |
| 48 | S65–63943 | S65–65048 | 193 | Dec. 17, 1965 | 15:28 | 160 | **Cuba: Oriente Province, Guantanamo Bay. |
| 49 | S65–63942 | S65–65049 | ........... | ........... | ...... | ....... | **Clouds. |
| 50 | S65–63941 | S65–65050 | 194 | ........... | ...... | ....... | **Clouds, west of Panama. |
| 51 | S65–63940 | S65–65051 | 195 | Dec. 17, 1965 | 18:41 | 161 | Peru, Ecuador: Rio Napo, Rio Cururary. |
| 52 | S65–63939 | S65–65052 | 195 | Dec. 17, 1965 | 18:42 | 161 | Peru, Brazil: Upper Amazon Basin. |
| 53 | S65–63938 | S65–65053 | 195 | Dec. 17, 1965 | 18:43 | 161 | Brazil, Colombia: Upper Amazon Basin. |
| 54 | S65–63937 | S65–65054 | 195 | Dec. 17, 1965 | ...... | ....... | Brazil: Overexposed. |
| 55 | S65–63936 | S65–65055 | 195 | Dec. 17, 1965 | ...... | ....... | Brazil: Matto Grosso, clouds. |
| 56 | S65–63935 | S65–65056 | 195 | Dec. 17, 1965 | ...... | ....... | Brazil: Matto Grosso, clouds. |
| 57 | S65–63934 | S65–65057 | 195 | Dec. 17, 1965 | ...... | ....... | Brazil: Matto Grosso. |
| 58 | S65–63933 | S65–65058 | 195 | Dec. 17, 1965 | ...... | ....... | Brazil: Matto Grosso. |
| 59 | S65–63932 | S65–65059 | 195 | Dec. 17, 1965 | 18:51 | 163 | Brazil: Coastline north of Vitoria, clouds. |
| 60 | S65–63931 | S65–65060 | 195 | Dec. 17, 1965 | ...... | ....... | Clouds over Atlantic. |

MAGAZINE 26

| Frame | NASA/MSC Color No. | NASA/MSC B&W No. | Revolution | Date | GMT | Alt, N. Mi. | Area description |
|---|---|---|---|---|---|---|---|
| 1 | ........... | ........... | ........... | ........... | ...... | ....... | Blank. |
| 2 | S65–64050 | ........... | 45 | Dec. 7, 1965 | 19:21 | 130 | Gulf coast: New Orleans, Baton Rouge, Mobile, Gulfport; *f*/11, 1/250 sec. |
| 3 | S65–64051 | ........... | 45 | Dec. 7, 1965 | 19:21 | 129 | Gulf coast: Mobile, Gulfport, Pensacola; *f*/11, 1/250 sec. |

MAGAZINE 26 Continued

| Frame | NASA/MSC | | Revolution | Date | GMT | Alt, N. Mi. | Area description |
|---|---|---|---|---|---|---|---|
| | Color No. | B&W No. | | | | | |
| *4* | *S65–64052* | ... | *45* | *Dec. 7, 1965* | *19:22* | *129* | *Gulf coast: Pensacola, Panama City, Montgomery, Birmingham; f/11, 1/250 sec.* |
| *5* | *S65–64053* | ... | *45* | *Dec. 7, 1965* | *19:22* | *129* | *Gulf coast: Apalachicola, Tallahassee; forest fires.* |
| 6 | S65–64054 | ... | ... | ... | ... | ... | Gulf coast: Florida; underexposed, *f*/16, 1/250 sec. |
| 7 | S65–64055 | ... | ... | ... | ... | ... | Florida, Georgia coast: Jacksonville; underexposed. |
| 8 | S65–64056 | ... | 45 | Dec. 7, 1965 | 19:22 | 129 | Florida: Jacksonville; highlights underexposed. |
| 9 | S65–64057 | ... | 121 | Dec. 12, 1965 | 19:51 | 160 | Brazil: Para and Maranhao States; Atlantic Ocean; no filter. |
| 10 | S65–64058 | ... | 121 | Dec. 12, 1965 | 19:51 | 160 | Brazil; Maranhao State, Baia de Sao Luis; no filter. |
| 11 | S65–64059 | ... | 121 | Dec. 12, 1965 | 19:51 | 160 | Brazil: Maranhao State, Baia de Sao Luis; no filter. |
| 12 | S65–64060 | ... | 121 | Dec. 12, 1965 | ... | ... | Clouds along Brazil coast; underexposed. |
| 13 | S65–64061 | ... | 121 | Dec. 12, 1965 | ... | ... | Clouds along Brazil coast; underexposed. |
| 14 | S65–64062 | ... | 121 | Dec. 12, 1965 | ... | ... | Clouds along Brazil coast; underexposed. |
| 15 | S65–64063 | ... | 121 | Dec. 12, 1965 | 19:54 | 160 | Brazil: mouth of Sao Francisco River; no filter. |
| 16 | S65–64064 | ... | 194 | Dec. 17, 1965 | ... | ... | Brazil: Amazon River; bad exposure, trouble with film advance. |
| 17 | S65–64065 | ... | 194 | Dec. 17, 1965 | ... | ... | Brazil: Amazon and Purus Rivers; bad exposure, trouble with film advance. |
| 18 | S65–64066 | ... | 194 | Dec. 17, 1965 | ... | ... | Overexposed. |
| 19 | S65–64067 | ... | 194 | Dec. 17, 1965 | ... | ... | Brazil: Maranhao State; clouds. |
| 20 | S65–64068 | ... | 194 | Dec. 17, 1965 | 17:11 | 161 | Brazil: Maranhao State; clouds. |
| *21* | *S65–64069* | ... | *194* | *Dec. 17, 1965* | *17:11* | *161* | *Brazil: Maranhao State Sao Luis; Atlantic Ocean; clouds.* |
| *22* | *S65–64070* | ... | *194* | *Dec. 17, 1965* | *17:12* | *161* | *Brazil: Maranhao, Piaui, Ceara States; Atlantic Ocean, clouds.* |
| 23 | S65–64071 | ... | 194 | Dec. 17, 1965 | 17:12 | 161 | Brazil: Paiui and Ceara States; clouds. |
| 24 | S65–64072 | ... | 194 | Dec. 17, 1965 | 17:12 | 161 | Brazil: Ceara State, south of Fortaleza; clouds. |
| *25* | *S65–64073* | ... | *194* | *Dec. 17, 1965* | *17:13* | *161* | *Brazil: Ceara and Rio Grande do Norte States, Fortaleza; Atlantic coast; clouds.* |
| 26 | S65–64074 | ... | 194 | Dec. 17, 1965 | 17:13 | 162 | Brazil: Ceara and Rio Grande do Norte States; clouds. |
| 27 | S65–64075 | ... | 194 | Dec. 17, 1965 | 17:13 | 162 | Brazil: Ceara, Rio Grande do Norte and Paraiba States, Natal; clouds. |
| 28 | S65–64076 | ... | 194 | Dec. 17, 1965 | 17:13 | 162 | Brazil: Rio Grande do Norte, Paraiba and Pernambuco States, Natal; clouds. |
| 29 | S65–64077 | ... | 194 | Dec. 17, 1965 | 17:13 | 162 | Brazil: Ceara, Rio Grande do Norte and Paraiba States, Fortaleza; clouds. |
| 30 | S65–64078 | ... | 194 | Dec. 17, 1965 | 17:13 | 162 | Brazil: Ceara, Rio Grande do Norte and Paraiba States, Natal; clouds. |
| 31 | S65–64079 | ... | 194 | Dec. 17, 1965 | 17:15 | 161 | Brazil: Atlantic coast, mouth of Sao Francisco River. |

## GEMINI VIII

MAGAZINE 20

| Frame | NASA/MSC | | Revolution | Date | GMT | Alt, N. Mi. | Area description |
|---|---|---|---|---|---|---|---|
| | Color No. | B&W No. | | | | | |
| *1* | *S66–25771* | *S66–25752* | *3* | *Mar. 16, 1966* | *20:56* | ... | *Earth limb with cloud layers in silhouette, sunrise over Guam.* |
| 2 | S66–25772 | S66–25753 | 3 | Mar. 16, 1966 | 21:05 | ... | Agena at approximately 1000 ft; overexposed; near Midway Island. |
| 3 | S66–25773 | S66–25754 | 3 | Mar. 16, 1966 | 21:05 | ... | Agena at approximately 1000 ft; overexposed; near Midway Island. |
| 4 | S66–25774 | S66–25755 | 3 | Mar. 16, 1966 | 21:06 | ... | Agena at approximately 1000 ft; dark sky background; near Midway Island. |

MAGAZINE 20 Continued

| Frame | NASA/MSC Color No. | NASA/MSC B&W No. | Revolution | Date | GMT | Alt, N. Mi. | Area description |
|---|---|---|---|---|---|---|---|
| 5 | S66–25775 | S66–25756 | 3 | Mar. 16, 1966 | 21:06 | ....... | Agena at approximately 1000 ft; dark sky background; near Midway Island. |
| 6 | S66–25776 | S66–25757 | 3 | Mar. 16, 1966 | 21:07 | ....... | Agena at approximately 750 ft; dark sky background; north of Hawaii. |
| 7 | S66–25777 | S66–25758 | 3 | Mar. 16, 1966 | 21:08 | ....... | Agena at approximately 450 ft; dark sky background; north of Hawaii. |
| 8 | S66–25778 | S66–25759 | 3 | Mar. 16, 1966 | 21:09 | ....... | Agena at 250 ft, motor end turned 45° toward Gemini VIII; sky background; north of Hawaii. |
| 9 | S66–25779 | S66–25760 | 3 | Mar. 16, 1966 | 21:09 | 147 | Agena at 210 ft; motor end turned 45° toward Gemini VIII; sea, clouds, sky in background. |
| 10 | S66–25780 | S66–25761 | 3 | Mar. 16, 1966 | 21:10 | 147 | Agena at 190 ft, motor end turned 45° toward Gemini VIII; sea, clouds, sky in background. |
| 11 | S66–25781 | S66–25762 | 3 | Mar. 16, 1966 | 21:14 | ....... | Agena at 55 ft, docking adapter end turned partially toward Gemini VIII; clouds, sky in background. |
| 12 | S66–25782 | S66–25763 | 3 | Mar. 16, 1966 | 21:21 | ........ | Agena at 45 ft, side view of entire Agena; good stereo with frame 13; off west coast of Mexico. |
| 13 | S66–25783 | S66–25764 | 3 | Mar. 16, 1966 | 21:21 | ........ | Agena at 44 ft, side view of entire Agena; good stereo with frame 12; off west coast of Mexico. |
| 14 | S66–25784 | S66–25765 | 4 | Mar. 16, 1966 | 21:38 | ........ | Agena at 24 in. from nose of Gemini VIII, docking adapter end and instrument panel of Agena visible; over coast of Brazil near Rio de Janeiro. |
| 15 | S66–25785 | S66–25766 | 4 | Mar. 16, 1966 | 21:57 | ........ | Docking, instrument panel and L-band antenna of Agena, slightly out of focus; over South Africa. |
| 16 | S66–25786 | S66–25767 | 4 | Mar. 16, 1966 | 21:57 | ........ | Agena instrument panel while docked; out of focus. |
| 17 | S66–25787 | S66–25768 | 4 | Mar. 16, 1966 | 22:21 | ........ | Docked with Agena; clouds, sea, sky, solar backlighting, near Philippine Islands. |
| 18 | S66–25788 | S66–25769 | 4 | Mar. 16, 1966 | 22:21 | ........ | Docked with Agena; shadow side of Agena; clouds, sea, sky, near Philippine Islands. |
| 19 | S66–25789 | S66–25770 | 4 | Mar. 16, 1966 | ....... | ........ | Sunlight in lens, no photo. |

## GEMINI IX

### MAGAZINE A

| Frame | NASA/MSC Color No. | NASA/MSC B&W No. | Revolution | Date | GMT | Alt, N. Mi. | Area description |
|---|---|---|---|---|---|---|---|
| 1 | S66–37906 | S66–37806 | 1 | June 3, 1966 | 15:11 | 130 | Mexico: Torreon, Monterrey; looking over cloudy Coahuila Basin to folded mountains of Sierra Madre Oriental. |
| *2* | *S66–37907* | *S66–37807* | *1* | *June 3, 1966* | *15:11* | *130* | *Mexico: Torreon, Monterrey; looking over cloudy Coahuila Basin to folded mountains of Sierra Madre Oriental.* |
| 3 | S66–37908 | S66–37808 | 1 | June 3, 1966 | 15:11 | 130 | Mexico: Coahuila, Nuevo Leon States; Serranias del Burro, northern Sierra Madre Oriental. |
| *4* | *S66–37909* | *S66–37809* | *1* | *June 3, 1966* | *15:14* | *129* | *Louisiana, gulf coast: Cameron to Mobile; Mississippi River and delta; cloudy.* |
| *5* | *S66–37910* | *S66–37810* | *1* | *June 3, 1966* | *15:15* | *128* | *Louisiana, Alabama, Florida: gulf coast, Grand Isle to Apalachicola; Mississippi Delta, Mobile Bay.* |
| 6 | S66–37911 | S66–37811 | 3 | June 3, 1966 | 18:27 | ........ | ATDA, backlit, range 65 ft; sky background. |
| 7 | S66–37912 | S66–37812 | 3 | June 3, 1966 | 18:27 | ........ | ATDA, backlit, range 65 ft; sky background. |
| 8 | S66–37913 | S66–37813 | 3 | June 3, 1966 | 18:27 | ........ | ATDA, backlit, range 70 ft; sky background. |
| 9 | S66–37914 | S66–37814 | 3 | June 3, 1966 | 18:28 | ........ | ATDA, backlit, range 65 ft; sky background. |
| 10 | S66–37915 | S66–37815 | 3 | June 3, 1966 | 18:29 | ........ | ATDA, backlit, range 45 ft; sky background. |

MAGAZINE A Continued

| Frame | NASA/MSC Color No. | NASA/MSC B&W No. | Revolution | Date | GMT | Alt, N. Mi. | Area description |
|---|---|---|---|---|---|---|---|
| 11 | S66–37916 | S66–37816 | 3 | June 3, 1966 | 18:29 | ....... | ATDA, backlit, range 38 ft; sky background. |
| 12 | S66–37917 | S66–37817 | 3 | June 3, 1966 | 18:29 | ........ | ATDA, side view, range 45 ft; off coast of Honduras. |
| 13 | S66–37918 | S66–37818 | 4 | June 3, 1966 | 18:30 | ........ | ATDA, back end view, range 75 ft; sky background. |
| 14 | S66–37919 | S66–37819 | 4 | June 3, 1966 | 18:31 | ........ | ATDA, side view, range 30 ft; sky background. |
| 15 | S66–37920 | S66–37820 | 4 | June 3, 1966 | 18:31 | ........ | ATDA, side view, range 25 ft; sky background. |
| 16 | S66–37921 | S66–37821 | 4 | June 3, 1966 | 18:31 | ........ | ATDA, side view, range 25 ft; sky background. |
| 17 | S66–37922 | S66–37822 | 4 | June 3, 1966 | 18:32 | 157 | ATDA, side view, range 70 ft; Venezuela coast, Isla Los Roques. |
| 18 | S66–37923 | S66–37823 | 4 | June 3, 1966 | 18:32 | 157 | ATDA, side view, range 75 ft; Venezuela coast, Isla Los Roques, Isla La Orchila. |
| 19 | S66–37924 | S66–37824 | 4 | June 3, 1966 | 18:32 | 157 | ATDA, side view, range 85 ft; Venezuela coast, Isla La Tortuga. |
| 20 | S66–37925 | S66–37825 | 4 | June 3, 1966 | 18:32 | 157 | ATDA, side view, range 105 ft; Venezuela coast, Isla La Tortuga. |
| 21 | S66–37926 | S66–37826 | 4 | June 3, 1966 | 18:32 | 157 | ATDA, side view, range, 110 ft; Venezuela coast, Isla La Tortuga, Peninsula de Araya. |
| 22 | S66–37927 | S66–37827 | 4 | June 3, 1966 | 18:33 | 157 | ATDA, shroud, range 45 ft; Venezuelan jungles, clouds in background. |
| 23 | S66–37928 | S66–37828 | 4 | June 3, 1966 | 18:33 | 157 | ATDA, shroud, range 40 ft; Venezuelan jungles, clouds in background. |
| 24 | S66–37929 | S66–37829 | 4 | June 3, 1966 | 19:13 | ........ | Moon, full; ATDA, range approximately 750 ft. |
| 25 | S66–37930 | S66–37830 | 4 | June 3, 1966 | 19:13 | ........ | Moon, full; ATDA, range approximately 750 ft. |
| 26 | S66–37931 | S66–37831 | 4 | June 3, 1966 | 19:13 | ........ | Moon, full. |
| 27 | S66–37932 | S66–37832 | 15 | June 4, 1966 | 12:16 | ........ | ATDA, fore side view, range 125 ft; sky background. |
| 28 | S66–37933 | S66–37833 | 15 | June 4, 1966 | 12:16 | ........ | ATDA, side view, range 140 ft; sky background. |
| 29 | S66–37934 | S66–37834 | 15 | June 4, 1966 | 12:16 | ........ | ATDA, rear quarter view, range 140 ft; sky background. |
| 30 | S66–37935 | S66–37835 | 15 | June 4, 1966 | 12:17 | ........ | ATDA, side view, range 150 ft; sky background. |
| 31 | S66–37936 | S66–37836 | 15 | June 4, 1966 | 12:17 | ........ | ATDA, nose view, range 150 ft; sky background. |
| 32 | S66–37937 | S66–37837 | 15 | June 4, 1966 | 12:17 | ........ | ATDA, view of shroud, range 150 ft; sky background. |
| 33 | S66–37938 | S66–37838 | 15 | June 4, 1966 | 12:17 | ........ | ATDA, nose view, range 170 ft; sky background. |
| 34 | S66–37939 | S66–37839 | 15 | June 4, 1966 | 12:18 | ........ | ATDA, rear and side view, range 150 ft; sky background. |
| 35 | S66–37940 | S66–37840 | 15 | June 4, 1966 | 12:18 | ........ | ATDA, side view, range 140 ft; sky background. |
| 36 | S66–37941 | S66–37841 | 15 | June 4, 1966 | 12:18 | ........ | ATDA, side view, range 100 ft; sky background. |
| 37 | S66–37942 | S66–37842 | 15 | June 4, 1966 | 12:18 | ........ | ATDA, side view, range 100 ft; sky background. |
| 38 | S66–37943 | S66–37843 | 15 | June 4, 1966 | 12:19 | ........ | ATDA, forward quarter view, range 80 ft; sky background. |
| 39 | S66–37944 | S66–37844 | 15 | June 4, 1966 | 12:19 | ........ | ATDA, side rear half view, range 135 ft; sky background. |
| 40 | S66–37945 | S66–37845 | 15 | June 4, 1966 | 12:19 | ........ | ATDA, side rear half view, range 130 ft; sky background. |
| 41 | S66–37946 | S66–37846 | 15 | June 4, 1966 | 12:19 | ........ | ATDA, side rear half view, range 145 ft; sky background. |
| 42 | S66–37947 | S66–37847 | 15 | June 4, 1966 | 12:19 | ........ | ATDA, side rear half view, range 120 ft; sky background. |
| 43 | S66–37948 | S66–37848 | 15 | June 4, 1966 | 12:20 | ........ | ATDA, side view, range 110 ft; sky background. |
| 44 | S66–37949 | S66–37849 | 15 | June 4, 1966 | 12:20 | ........ | ATDA, side view, range 120 ft; sky-horizon-ocean. |
| 45 | S66–37950 | S66–37850 | 15 | June 4, 1966 | 12:20 | ........ | ATDA, side view, range 80 ft; sky-horizon-ocean. |
| 46 | S66–37951 | S66–37851 | 15 | June 4, 1966 | 12:20 | ........ | ATDA, fore quarter view, range 75 ft; sky-horizon-ocean. |
| 47 | S66–37952 | S66–37852 | 15 | June 4, 1966 | 12:21 | ........ | ATDA, side rear half view, range 65 ft; sky-horizon-ocean. |

MAGAZINE A Continued

| Frame | NASA/MSC Color No. | NASA/MSC B&W No. | Revolution | Date | GMT | Alt, N. Mi. | Area description |
|---|---|---|---|---|---|---|---|
| 48 | S66–37953 | S66–37853 | 15 | June 4, 1966 | 12:21 | ........ | ATDA, side rear half view, range 55 ft; sky-horizon-ocean. |
| 49 | S66–37954 | S66–37854 | 15 | June 4, 1966 | 12:21 | ........ | ATDA, shroud side view, range 25 ft; sky-horizon-ocean. |
| 50 | S66–37955 | S66–37855 | 15 | June 4, 1966 | 12:21 | ........ | ATDA, shroud side view, range 25 ft; sky-horizon-ocean. |
| 51 | S66–37956 | S66–37856 | 15 | June 4, 1966 | 12:21 | ........ | ATDA, partial shroud and side view, range 25 ft; sky-horizon-ocean. |
| 52 | S66–37957 | S66–37857 | 15 | June 4, 1966 | 12:22 | ........ | ATDA, shroud side view, range 25 ft; sky background. |
| 53 | S66–37958 | S66–37858 | 15 | June 4, 1966 | 12:22 | ........ | ATDA, partial shroud view, range 22 ft; sky background. |
| 54 | S66–37959 | S66–37859 | 15 | June 4, 1966 | 12:22 | ........ | ATDA, shroud view, range 22 ft; sky background. |
| 55 | S66–37960 | S66–37860 | 15 | June 4, 1966 | 12:22 | ........ | ATDA, partial shroud view, range 26 ft; sky background. |
| 56 | S66–37961 | S66–37861 | 15 | June 4, 1966 | 12:22 | ........ | ATDA, partial shroud view, range 28 ft; sky background. |
| 57 | S66–37962 | S66–37862 | 15 | June 4, 1966 | 12:22 | ........ | ATDA, partial longitudinal view, range 25 ft; sky background. |
| 58 | S66–37963 | S66–37863 | 15 | June 4, 1966 | 12:23 | ........ | ATDA, partial longitudinal view, range 27 ft; ocean, clouds west of Africa. |
| 59 | S66–37964 | S66–37864 | 15 | June 4, 1966 | 12:23 | ........ | ATDA, side rear half view, range 30 ft; oceans, clouds west of Africa. |
| 60 | S66–37965 | S66–37865 | 15 | June 4, 1966 | 12:23 | ........ | ATDA, side view, range 33 ft; ocean, clouds west of Africa. |
| 61 | S66–37966 | S66–37866 | 15 | June 4, 1966 | 12:23 | ........ | ATDA, side view, range 38 ft; ocean, clouds west of Africa. |
| 62 | S66–37967 | S66–37867 | 15 | June 4, 1966 | 12:23 | ........ | ATDA, rear quarter view, range 40 ft; ocean, clouds west of Africa. |
| 63 | S66–37968 | S66–37868 | 15 | June 4, 1966 | 12:24 | ........ | ATDA, rear view, range 44 ft; ocean, clouds, Mauritania coastline. |
| 64 | S66–37969 | S66–37869 | 15 | June 4, 1966 | 12:24 | ........ | ATDA, rear view, range 47 ft; ocean, clouds, Mauritania coastline. |
| 65 | S66–37970 | S66–37870 | 15 | June 4, 1966 | 12:24 | ........ | ATDA, rear quarter view, range 47 ft; ocean, clouds, Mauritania coastline. |
| 66 | S66–37971 | S66–37871 | 15 | June 4, 1966 | 12:24 | ........ | ATDA, side view, range 47 ft; ocean, clouds, Mauritania coastline. |
| 67 | S66–37972 | S66–37872 | 15 | June 4, 1966 | 12:24 | ........ | ATDA, side view, range 44 ft; ocean, clouds, Mauritania coastline. |

MAGAZINE F

| Frame | NASA/MSC Color No. | NASA/MSC B&W No. | Revolution | Date | GMT | Alt, N. Mi. | Area description |
|---|---|---|---|---|---|---|---|
| 1 | S66–38141 | S66–38089 | 12 | June 4, 1966 | 07:55 | 157 | Iran, West Pakistan: Arabian Sea coast, Makran Mountains. |
| 2 | S66–38142 | S66–38090 | 15 | June 4, 1966 | 12:14 | ........ | ATDA, side view, range 125 ft; sky background. |
| 3 | S66–38143 | S66–38091 | 15 | June 4, 1966 | 12:15 | ........ | ATDA, nose view, range 120 ft; sky background. |
| 4 | S66–38144 | S66–38092 | 15 | June 4, 1966 | 12:15 | ........ | ATDA, side view, range 115 ft; sky background. |
| 5 | S66–38145 | S66–38093 | 15 | June 4, 1966 | 12:15 | ........ | ATDA, end view, range 130 ft; sky background. |
| 6 | S66–38146 | S66–38094 | 15 | June 4, 1966 | 12:16 | ........ | ATDA, side view, range 140 ft; sky background. |
| 7 | S66–38147 | S66–38095 | 15 | June 4, 1966 | 12:16 | ........ | ATDA, side view, range 140 ft; sky-horizon-ocean. |
| 8 | S66–38148 | S66–38096 | 15 | June 4, 1966 | 12:16 | ........ | ATDA, side view, range 75 ft; sky-horizon-ocean. |
| 9 | S66–38149 | S66–38097 | 15 | June 4, 1966 | 12:17 | ........ | ATDA, side view, range 60 ft; sky-horizon-ocean. |
| 10 | S66–38150 | S66–38098 | 15 | June 4, 1966 | 12:18 | ........ | ATDA, side view, range 50 ft; sky-horizon-ocean. |
| 11 | S66–38151 | S66–38099 | 15 | June 4, 1966 | 12:18 | ........ | ATDA, side rear half view, range 37 ft; sky-horizon-ocean. |

MAGAZINE F Continued

| Frame | NASA/MSC Color No. | NASA/MSC B&W No. | Revolution | Date | GMT | Alt, N. Mi. | Area description |
|---|---|---|---|---|---|---|---|
| 12 | S66–38152 | S66–38100 | 15 | June 4, 1966 | 12:18 | ........ | ATDA, side rear half view, range 37 ft; sky-horizon-ocean. |
| 13 | S66–38153 | S66–38101 | 15 | June 4, 1966 | 12:19 | ........ | ATDA, side view, range 30 ft; sky background, image blurred. |
| 14 | S66–38154 | S66–38102 | 15 | June 4, 1966 | 12:19 | ........ | ATDA, side view, range 27 ft; sky background. |
| 15 | S66–38155 | S66–38103 | 15 | June 4, 1966 | 12:20 | ........ | ATDA, rear quarter view, range 27 ft; sky background. |
| 16 | S66–38156 | S66–38104 | 15 | June 4, 1966 | 12:20 | ........ | ATDA, rear quarter view, range 27 ft; sky background. |
| 17 | S66–38157 | S66–38105 | 15 | June 4, 1966 | 12:20 | ........ | ATDA, shroud view, range 24 ft; sky-horizon-ocean. |
| 18 | S66–38158 | S66–38106 | 15 | June 4, 1966 | 12:20 | ........ | ATDA, shroud view, range 22 ft; sky-horizon-ocean. |
| 19 | S66–38159 | S66–38107 | 15 | June 4, 1966 | 12:21 | ........ | ATDA, shroud view, range 23 ft; sky-horizon-ocean. |
| 20 | S66–38160 | S66–38108 | 15 | June 4, 1966 | 12:21 | ........ | ATDA, shroud view, range 24 ft; sky-horizon-ocean. |
| 21 | S66–38161 | S66–38109 | 15 | June 4, 1966 | 12:21 | ........ | ATDA, shroud view, range 25 ft; sky-horizon-ocean. |
| 22 | S66–38162 | S66–38110 | 15 | June 4, 1966 | 12:21 | ........ | ATDA, shroud view, range 20 ft; sky-horizon-ocean. |
| 23 | S66–38163 | S66–38111 | 15 | June 4, 1966 | 12:21 | ........ | ATDA, shroud view, range 17 ft; sky-horizon-ocean. |
| 24 | S66–38164 | S66–38112 | 15 | June 4, 1966 | 12:22 | ........ | ATDA, shroud view, range 16 ft; sky-horizon-ocean. |
| 25 | S66–38165 | S66–38113 | 15 | June 4, 1966 | 12:22 | ........ | ATDA, shroud view, range 21 ft; sky-horizon-ocean; image blurred. |
| 26 | S66–38166 | S66–38114 | 15 | June 4, 1966 | 12:22 | ........ | ATDA, side view, range 33 ft; sky-horizon-ocean. |
| 27 | S66–38167 | S66–38115 | 15 | June 4, 1966 | 12:22 | ........ | ATDA, side view, range 36 ft; sky-horizon-ocean. |
| 28 | S66–38168 | S66–38116 | 15 | June 4, 1966 | 12:23 | ........ | ATDA, rear quarter view, range 37 ft; sky-horizon-ocean. |
| 29 | S66–38169 | S66–38117 | 15 | June 4, 1966 | 12:23 | ........ | ATDA, rear quarter view, range 40 ft; Mauritania coast in background. |
| 30 | S66–38170 | S66–38118 | 15 | June 4, 1966 | 12:23 | ........ | ATDA, rear quarter view, range 40 ft.; Mauritania coast in background. |
| 31 | S66–38171 | S66–38119 | 15 | June 4, 1966 | 12:24 | ........ | ATDA, rear quarter view, range 40 ft; Mauritania coast in background. |
| 32 | S66–38172 | S66–38120 | 15 | June 4, 1966 | 12:24 | ........ | ATDA, side view, range 40 ft; Mauritania coast in bakground. |
| 33 | S66–38173 | S66–38121 | 15 | June 4, 1966 | 12:24 | ........ | ATDA, side view, range 38 ft; Mauritania coast in background. |
| 34 | S66–38174 | S66–38122 | 15 | June 4, 1966 | 12:28 | 159 | Mauritania, Mali; Aouker Basin, Irrigi Plain: ATDA, partial view, range 60 ft. |
| 35 | S66–38175 | S66–38123 | 15 | June 4, 1966 | 12:28 | 159 | Mauritania, Mali: Aouker Basin, Irrigi Plain, Niger River; ATDA, partial view, range 60 ft. |
| 36 | S66–38176 | S66–38124 | 15 | June 4, 1966 | 12:28 | 159 | Mauritania, Mali: Aouker Basin, Niger River, Lake Faguibine; ATDA, nose view, range 60 ft. |
| 37 | S66–38177 | S66–38125 | 15 | June 4, 1966 | 12:28 | 159 | Mauritania, Mali: Niger River, Lake Faguibine; ATDA, nose view, range 65 ft. |
| 38 | S66–38178 | S66–38126 | 15 | June 4, 1966 | 12:29 | 159 | Mauritania, Mali: Timbuktu; Niger River, Lake Faguibine; ATDA, nose view, range 60 ft. |
| 39 | S66–38179 | S66–38127 | 15 | June 4, 1966 | 12:29 | 159 | Mauritania, Mali: Timbuktu; Niger River, Lake Faguibine; ATDA, nose view, range 60 ft. |
| 40 | S66–38180 | S66–38128 | 15 | June 4, 1966 | 12:29 | 159 | Mali, Upper Volta: Timbuktu; false delta of Niger River; ATDA, side view, range 60 ft. |
| 41 | S66–38181 | S66–38129 | 15 | June 4, 1966 | 12:30 | 159 | Mali, Upper Volta: Niger River; ATDA, side view, range 60 ft. |

MAGAZINE F Continued

| Frame | NASA/MSC Color No. | NASA/MSC B&W No. | Revolution | Date | GMT | Alt, N. Mi. | Area description |
|---|---|---|---|---|---|---|---|
| 42 | S66–38182 | S66–38130 | 15 | June 4, 1966 | 12:31 | 159 | Mali, Upper Volta: Hombori Mountains; ATDA, side view, range 65 ft. |
| 43 | S66–38183 | S66–38131 | 15 | June 4, 1966 | 12:31 | 159 | Mali, Upper Volta, Niger: Hombori Mountains; ATDA, side view, range 70 ft. |
| 44 | S66–38184 | S66–38132 | 15 | June 4, 1966 | 12:31 | 159 | Mali, Upper Volta, Niger: Niger River; ATDA, rear view, range 75 ft. |
| 45 | S66–38185 | S66–38133 | 15 | June 4, 1966 | 12:32 | 159 | Upper Volta, Niger, Dahomey, Nigeria: Niger River; ATDA, side view, range 75 ft. |
| 46 | S66–38186 | S66–38134 | 15 | June 4, 1966 | 12:32 | 159 | Upper Volta, Niger, Dahomey, Nigeria: Niger River; ATDA, side view, range 80 ft. |
| 47 | S66–38187 | S66–38135 | 15 | June 4, 1966 | 12:33 | 159 | ATDA, side view, range 42 ft; sky background. |
| 48 | S66–38188 | S66–38136 | 15 | June 4, 1966 | 12:33 | 159 | ATDA, side view, range 46 ft; sky background. |
| *49* | *S66–38189* | *S66–38137* | *15* | *June 4, 1966* | *17:01* | *159* | *Venezuela: Caribbean coast, islands of Aruba, Curaçao, Bonaire, Roques, Tortugas.* |
| 50 | S66–38190 | S66–38138 | 15 | June 4, 1966 | 17:01 | 159 | Venezuela: Caribbean coast, islands of Aruba, Curaçao, Bonaire, Roques, Tortugas, Margarita. |
| *51* | *S66–38191* | *S66–38139* | *15* | *June 4, 1966* | *17:08* | *158* | *Brazil: Atlantic coast, mouth of Amazon and Para Rivers.* |
| 52 | S66–38192 | S66–38140 | 15 | June 4, 1966 | 17:09 | 158 | Brazil: Atlantic coast, Baia de Sao Marcos. |

MAGAZINE C

| Frame | NASA/MSC Color No. | NASA/MSC B&W No. | Revolution | Date | GMT | Alt, N. Mi. | Area description |
|---|---|---|---|---|---|---|---|
| 1 | S66–38263 | S66–38193 | 19 | June 4, 1966 | 19:18 | 155 | Clouds over water. |
| 2 | S66–38264 | S66–38194 | 19 | June 4, 1966 | 19:18 | 155 | Clouds over water. |
| 3 | S66–38265 | S66–38195 | 19 | June 4, 1966 | 19:22 | 156 | Clouds over water. |
| 4 | S66–38266 | S66–38196 | 19 | June 4, 1966 | 19:22 | 156 | Clouds over water. |
| 5 | S66–38267 | S66–38197 | 19 | June 4, 1966 | 20:01 | 159 | Mexico: Pacific coast, Baja California, Sonora, Sinaloa. |
| 6 | S66–38268 | S66–38198 | 19 | June 4, 1966 | 20:01 | 159 | Mexico: Pacific coast, Baja California,, Sonora, Sinaloa. |
| 7 | S66–38269 | S66–38199 | 19 | June 4, 1966 | 20:01 | 159 | Mexico: Pacific coast near Mazatlan, entire gulf coast. |
| 8 | S66–38270 | S66–38200 | 19 | June 4, 1966 | 20:02 | 159 | Mexico, Central America: Istmo de Tehuantepec, Yucatan. |
| 9 | S66–38271 | S66–38201 | 19 | June 4, 1966 | 20:11 | 158 | Ecuador, Columbia, Peru: Andes, cloud-filled upper Amazon Basin. |
| 10 | S66–38272 | S66–38202 | 19 | June 4, 1966 | 20:11 | 158 | Ecuador: Guayaquil, beneath clouds; Chimborazo (20 561 ft). |
| *11* | *S66–38273* | *S66–38203* | *20* | *June 4, 1966* | *20:11* | *158* | *Ecuador, Peru: Gulf of Guayaquil, Andes, Pacific coast south of Punta Negra.* |
| 12 | S66–38274 | S66–38204 | 20 | June 4, 1966 | 20:50 | 156 | Limb, sunrise. |
| 13 | S66–38275 | S66–38205 | 20 | June 4, 1966 | 20:50 | 156 | Limb, sunrise. |
| 14 | S66–38276 | S66–38206 | 20 | June 4, 1966 | 21:22 | 159 | Clouds over water. |
| 15 | S66–38277 | S66–38207 | 20 | June 4, 1966 | 21:43 | 159 | Galapagos Islands: clouds over water. |
| 16 | S66–38278 | S66–38208 | 20 | June 4, 1966 | 21:44 | 159 | Galapagos Islands: clouds over water. |
| 17 | S66–38279 | S66–38209 | 20 | June 4, 1966 | 21:45 | 159 | Galapagos Islands: clouds over water. |
| 18 | S66–38280 | S66–38210 | 20 | June 4, 1966 | 21:47 | 159 | Clouds over Pacific Ocean, east of Galapagos Islands, cell structure. |
| *19* | *S66–38281* | *S66–38211* | *20* | *June 4, 1966* | *21:48* | *159* | *Peru: Pacific coast at Peninsula Paracas, Andes, Amazon Basin; twilight.* |
| 20 | S66–38282 | S66–38212 | 21 | June 4, 1966 | 21:50 | 159 | Peru: Andes; underexposed. |
| 21 | S66–38283 | S66–38213 | 21 | June 4, 1966 | 21:50 | 159 | Peru, Bolivia: Lake Titicaca, sunlit Cordillera Real peaks; twilight. |
| 22 | S66–38284 | S66–38214 | 21 | June 4, 1966 | 21:51 | 159 | Peru, Bolivia: Lake Titicaca, sunlit Cordillera Real peaks; twilight. |

MAGAZINE C Continued

| Frame | NASA/MSC Color No. | NASA/MSC B&W No. | Revolution | Date | GMT | Alt, N. Mi. | Area description |
|---|---|---|---|---|---|---|---|
| 23 | S66–38285 | S66–38215 | 21 | June 4, 1966 | 21:51 | 159 | Peru, Bolivia: sunlit Illimani volcano (21 300 ft); underexposed. |
| 24 | S66–38286 | S66–38216 | 21 | June 4, 1966 | 21:51 | 159 | Peru, Bolivia: La Paz; Lake Titicaca, sunlit Illimani volcano (21 300 ft); twilight. |
| 25 | S66–38287 | S66–38217 | 21 | June 4, 1966 | 21:55 | 160 | At sunset, long shadows from cumulus buildups. |
| 26 | S66–38288 | S66–38218 | 21 | June 4, 1966 | 21:55 | 160 | At sunset, long shadows from cumulus buildups. |
| 27 | S66–38289 | S66–38219 | 21 | June 4, 1966 | 22:19 | 160 | Nearly full Moon. |
| 28 | S66–38290 | S66–38220 | 34 | June 5, 1966 | 20:15 | 146 | Peru, Ecuador: Bay and Desert of Sechura, Andes Mountains, Amazon Basin. |
| *29* | *S66–38291* | *S66–38221* | *34* | *June 5, 1966* | *20:16* | *146* | *Peru, Ecuador: Bay and Desert of Sechura, Andes Mountains.* |
| 30 | S66–38292 | S66–38222 | 34 | June 5, 1966 | 20:16 | 146 | Peru, Ecuador: Bay and Desert of Sechura, Andes Mountains. |
| 31 | S66–38293 | S66–38223 | 34 | June 5, 1966 | 20:16 | 146 | Peru: Bay and Desert of Sechura, Andes Mountains. |
| 32 | S66–38294 | S66–38224 | 35 | June 5, 1966 | 20:16 | 146 | Peru: North coastal area, Chiclayo to Trujillo; Andes Mountains. |
| 33 | S66–38295 | S66–38225 | 35 | June 5, 1966 | 20:17 | 146 | Peru: North coastal area, Chiclayo to Trujillo; Andes Mountains. |
| 34 | S66–38296 | S66–38226 | 35 | June 5, 1966 | 20:17 | 146 | Peru: North coastal area, Chiclayo to Trujillo; Andes Mountains. |
| 35 | S66–38297 | S66–38227 | 35 | June 5, 1966 | 20:17 | 146 | Peru: North coastal area, Trujillo to Casma; Andes Mountains. |
| *36* | *S66–38298* | *S66–38228* | *35* | *June 5, 1966* | *20:17* | *146* | *Peru: Central coastal area, Chimbote to Paramonga; Andes Mountains, Cordillera Blanca, Huascaran (22 205 ft.)—path of disastrous avalanche of 1962 clearly visible.* |
| 37 | S66–38299 | S66–38229 | 35 | June 5, 1966 | 20:18 | 146 | Peru: Cerro de Pasco; Andes Mountains, branches of Ucayali River. |
| *38* | *S66–38300* | *S66–38230* | *35* | *June 5, 1966* | *20:18* | *147* | *Peru: Coastline, Lima to Peninsula Paracas; Andes Mountains, Lago de Junin.* |
| 39 | S66–38301 | S66–38231 | 35 | June 5, 1966 | 20:18 | 147 | Peru: Andes Mountains, Ucayali River, Upper Amazon Basin. |
| 40 | S66–38302 | S66–38232 | 35 | June 5, 1966 | 20:18 | 147 | Peru: Eastern edge of Andes Mountains, Ucayali River, Upper Amazon Basin. |
| *41* | *S66–38303* | *S66–38233* | *35* | *June 5, 1966* | *20:19* | *147* | *Peru: Cusco-Ayacucho area; Andes Mountains, Rio Apurimac, Rio Urubamba.* |
| 42 | S66–38304 | S66–38234 | 35 | June 5, 1966 | 20:19 | 147 | Peru: Cusco-Ayacucho area: Andes Mountains, Rio Apurimac, Rio Urubamba. |
| 43 | S66–38305 | S66–38235 | 35 | June 5, 1966 | 20:19 | 147 | Peru: Cusco-Ayacucho area; Andes Mountains, Rio Apurimac, Rio Urubamba, Nevado Ampato. |
| *44* | *S66–38306* | *S66–38236* | *35* | *June 5, 1966* | *20:19* | *147* | *Peru: Cusco area; Andes Mountains, Apurimac-Urubamba-Madre de Dios Rivers.* |
| 45 | S66–38307 | S66–38237 | 35 | June 5, 1966 | 20:19 | 147 | Peru, Chile: Arequipa, coastline from Chala south; Andes Mountains, Volcan Misti. |
| 46 | S66–38308 | S66–38238 | 35 | June 5, 1966 | 20:19 | 147 | Peru, Bolivia, Chile; Arequipa, coastline from Mollendo south; Andes Mountains, Volcan Misti. |
| 47 | S66–38309 | S66–38239 | 35 | June 5, 1966 | 20:20 | 148 | Peru, Bolivia, Chile: Arequipa, Lake Titicaca, Andes Mountains, salt basins, coastline. |
| 48 | S66–38310 | S66–38240 | 35 | June 5, 1966 | 20:20 | 148 | Peru, Bolivia, Chile: Arequipa, Lake Titicaca, Andes Mountains, salt basins, coastline. |
| 49 | S66–38311 | S66–38241 | 35 | June 5, 1966 | 20:20 | 148 | Peru, Bolivia, Chile: La Paz; Lake Titicaca, Andes Mountains, salt basins, coastline. |
| *50* | *S66–38312* | *S66–38242* | *35* | *June 5, 1966* | *20:20* | *148* | *Peru, Bolivia, Chile: La Paz; Lake Titicaca, Andes Mountains, salt basins, coastline.* |

MAGAZINE C Continued

| Frame | NASA/MSC Color No. | NASA/MSC B&W No. | Revolution | Date | GMT | Alt, N. Mi. | Area description |
|---|---|---|---|---|---|---|---|
| *51* | *S66–38313* | *S66–38243* | *35* | *June 5, 1966* | *20:20* | *148* | *Peru, Bolivia, Chile: La Paz; Lake Titicaca, Lake Poopo, Salar de Uyuni, Andes Mountains.* |
| 52 | S66–38314 | S66–38244 | 35 | June 5, 1966 | 20:21 | 148 | Peru, Bolivia, Chile: La Paz; Lake Titicaca, Lake Poopo, Salar de Uyuni, Andes Mountains. |
| *53* | *S66–38315* | *S66–38245* | *35* | *June 5, 1966* | *20:21* | *148* | *Bolivia, Chile, Argentina: Sucre; Lake Poopo, Salar de Uyuni, Andes Mountains, Gran Chaco.* |
| 54 | S66–38316 | S66–38246 | 35 | June 5, 1966 | 20:21 | 148 | Bolivia, Argentina, Paraguay: Sucre; Cordillera Central, Cordillera Oriental, Gran Chaco, Rio Grande. |
| 55 | S66–38317 | S66–38247 | 35 | June 5, 1966 | 20:21 | 148 | Bolivia, Argentina, Paraguay: Cordillera Oriental, Gran Chaco, Rio Grande, Rio Parapeti. |
| 56 | S66–38318 | S66–38248 | 35 | June 5, 1966 | 20:22 | 149 | Bolivia, Paraguay: Cordillera Oriental, Gran Chaco, Rio Grande, Rio Parapeti, Serrania de San Jose. |
| 57 | S66–38319 | S66–38249 | 35 | June 5, 1966 | 20:22 | 149 | Boliva, Paraguay: Gran Chaco, Rio Parapeti, Serra de San Jose, Serrania de Santiago. |
| 58 | S66–38320 | S66–38250 | 35 | June 5, 1966 | 20:22 | 149 | Bolivia, Paraguay: Chaco Boreal, Serrania de Santiago, Serrania de Sunsas. |
| 59 | S66–38321 | S66–38251 | 35 | June 5, 1966 | 20:22 | 149 | Bolivia, Paraguay: Chaco Boreal, Serrania de Santiago. |
| 60 | S66–38322 | S66–38252 | 35 | June 5, 1966 | ....... | ........ | Blank. |
| 61 | S66–38323 | S66–38253 | 35 | June 5, 1966 | ....... | ........ | Light spot, probably Moon time exposure. |
| 62 | S66–38324 | S66–38254 | 35 | June 5, 1966 | 20:28 | ........ | Earth terminator at sunset, South America. |
| 63 | S66–38325 | S66–38255 | 35 | June 5, 1966 | 20:28 | ........ | Earth terminator at sunset, South America. |
| 64 | S66–38326 | S66–38256 | 35 | June 5, 1966 | 20:28 | ........ | Earth terminator at sunset, South America. |
| 65 | S66–38327 | S66–38257 | ............ | .............. | ....... | ........ | Cirriform clouds. |
| 66 | S66–38328 | S66–38258 | ............ | .............. | ....... | ........ | Cirriform clouds. |
| 67 | S66–38329 | S66–38259 | ............ | .............. | ....... | ........ | Cirriform clouds. |
| 68 | S66–38330 | S66–38260 | ............ | .............. | ....... | ........ | Cirriform clouds. |
| 69 | S66–38331 | S66–38261 | ............ | .............. | ....... | ........ | Blank. |
| 70 | S66–38332 | S66–38262 | ............ | .............. | ....... | ........ | Blank. |

MAGAZINE D

| Frame | NASA/MSC Color No. | NASA/MSC B&W No. | Revolution | Date | GMT | Alt, N. Mi. | Area description |
|---|---|---|---|---|---|---|---|
| 1 | S66–38031 | S66–37973 | ............ | .............. | ....... | ........ | Blank. |
| 2 | S66–38032 | S66–37974 | 31 | June 5, 1966 | 15:10 | 156 | Comdr. Cernan's EVA camera; standing in hatch over Pacific Ocean. |
| 3 | S66–38033 | S66–37975 | 31 | June 5, 1966 | 15:11 | 156 | Comdr. Cernan's EVA camera; standing in hatch over Pacific Ocean. |
| 4 | S66–38034 | S66–37976 | 31 | June 5, 1966 | 15:12 | 157 | Comdr. Cernan's EVA camera; clouds over Pacific Ocean. |
| 5 | S66–38035 | S66–37977 | 31 | June 5, 1966 | 15:14 | 157 | Comdr. Cernan's EVA camera; clouds over Pacific Ocean. |
| 6 | S66–38036 | S66–37978 | 31 | June 5, 1966 | 15:14 | 157 | Comdr. Cernan's EVA camera; clouds over Pacific Ocean. |
| 7 | S66–38037 | S66–37979 | 31 | June 5, 1966 | 15:15 | 157 | Comdr. Cernan's EVA camera; clouds over Pacific Ocean. |
| 8 | S66–38038 | S66–37980 | 31 | June 5, 1966 | 15:16 | 158 | Comdr. Cernan's EVA camera; California/Arizona/Mexico: Baja California, Sonora. |
| 9 | S66–38039 | S66–37981 | 31 | June 5, 1966 | 15:16 | 158 | Comdr. Cernan's EVA camera; California/Arizona/Mexico: Baja California, Sonora. |
| 10 | S66–38040 | S66–37982 | 31 | June 5, 1966 | 15:16 | 158 | Comdr. Cernan's EVA camera; California/Arizona/Mexico: Baja California, Sonora. |
| 11 | S66–38041 | S66–37983 | 31 | June 5, 1966 | 15:16 | 158 | Comdr. Cernan's EVA camera; California/Arizona/Mexico: Baja California, Sonora. |

MAGAZINE D Continued

| Frame | NASA/MSC Color No. | NASA/MSC B&W No. | Revolution | Date | GMT | Alt, N. Mi. | Area description |
|---|---|---|---|---|---|---|---|
| 12 | S66–38042 | S66–37984 | 31 | June 5, 1966 | 15:19 | 158 | Comdr. Cernan's EVA camera; open hatch, gear deployment. |
| 13 | S66–38043 | S66–37985 | 31 | June 5, 1966 | 15:19 | 158 | Comdr. Cernan's EVA camera; open hatch, gear deployment; Arizona/New Mexico background. |
| 14 | S66–38044 | S66–37986 | 31 | June 5, 1966 | 15:20 | 158 | Comdr. Cernan's EVA camera; open hatch, gear deployment; Arizona/New Mexico background. |
| 15 | S66–38045 | S66–37987 | 31 | June 5, 1966 | 15:21 | 158 | Comdr. Cernan's EVA camera; command pilot side spacecraft; Arizona/New Mexico/Texas/ Mexico background. |
| 16 | S66–38046 | S66–37988 | 31 | June 5, 1966 | 15:21 | 158 | Comdr. Cernan's EVA camera; open hatch, gear deployment; Mexico background. |
| 17 | S66–38047 | S66–37989 | 31 | June 5, 1966 | 15:23 | 158 | Comdr. Cernan's EVA camera; side of spacecraft. |
| 18 | S66–38048 | S66–37990 | 31 | June 5, 1966 | 15:24 | 159 | Comdr. Cernan's EVA camera; nose view of spacecraft. |
| 19 | S66–38049 | S66–37991 | 31 | June 5, 1966 | 15:24 | 159 | Comdr. Cernan's EVA camera; side view, open hatch, umbilical cord. |
| 20 | S66–38050 | S66–37992 | 31 | June 5, 1966 | 15:25 | 159 | Comdr. Cernan's EVA camera; side view of' Gemini IX. |
| 21 | S66–38051 | S66–37993 | 32 | June 5, 1966 | 15:28 | 159 | Comdr. Cernan's EVA camera; view of Gemini IX. |
| 22 | S66–38052 | S66–37994 | 32 | June 5, 1966 | 15:29 | 159 | Comdr. Cernan's EVA camera; umbilical cord, sea background. |
| 23 | S66–38053 | S66–37995 | 32 | June 5, 1966 | 15:29 | 159 | Comdr. Cernan's EVA camera; nose of Gemini IX |
| 24 | S66–38054 | S66–37996 | 32 | June 5, 1966 | 15:30 | 159 | Comdr. Cernan's EVA camera; sea, umbilical cord, hatch. |
| 25 | S66–38055 | S66–37997 | 32 | June 5, 1966 | 15:30 | 159 | Comdr. Cernan's EVA camera; side of Gemini IX adapter section. |
| 26 | S66–38056 | S66–37998 | 32 | June 5, 1966 | 15:31 | 159 | Comdr. Cernan's EVA camera; out of focus. |
| 27 | S66–38057 | S66–37999 | 32 | June 5, 1966 | ...... | ........ | Blank. |
| 28 | S66–38058 | S66–38000 | 32 | June 5, 1966 | ...... | ........ | Blank. |
| 29 | S66–38059 | S66–38001 | 32 | June 5, 1966 | ...... | ........ | Blank. |
| 30 | S66–38060 | S66–38002 | 32 | June 5, 1966 | ...... | ........ | Blank. |
| 31 | S66–38061 | S66–38003 | 32 | June 5, 1966 | ...... | ........ | Comd. Cernan's EVA camera; out of focus. |
| 32 | S66–38062 | S66–38004 | 32 | June 5, 1966 | 16:40 | 156 | Comdr. Cernan's EVA camera; adapter section. |
| 33 | S66–38063 | S66–38005 | 32 | June 5, 1966 | 16:49 | 157 | Comdr. Cernan's EVA camera; nose of Gemini IX, umbilical cord. |
| 34 | S66–38064 | S66–38006 | 32 | June 5, 1966 | 16:49 | 158 | Comdr. Cernan's EVA camera; nose of Gemini IX, umbilical cord. |
| 35 | S66–38065 | S66–38007 | 32 | June 5, 1966 | 16:50 | 158 | Comdr. Cernan's EVA camera; nose of Gemini IX, umbilical cord. |
| 36 | S66–38066 | S66–38008 | 32 | June 5, 1966 | 16:50 | 158 | Comdr. Cernan's EVA camera; nose of Gemini IX, umbilical cord, California. |
| 37 | S66–38067 | S66–38009 | 32 | June 5, 1966 | 16:51 | 158 | Comdr. Cernan's EVA camera; umbilical cord; California, Los Angeles area. |
| *38* | *S66–38068* | *S66–38010* | *32* | *June 5, 1966* | *16:53* | *158* | *Comdr. Cernan's EVA camera; umbilical cord; California/Arizona/Sonora.* |
| 39 | S66–38069 | S66–38011 | 32 | June 5, 1966 | 16:53 | 158 | Comdr. Cernan's EVA camera; umbilical cord; Arizona/New Mexico/Sonora. |
| *40* | *S66–38070* | *S66–38012* | *32* | *June 5, 1966* | *16:54* | *158* | *Comdr. Cernan's EVA camera; nose of Gemini IX, Baja California/Sonora.* |
| 41 | S66–38071 | S66–38013 | 33 | June 5, 1966 | 17:12 | ........ | Comdr. Cernan's EVA camera; underexposed. |
| 42 | S66–38072 | S66–38014 | 33 | June 5, 1966 | 17:12 | ........ | Comdr. Cernan's EVA camera; underexposed. |
| 43 | S66–38073 | S66–38015 | 33 | June 5, 1966 | 17:13 | ........ | Comdr. Cernan's EVA camera; underexposed. |
| 44 | S66–38074 | S66–38016 | 33 | June 5, 1966 | 17:13 | ........ | Comdr. Cernan's EVA camera; underexposed. |
| 45 | S66–38075 | S66–38017 | 33 | June 5, 1966 | 17:13 | ........ | Comdr. Cernan's EVA camera; underexposed. |

MAGAZINE D Continued

| Frame | NASA/MSC Color No. | NASA/MSC B&W No. | Revolution | Date | GMT | Alt, N. Mi. | Area description |
|---|---|---|---|---|---|---|---|
| 46 | S66–38076 | S66–38018 | 34 | June 5, 1966 | 18:40 | ........ | Inside Gemini IX, Lt. Col. Stafford. |
| 47 | S66–38077 | S66–38019 | 34 | June 5, 1966 | 18:40 | ........ | Inside Gemini IX, Lt. Col. Stafford. |
| 48 | S66–38078 | S66–38020 | 34 | June 5, 1966 | 18:41 | ........ | Inside Gemini IX, Lt. Col. Stafford; image blurred. |
| 49 | S66–38079 | S66–38021 | 34 | June 5, 1966 | 18:41 | ........ | Inside Gemini IX, Lt. Col. Stafford; image blurred. |
| 50 | S66–38080 | S66–38022 | 34 | June 5, 1966 | 18:41 | ........ | Inside Gemini IX, Lt. Col. Stafford. |
| 51 | S66–38081 | S66–38023 | 34 | June 5, 1966 | 18:42 | ........ | Inside Gemini IX, Lt. Comdr. Cernan; image blurred. |
| 52 | S66–38082 | S66–38024 | 34 | June 5, 1966 | 18:42 | ........ | Inside Gemini IX, Lt. Comdr. Cernan; image blurred. |
| 53 | S66–38083 | S66–38025 | 34 | June 5, 1966 | 18:55 | ........ | Inside Gemini IX, Lt. Comdr. Cernan; image blurred. |
| 54 | S66–38084 | S66–38026 | 34 | June 5, 1966 | 18:55 | ........ | Limb; sunset. |
| 55 | S66–38085 | S66–38027 | 34 | June 5, 1966 | 18:56 | ........ | Limb; sunset. |
| 56 | S66–38086 | S66–38028 | 34 | June 5, 1966 | 18:56 | ........ | Clouds; out of focus. |
| 57 | S66–38087 | S66–38029 | 34 | June 5, 1966 | 18:57 | ........ | Clouds; out of focus |
| 58 | S66–38088 | S66–38030 | 34 | June 5, 1966 | 18:58 | ........ | Red light streak. |

MAGAZINE G

| Frame | NASA/MSC Color No. | NASA/MSC B&W No. | Revolution | Date | GMT | Alt, N. Mi. | Area description |
|---|---|---|---|---|---|---|---|
| 1 | S66–38510 | S66–38459 | 31 | June 5, 1966 | 15:23 | ........ | EVA, Lt. Comdr. Cernan outside; solar reflection degrades photo. |
| 2 | S66–38511 | S66–38460 | 31 | June 5, 1966 | 15:24 | ........ | EVA, Lt. Comdr. Cernan outside; solar reflection degrades photo. |
| 3 | S66–38512 | S66–38461 | 31 | June 5, 1966 | 15:24 | ........ | EVA Lt. Comdr. Cernan outside; solar reflection degrades photo. |
| 4 | S66–38513 | S66–38462 | 31 | June 5, 1966 | 15:24 | ........ | EVA, umbilical cord; out of focus, light reflection. |
| 5 | S66–38514 | S66–38463 | 31 | June 5, 1966 | 15:24 | ........ | EVA, partial view of Lt. Comdr. Cernan outside. |
| 6 | S66–38515 | S66–38464 | 31 | June 5, 1966 | 15:25 | ........ | EVA, partial view of Lt. Comdr. Cernan outside. |
| 7 | S66–38516 | S66–38465 | 31 | June 5, 1966 | 15:25 | ........ | EVA, partial view of Lt. Comdr. Cernan outside, image blurred. |
| 8 | S66–38517 | S66–38466 | 31 | June 5, 1966 | 15:25 | ........ | EVA, closeup of Lt. Comdr. Cernan outside, out of focus. |
| 9 | S66–38518 | S66–38467 | 31 | June 5, 1966 | 15:26 | ........ | EVA, umbilical cord. |
| 10 | S66–38519 | S66–38468 | 34 | June 5, 1966 | 19:48 | ........ | Limb, red-yellow-blue; focus not sharp. |
| 11 | S66–38520 | S66–38469 | 34 | June 5, 1966 | 19:48 | ........ | Limb, red-yellow-blue; focus not sharp. |
| 12 | S66–38521 | S66–38470 | 34 | June 5, 1966 | 19:49 | ........ | Limb, red-yellow-blue; focus not sharp. |
| 13 | S66–38522 | S66–38471 | 34 | June 5, 1966 | 20:16 | 146 | Peru, Ecuador: Bay and Desert of Sechura, Andes Mountains, Amazon Basin. |
| 14 | S66–38523 | S66–38472 | 34 | June 5, 1966 | 20:16 | 146 | Peru: Desert of Sechura, Andes Mountains, Amazon Basin. |
| 15 | S66–38524 | S66–38473 | 35 | June 5, 1966 | 20:17 | 146 | Peru: Andes Mountains, Rio Maranon, east of Trujillo. |
| *16* | *S66–38525* | *S66–38474* | *35* | *June 5, 1966* | *20:17* | *146* | *Peru: Andes Mountains, Rio Maranon, Rio Huallaga, east of Trujillo.* |
| 17 | S66–38526 | S66–38475 | 35 | June 5, 1966 | 20:17 | 146 | Peru: Andes Mountains, Rio Maranon, Rio Huallaga, east of Trujillo. |
| 18 | S66–38527 | S66–38476 | 35 | June 5, 1966 | 20:18 | 147 | Peru: Andes Mountains, Amazon Basin, Rio Ucayali. |
| 19 | S66–38528 | S66–38477 | 35 | June 5, 1966 | 20:18 | 147 | Peru: Andes Mountains, Amazon Basin, Rio Ucayali. |
| 20 | S66–38529 | S66–38478 | 35 | June 5, 1966 | 20:19 | 147 | Peru: Andes Mountains, Amazon Basin, Rio Madre de Dios, Rio Urubamba. |
| 21 | S66–38530 | S66–38479 | 35 | June 5, 1966 | 20:19 | 147 | Peru, Bolivia: Andes Mountains, Lake Titicaca, Rio Madre de Dios, Amazon Basin. |

MAGAZINE G Continued

| Frame | NASA/MSC Color No. | NASA/MSC B&W No. | Revolution | Date | GMT | Alt, N. Mi. | Area description |
|---|---|---|---|---|---|---|---|
| 22 | S66–38531 | S66–38480 | 35 | June 5, 1966 | 20:20 | 147 | Peru, Bolivia: Andes Mountains, Lake Titicaca, Rio Madre de Dios, Amazon Basin. |
| 23 | S66–38532 | S66–38481 | 35 | June 5, 1966 | 20:20 | 148 | Peru, Bolivia: Andes Mountains, Rio Madre de Dios, Amazon Basin. |
| 24 | S66–38533 | S66–38482 | 35 | June 5, 1966 | 20:20 | 148 | Peru, Bolivia: Andes Mountains, Lake Titicaca, Lake Poopo, Salar de Uyuni, Rio Beni, Amazon Basin. |
| 25 | S66–38534 | S66–38483 | 35 | June 5, 1966 | 20:20 | 148 | Bolivia: Andes Mountains, Rio Beni, Amazon Basin. |
| 26 | S66–38535 | S66–38484 | 35 | June 5, 1966 | 20:21 | 148 | Bolivia: Eastern slope of Andes, Amazon Basin, Rio Mamore, Rio Grande. |
| 27 | S66–38536 | S66–38485 | 35 | June 5, 1966 | 20:21 | 148 | Bolivia: Amazon Basin, Rio Mamore, Rio Grande. |
| 28 | S66–38537 | S66–38486 | 35 | June 5, 1966 | 20:21 | 148 | Bolivia: San Javier; Amazon Basin, Rio Grande. |
| 29 | S66–38538 | S66–38487 | 35 | June 5, 1966 | 20:22 | 149 | Bolivia: San Javier; Amazon Basin. |
| 30 | S66–38539 | S66–38488 | 35 | June 5, 1966 | 20:22 | 149 | Bolivia, Brazil: Serra Aguapei, Mato Grosso, headwaters of Rio Paraguay. |
| 31 | S66–38540 | S66–38489 | 35 | June 5, 1966 | 20:23 | 149 | Bolivia, Brazil: Serrana de Sunsas, Mato Grosso, headwaters of Rio Paraguay at Lago Mandiore. |
| 32 | S66–38541 | S66–38490 | 35 | June 5, 1966 | 20:23 | 149 | Bolivia, Brazil: Mato Grosso, Serra Azul, headwaters of Rio Paraguay. |
| 33 | S66–38542 | S66–38491 | 43 | June 6, 1966 | 09:19 | 148 | Canary Islands near horizon. |
| 34 | S66–38543 | S66–38492 | 43 | June 6, 1966 | 09:20 | 148 | Canary Islands; image degraded because of window obscuration. |
| 35 | S66–38544 | S66–38493 | 43 | June 6, 1966 | 09:20 | 148 | Canary Islands; image degraded because of window obscuration. |
| 36 | S66–38545 | S66–38494 | 43 | June 6, 1966 | 09:22 | 147 | Spanish Sahara, Morocco: Hamada du Dra, Tindouf Basin. |
| 37 | S66–38546 | S66–38495 | 43 | June 6, 1966 | 09:23 | 147 | Spanish Sahara, Morocco, Mauritania, Algeria: Tindouf Basin, Yetti Plains. |
| 38 | S66–38547 | S66–38496 | 43 | June 6, 1966 | 09:23 | 147 | Spanish Sahara, Morocco, Mauritania, Algeria: Hamada du Dra, Tindouf Basin. |
| 39 | S66–38548 | S66–38497 | 43 | June 6, 1966 | 09:23 | 147 | Algeria: Erg Iguidi, Erg Chech; image degraded because of window obscuration. |
| 40 | S66–38549 | S66–38498 | 43 | June 6, 1966 | 09:24 | 147 | Algeria: Erg Iguidi, Erg Chech; image degraded because of window obscuration. |
| 41 | S66–38550 | S66–38499 | 43 | June 6, 1966 | 09:25 | 146 | Algeria: Grand Erg Oriental, Ajjer Plateau; image degraded because of window obscuration. |
| 42 | S66–38551 | S66–38500 | 43 | June 6, 1966 | 09:26 | 146 | Algeria, Libya: Ajjer Plateau, Marzuq Sand Plain. |
| 43 | S66–38552 | S66–38501 | 43 | June 6, 1966 | 09:27 | 146 | Algeria, Libya: Ajjer Plateau, Marzuq Sand Plain. |
| 44 | S66–38553 | S66–38502 | 43 | June 6, 1966 | 09:28 | 145 | Libya, Chad, Niger: Tibesti Mountains and Gravel Desert. |
| 45 | S66–38554 | S66–38503 | 43 | June 6, 1966 | 09:29 | 145 | Libya, Chad: Northern Tibesti Mountains; cloudy. |
| 46 | S66–38555 | S66–38504 | 43 | June 6, 1966 | 09:29 | 145 | Libya: Northern Tibesti Mountains, Kufra Oasis, Sarra Gravel Desert. |
| 47 | S66–38556 | S66–38505 | 43 | June 6, 1966 | 09:31 | 144 | Sudan: Great Bend of Nile River, Ethiopia, Red Sea, Saudi Arabia in background. |
| 48 | S66–38557 | S66–38506 | 43 | June 6, 1966 | 09:32 | 144 | Sudan: Great Bend of Nile River, Ethiopia, Red Sea, Saudi Arabia in background. |
| 49 | S66–38558 | S66–38507 | 43 | June 6, 1966 | 09:33 | 144 | Sudan, Ethiopia, Saudi Arabia: Red Sea. |
| 50 | S66–38559 | S66–38508 | 43 | June 6, 1966 | 09:34 | 144 | Ethiopia, Yemen, Saudi Arabia: Danakil Depression, Red Sea, Gulf of Aden. |
| 51 | S66–38560 | S66–38509 | 43 | June 6, 1966 | 09:35 | 144 | Ethiopia, French Somaliland, Somali Republic: Gulf of Aden; partial frame. |

MAGAZINE B

| Frame | NASA/MSC Color No. | NASA/MSC B&W No. | Revolution | Date | GMT | Alt, N. Mi. | Area description |
|---|---|---|---|---|---|---|---|
| 1 | .......... | .......... | | | | | |
| 2 | S66-38396 | S66-38333 | .......... | .......... | ...... | ...... | Blank. |
| 3 | S66-38397 | S66-38334 | .......... | .......... | ...... | ...... | Blank. |
| 4 | S66-38398 | S66-38335 | 43 | June 6, 1966 | ...... | ...... | Limb, blue. |
| 5 | S66-38399 | S66-38336 | 43 | June 6, 1966 | ...... | ...... | Limb, blue. |
| 6 | S66-38400 | S66-38337 | 43 | June 6, 1966 | 09:18 | 148 | Canary Islands. |
| 7 | S66-38401 | S66-38338 | 43 | June 6, 1966 | 09:19 | 148 | Canary Islands. |
| 8 | S66-38402 | S66-38339 | 43 | June 6, 1966 | 09:19 | 148 | Canary Islands. |
| 9 | S66-38403 | S66-38340 | 43 | June 6, 1966 | 09:19 | 148 | Canary Islands, coast of Africa. |
| *10* | *S66-38404* | *S66-38341* | *43* | *June 6, 1966* | *09:20* | *148* | *Canary Islands, coast of Africa.* |
| *11* | *S66-38405* | *S66-38342* | *43* | *June 6, 1966* | *09:20* | *148* | *Canary Islands, coast of Morocco and Spanish Sahara.* |
| 12 | S66-38406 | S66-38343 | 43 | June 6, 1966 | 09:20 | 148 | Canary Islands, coast of Morocco and Spanish Sahara. |
| 13 | S66-38407 | S66-38344 | 43 | June 6, 1966 | 09:21 | 148 | Canary Islands, coast of Morocco and Spanish Sahara. |
| *14* | *S66-38408* | *S66-38345* | *43* | *June 6, 1966* | *09:21* | *147* | *Fuerteventura Islands, coast of Morocco and Spanish Sahara.* |
| *15* | *S66-38409* | *S66-38346* | *43* | *June 6, 1966* | *09:22* | *147* | *Morocco, Spanish Sahara, Mauritania, Algeria: Hamada du Dra, Tindouf Basin, Yetti Plain.* |
| 16 | S66-38410 | S66-38347 | 43 | June 6, 1966 | ...... | ...... | Blank. |
| 17 | S66-38411 | S66-38348 | 43 | .......... | 09:22 | 147 | Spanish Sahara, Mauritania: South edge of Tindouf Basin, Yetti Plain. |
| 18 | S66-38412 | S66-38349 | 43 | June 6, 1966 | 09:23 | 147 | Algeria: Erg Iguidi, Erg Chech. |
| *19* | *S66-38413* | *S66-38350* | *43* | *June 6, 1966* | *09:23* | *147* | *Algeria: Erg Iguidi, Erg Chech.* |
| 20 | S66-38414 | S66-38351 | 43 | June 6, 1966 | 09:24 | 147 | Algeria: Erg Chech, Tademait Plateau. |
| 21 | S66-38415 | S66-38352 | 43 | June 6, 1966 | 09:24 | 146 | Algeria: Erg Chech, Tanezrouft area. |
| 22 | S66-38416 | S66-38353 | 43 | June 6, 1966 | 09:25 | 146 | Algeria: Tademait Plateau, Ahellakane Escarpment. |
| 23 | S66-38417 | S66-38354 | 43 | June 6, 1966 | 09:26 | 146 | Algeria: Iraquene and Ahellakane Escarpments. |
| *24* | *S66-38418* | *S66-38355* | *43* | *June 6, 1966* | *09:27* | *146* | *Algeria, Libya: Ajjer Plateau, Ahaggar Mountains.* |
| 25 | S66-38419 | S66-38356 | 43 | June 6, 1966 | 09:28 | 145 | Libya, Niger, Chad: Tibesti Mountains and Gravel Desert. |
| 26 | S66-38420 | S66-38357 | 43 | June 6, 1966 | 09:29 | 145 | Niger, Chad: Tibesti Mountains, volcanoes, lava. |
| 27 | S66-38421 | S66-38358 | 43 | June 6, 1966 | 09:31 | 145 | Libya, Chad, Sudan: featureless desert. |
| 28 | S66-38422 | S66-38359 | 43 | June 6, 1966 | 09:33 | 144 | Sudan: Great Bend of Nile River. |
| 29 | S66-38423 | S66-38360 | 43 | June 6, 1966 | 09:35 | 144 | Ethiopia, French Somaliland, Yemen, South Arabia: Red Sea, Gulf of Aden, Danakil Depression. |
| *30* | *S66-38424* | *S66-38361* | *43* | *June 6, 1966* | *09:35* | *144* | *Ethiopia, Somali Republic: Berbera; Gulf of Aden.* |
| 31 | S66-38425 | S66-38362 | 43 | June 6, 1966 | 09:36 | 144 | Ethiopia, Somali Republic; Heavy cloud cover. |
| 32 | S66-38426 | S66-38363 | 43 | June 6, 1966 | 09:37 | 144 | Somali Republic: Ras Azir, Ras Hafun, Indian Ocean, Socotra Island. |
| 33 | S66-38427 | S66-38364 | 43 | June 6, 1966 | 09:38 | 144 | Somali Republic: Ras Azir, Ras Hafun, Indian Ocean, Socotra Island. |
| 34 | S66-38428 | S66-38365 | 43 | June 6, 1966 | 09:50 | 148 | Clouds over water. |
| *35* | *S66-38429* | *S66-38366* | *43* | *June 6, 1966* | *09:51* | *148* | *Clouds over water.* |
| 36 | S66-38430 | S66-38367 | 44 | June 6, 1966 | 10:46 | 149 | Clouds, underexposed. |
| 37 | S66-38431 | S66-38368 | 44 | June 6, 1966 | 10:46 | 149 | Clouds, underexposed. |
| 38 | S66-38432 | S66-38369 | 44 | June 6, 1966 | 10:47 | 149 | Clouds, near terminator. |
| 39 | S66-38433 | S66-38370 | 44 | June 6, 1966 | 10:47 | 149 | Clouds, near terminator. |
| 40 | S66-38434 | S66-38371 | 44 | June 6, 1966 | 10:47 | 149 | Clouds, near terminator. |
| 41 | S66-38435 | S66-38372 | 44 | June 6, 1966 | 10:48 | 148 | Clouds, near terminator. |
| 42 | S66-38436 | S66-38373 | 44 | June 6, 1966 | 10:48 | 148 | Clouds, near terminator. |
| 43 | S66-38437 | S66-38374 | 44 | June 6, 1966 | 10:48 | 148 | Clouds. |
| 44 | S66-38438 | S66-38375 | 44 | June 6, 1966 | 10:49 | 148 | Clouds. |
| 45 | S66-38439 | S66-38376 | 44 | June 6, 1966 | 10:49 | 148 | Clouds. |
| *46* | *S66-38440* | *S66-38377* | *44* | *June 6, 1966* | *10:55* | *146* | *Clouds.* |

MAGAZINE B Continued

| Frame | NASA/MSC Color No. | NASA/MSC B&W No. | Revolution | Date | GMT | Alt, N. Mi. | Area description |
|---|---|---|---|---|---|---|---|
| 47 | S66–38441 | S66–38378 | 44 | June 6, 1966 | 10:56 | 145 | Canary Islands. |
| *48* | *S66–38442* | *S66–38379* | *44* | *June 6, 1966* | *10:57* | *145* | *Canary Islands.* |
| 49 | S66–38443 | S66–38380 | 44 | June 6, 1966 | 11:04 | 144 | Chad, Niger, Nigeria: Lake Chad, inundated dunes. |
| *50* | *S66–38444* | *S66–38381* | *44* | *June 6, 1966* | *11:05* | *144* | *Chad, Niger, Nigeria, Cameroun: Lake Chad, inundated dunes.* |
| *51* | *S66–38445* | *S66–38382* | *44* | *June 6, 1966* | *11:08* | *144* | *Central African Republic: cloudy.* |
| 52 | S66–38446 | S66–38383 | 44 | June 6, 1966 | 11:09 | 144 | Central African Republic, Republic of the Congo: hazy. |
| 53 | S66–38447 | S66–38384 | 44 | June 6, 1966 | 11:10 | 144 | Republic of the Congo, Uganda: Lake Albert, Lake Edward; hazy. |
| 54 | S66–38448 | S66–38385 | 44 | June 6, 1966 | 11:11 | 144 | Republic of the Congo, Uganda: Lake Albert, Lake Edward, Lake Kyoga; hazy. |
| 55 | S66–38449 | S66–38386 | 44 | June 6, 1966 | 11:11 | 144 | Kenya, Tanzania, Uganda: Lake Victoria, Kavirondo Gulf; hazy. |
| 56 | S66–38450 | S66–38387 | 44 | June 6, 1966 | 11:11 | 144 | Kenya, Tanzania, Uganda: Lake Victoria, Kavirondo Gulf; hazy. |
| 57 | S66–38451 | S66–38388 | 44 | June 6, 1966 | 11:13 | 144 | Kenya, Tanzania: Indian Ocean coast; hazy. |
| 58 | S66–38452 | S66–38389 | 44 | June 6, 1966 | 11:13 | 145 | Kenya, Somali Republic: Indian Ocean coast; hazy. |
| *59* | *S66–38453* | *S66–38390* | *44* | *June 6, 1966* | *11:14* | *145* | *Kenya, Somali Republic; Tanzania: Indian Ocean coast; hazy.* |
| *60* | *S66–38454* | *S66–38391* | *44* | *June 6, 1966* | *11:14* | *145* | *Somali Republic, Kenya: Indian Ocean coast; hazy.* |
| 61 | S66–38455 | S66–38392 | 44 | June 6, 1966 | 11:15 | 145 | Somali Republic, Kenya: Indian Ocean coast; hazy. |
| 62 | S66–38456 | S66–38393 | 44 | June 6, 1966 | 11:15 | 145 | Partial frame, Somali coast. |
| 63 | S66–38457 | S66–38394 | ........... | ............... | ...... | ....... | Blank. |
| 64 | S66–38458 | S66–38395 | ........... | ............... | ...... | ....... | Blank. |

# GEMINI X

## MAGAZINE 5

| Frame | NASA/MSC Color No. | NASA/MSC B&W No. | Revolution | Date | GMT | Alt, N. Mi. | Area description |
|---|---|---|---|---|---|---|---|
| 1 | .......... | .......... | ........... | ............... | ...... | ....... | Blank. |
| 2 | S66–46111 | S66–46171 | 4 | July 19, 1966 | 04:00 | 161 | Agena No. 5005, side view, range 98 ft; ocean, clouds. |
| 3 | S66–46112 | S66–46172 | 4 | July 19, 1966 | 04:00 | 161 | Agena No. 5005, side view, range 98 ft; ocean, clouds. |
| 4 | S66–46113 | S66–46173 | 4 | July 19, 1966 | 04:01 | 161 | Agena No. 5005, side view, range 85 ft; ocean, clouds. |
| 5 | S66–46114 | S66–46174 | 4 | July 19, 1966 | 04:01 | 161 | Agena No. 5005, side view, range 85 ft; ocean, clouds. |
| 6 | S66–46115 | S66–46175 | 4 | July 19, 1966 | 04:02 | 161 | Agena No. 5005, side view, range 65 ft; ocean, clouds. |
| 7 | S66–46116 | S66–46176 | 4 | July 19, 1966 | 04:02 | 161 | Agena No. 5005, side view, range 65 ft; ocean, clouds. |
| 8 | S66–46117 | S66–46177 | 4 | July 19, 1966 | 04:03 | 161 | Agena No. 5005, side view, range 62 ft; ocean, clouds. |
| 9 | S66–46118 | S66–46178 | 4 | July 19, 1966 | 04:03 | 161 | Agena No. 5005, side view, range 62 ft; ocean, clouds. |
| 10 | S66–46119 | S66–46179 | 4 | July 19, 1966 | 04:03 | 161 | Agena No. 5005, side view, range 52 ft; ocean, clouds. |
| 11 | S66–46120 | S66–46180 | 4 | July 19, 1966 | 04:03 | 161 | Agena No. 5005, side view, range 52 ft; ocean, clouds. |
| 12 | S66–46121 | S66–46181 | 4 | July 19, 1966 | 04:03 | 161 | Agena No. 5005, side view, range 46 ft; ocean, clouds. |

MAGAZINE 5 Continued

| Frame | NASA/MSC Color No. | NASA/MSC B&W No. | Revolution | Date | GMT | Alt, N. Mi. | Area description |
|---|---|---|---|---|---|---|---|
| 13 | S66-46122 | S66-46182 | 4 | July 19, 1966 | 04:04 | 161 | Agena No. 5005, side view, range 46 ft; ocean, clouds. |
| 14 | S66-46123 | S66-46183 | 4 | July 19, 1966 | 04:04 | 161 | Agena No. 5005, side view, range 51 ft; ocean, clouds. |
| 15 | S66-46124 | S66-46184 | 4 | July 19, 1966 | 04:04 | 162 | Agena No. 5005, side view, range 49 ft; ocean, clouds. |
| 16 | S66-46125 | S66-46185 | 4 | July 19, 1966 | 04:04 | 162 | Agena No. 5005, side view, range 51 ft; ocean, clouds. |
| 17 | S66-46126 | S66-46186 | 4 | July 19, 1966 | 04:04 | 162 | Agena No. 5005, side view, range 28 ft; ocean, clouds. |
| 18 | S66-46127 | S66-46187 | 4 | July 19, 1966 | 04:05 | 162 | Agena No. 5005, side view, range 27 ft; ocean, clouds. |
| 19 | S66-46128 | S66-46188 | 4 | July 19, 1966 | 04:05 | 162 | Agena No. 5005, docking adapter turning toward spacecraft, range 24 ft; ocean, clouds. |
| 20 | S66-46129 | S66-46189 | 4 | July 19, 1966 | 04:05 | 162 | Agena No. 5005, docking adapter turning toward spacecraft, range 23 ft; ocean, clouds. |
| 21 | S66-46130 | S66-46190 | 4 | July 19, 1966 | 04:05 | 162 | Agena No. 5005, docking adapter turning toward spacecraft, range 23 ft; ocean, clouds. |
| 22 | S66-46131 | S66-46191 | 4 | July 19, 1966 | 04:06 | 162 | Agena No. 5005, docking adapter turning toward spacecraft, range 26 ft; ocean, clouds. |
| 23 | S66-46132 | S66-46192 | 4 | July 19, 1966 | 04:06 | 162 | Agena No. 5005, docking adapter turning toward spacecraft, range 25 ft; ocean, clouds. |
| 24 | S66-46133 | S66-46193 | 4 | July 19, 1966 | 04:06 | 162 | Agena No. 5005, docking adapter turning toward spacecraft, range 25 ft; ocean, clouds. |
| 25 | S66-46134 | S66-46194 | 4 | July 19, 1966 | 04:08 | 161 | Blank. |
| 26 | S66-46135 | S66-46195 | 4 | July 19, 1966 | 04:09 | 161 | Agena No. 5005, docked. |
| 27 | S66-46136 | S66-46196 | 4 | July 19, 1966 | 04:25 | 160 | Agena No. 5005, docked. |
| 28 | S66-46137 | S66-46197 | 4 | July 19, 1966 | 04:25 | 160 | Agena No. 5005, docked, Agena display panel clearly seen. |
| 29 | S66-46138 | S66-46198 | 4 | July 19, 1966 | 04:25 | 160 | Agena No. 5005, docked, Agena display panel clearly seen. |
| 30 | S66-46139 | S66-46199 | 4 | July 19, 1966 | 04:26 | 159 | Agena No. 5005, docked, Agena display panel clearly seen. |
| 31 | S66-46140 | S66-46200 | 4 | July 19, 1966 | 04:26 | 159 | Agena No. 5005, docked, Agena display panel clearly seen. |
| 32 | S66-46141 | S66-46201 | 4 | July 19, 1966 | 04:26 | 159 | Agena No. 5005, docked, Agena display panel clearly seen. |
| 33 | S66-46142 | S66-46202 | 4 | July 19, 1966 | 04:26 | 159 | Agena No. 5005, docked, Agena display panel clearly seen. |
| 34 | S66-46143 | S66-46203 | 4 | July 19, 1966 | 04:26 | 159 | Agena No. 5005, docked, Agena display panel clearly seen. |
| 35 | S66-46144 | S66-46204 | 4 | July 19, 1966 | 04:27 | 159 | Agena No. 5005, docked, Agena display panel clearly seen. |
| 36 | S66-46145 | S66-46205 | 4 | July 19, 1966 | 04:27 | 159 | Agena No. 5005, docked, Agena display panel clearly seen. |
| 37 | S66-46146 | S66-46206 | 4 | July 19, 1966 | 04:27 | 159 | Agena No. 5005, docked. |
| 38 | S66-46147 | S66-46207 | 4 | July 19, 1966 | 04:28 | 159 | Agena No. 5005, docked. |
| 39 | S66-46148 | S66-46208 | 4 | July 19, 1966 | 04:28 | 159 | Agena No. 5005, docked. |
| 40 | S66-46149 | S66-46209 | 4 | July 19, 1966 | 04:28 | 159 | Agena No. 5005, docked. |
| 41 | S66-46150 | S66-46210 | 4 | July 19, 1966 | 04:29 | 159 | Agena No. 5005, docked. |
| 42 | S66-46151 | S66-46211 | 6 | July 19, 1966 | 07:00 | 371 | Small portion docked Agena No. 5005; Africa, Arabia, Red Sea, Gulf of Aden. |
| 43 | S66-46152 | S66-46212 | 6 | July 19, 1966 | 07:01 | 369 | Small portion docked Agena No. 5005; Africa, Arabia, Red Sea, Gulf of Aden. |
| 44 | S66-46153 | S66-46213 | 6 | July 19, 1966 | 07:01 | 367 | Small portion docked Agena No. 5005; Africa, Arabia, Red Sea, Gulf of Aden. |

MAGAZINE 5 Continued

| Frame | NASA/MSC Color No. | NASA/MSC B&W No. | Revolution | Date | GMT | Alt, N. Mi. | Area description |
|---|---|---|---|---|---|---|---|
| 45 | S66–46154 | S66–46214 | 6 | July 19, 1966 | 07:01 | 365 | Small portion docked Agena No. 5005; Africa, Arabia, Red Sea, Gulf of Aden. |
| 46 | .......... | .......... | .......... | .......... | ...... | ....... | Blank. |
| 47 | S66–46155 | S66–46215 | 10 | July 19, 1966 | 13:25 | 346 | Window, mostly sky, Earth limb; off west coast of Africa. |
| 48 | S66–46156 | S66–46216 | 10 | July 19, 1966 | 13:26 | 344 | Window, mostly sky, Earth limb; off west coast of Africa. |
| 49 | S66–46157 | S66–46217 | 10 | July 19, 1966 | 13:26 | 342 | Window, mostly sky, Earth limb; off west coast of Africa. |
| 50 | S66–46158 | S66–46218 | 10 | July 19, 1966 | 13:26 | 340 | Window, mostly sky, Earth limb; off west coast of Africa. |
| 51 | S66–46159 | S66–46219 | 10 | July 19, 1966 | 13:27 | 338 | Window, mostly sky, Earth limb; off west coast of Africa. |
| 52 | S66–46160 | S66–46220 | 10 | July 19, 1966 | 13:27 | 336 | Window, mostly sky, Earth limb; off west coast of Africa. |
| 53 | S66–46161 | S66–46221 | 10 | July 19, 1966 | 13:41 | 220 | Window, mostly sky, Earth limb; Mediterranean coast—Libya to Turkey. |
| 54 | S66–46162 | S66–46222 | 10 | July 19, 1966 | 13:42 | 216 | Window, mostly sky, Earth limb; Mediterranean coast—Libya to Turkey. |
| 55 | S66–46163 | S66–46223 | 11 | July 19, 1966 | 16:28 | 389 | Window, mostly sky, Earth limb; Mexico (Yucatan), Guatemala, British Honduras; Gulf of Mexico. |
| 56 | S66–46164 | S66–46224 | 11 | July 19, 1966 | 16:29 | 388 | Window, mostly sky, Earth limb; Mexico (Yucatan), Guatemala, British Honduras; Gulf of Mexico. |
| 57 | S66–46165 | S66–46225 | 11 | July 19, 1966 | 16:29 | 387 | Window, mostly sky, Earth limb; Mexico (Yucatan), Guatemala, British Honduras; Gulf of Mexico. |
| 58 | S66–46166 | S66–46226 | .......... | .......... | ...... | ....... | Agena No. 5005, docked. |
| 59 | S66–46167 | S66–46227 | .......... | .......... | ...... | ....... | Agena No. 5005, docked. |
| 60 | S66–46168 | S66–46228 | .......... | .......... | ...... | ....... | Agena No. 5005, docked, L-band antenna only. |
| 61 | S66–46169 | S66–46229 | .......... | .......... | ...... | ....... | Agena No. 5005, docked; sky and horizon. |
| 62 | S66–46170 | S66–46230 | .......... | .......... | ...... | ....... | Agena No. 5005, docked; sky and horizon. |

MAGAZINE 10

| Frame | NASA/MSC Color No. | NASA/MSC B&W No. | Revolution | Date | GMT | Alt, N. Mi. | Area description |
|---|---|---|---|---|---|---|---|
| 1 | S66–45651 | S66–45701 | 2 | July 19, 1966 | 00:03 | 91 | Clouds near terminator, sunlit tops. |
| 2 | S66–45652 | S66–45702 | 2 | July 19, 1966 | 00:03 | 91 | Clouds near terminator, sunlit tops. |
| *3* | *S66–45653* | *S66–45703* | *2* | *July 19, 1966* | *01:08* | *131* | *Murilo Atoll, Pacific Ocean.* |
| 4 | S66–45654 | S66–45704 | 2 | July 19, 1966 | 01:09 | 131 | Clouds over Pacific Ocean, northeast of Murilo Atoll. |
| 5 | S66–45655 | S66–45705 | 2 | July 19, 1966 | 01:22 | 178 | Guadalupe Island (in hole in clouds); Baja California, Gulf of California in background. |
| *6* | *S66–45656* | *S66–45706* | *2* | *July 19, 1966* | *01:23* | *178* | *Guadalupe Island (in hole in clouds); Baja California, Gulf of California in background.* |
| 7 | S66–45657 | S66–45707 | 2 | July 19, 1966 | 01:23 | 178 | Guadalupe Island (in hole in clouds); Southern California, Baja California area. |
| *8* | *S66–45658* | *S66–45708* | *2* | *July 19, 1966* | *01:23* | *178* | *California, Mexico: Los Angeles to Cabo Colnett.* |
| 9 | S66–45659 | S66–45709 | 5 | July 19, 1966 | 05:27 | 160 | Maldive Islands: Haddummati, Suvadiva Atolls. |
| 10 | S66–45660 | S66–45710 | .......... | July 19, 1966 | ...... | ....... | Docked, partial view of Agena; sky-ocean-clouds. |
| 11 | S66–45661 | S66–45711 | .......... | July 19, 1966 | ...... | ....... | Docked; sky-ocean-clouds. |
| 12 | S66–45662 | S66–45712 | .......... | July 19, 1966 | ...... | ....... | Docked; sky-ocean-clouds. |
| 13 | S66–45663 | S66–45713 | .......... | July 19, 1966 | ...... | ....... | Docked; sky-ocean-clouds. |
| 14 | S66–45664 | S66–45714 | .......... | July 19, 1966 | ...... | ....... | Docked; sky-ocean-clouds. |
| 15 | S66–45665 | S66–45715 | .......... | July 19, 1966 | ...... | ....... | Docked; sky-ocean-clouds. |
| 16 | S66–45666 | S66–45716 | .......... | July 19, 1966 | ...... | ....... | Docked; partial view of Agena; sky-ocean-clouds. |

MAGAZINE 10 Continued

| Frame | NASA/MSC Color No. | NASA/MSC B&W No. | Revolution | Date | GMT | Alt, N. Mi. | Area description |
|---|---|---|---|---|---|---|---|
| 17 | S66–45667 | S66–45717 | ............ | July 19, 1966 | ....... | ........ | Docked; partial view of Agena; sky-ocean-clouds. |
| 18 | S66–45668 | S66–45718 | ............ | July 19, 1966 | ....... | ........ | Docked; sky-ocean-clouds. |
| 19 | S66–45669 | S66–45719 | ............ | July 19, 1966 | ....... | ........ | Docked; sky-ocean-clouds. |
| 20 | S66–45670 | S66–45720 | ............ | July 19, 1966 | 13:34 | ........ | Mali, Mauritania: Upper Niger Basin. |
| 21 | S66–45671 | S66–45721 | 10 | July 19, 1966 | 13:35 | 267 | Mali, Niger, Upper Volta: Timbuktu; Niger River, Lake Faguibine. |
| 22 | S66–45672 | S66–45722 | 10 | July 19, 1966 | 13:37 | 247 | Mali, Niger, Algeria: Iforas Mountains, Niger Basin. |
| 23 | S66–45673 | S66–45723 | 10 | July 19, 1966 | 13:39 | 235 | Mali, Niger, Algeria: Ahaggar Mountains, Air ou Azbine. |
| 24 | S66–45674 | S66–45724 | 10 | July 19, 1966 | 13:39 | 231 | Niger, Algeria: Ahaggar Mountains, Air ou Azbine, northern Tenere. |
| 25 | S66–45675 | S66–45725 | 10 | July 19, 1966 | 13:40 | 227 | Niger, Algeria, Libya, Chad: Air ou Azbine, Tenere region. |
| 26 | S66–45676 | S66–45726 | 10 | July 19, 1966 | 13:41 | 220 | Niger, Algeria Libya, Chad: Tibesti Mountains, Tenere region. |
| 27 | S66–45677 | S66–45727 | 10 | July 19, 1966 | 13:41 | 216 | Niger, Libya, Chad: Tibesti Mountains, Bodele Basin. |
| 28 | S66–45678 | S66–45728 | 10 | July 19, 1966 | 13:42 | 210 | Libya, United Arab Republic, Sudan: Great Sand Sea, Jebel Uweinat. |
| 29 | S66–45679 | S66–45729 | 10 | July 19, 1966 | 13:45 | 194 | United Arab Republic, Sudan, Saudi Arabia: Eastern Desert, Foul Bay, Hejaz area, Red Sea. |
| 30 | S66–45680 | S66–45730 | 10 | July 19, 1966 | 13:46 | 188 | United Arab Republic, Sudan, Saudi Arabia: Eastern Desert, Foul Bay, Hejaz area, Red Sea. |
| 31 | S66–45681 | S66–45731 | 10 | July 19, 1966 | 13:46 | 185 | United Arab Republic, Sudan, Saudi Arabia: Hejaz Area, Red Sea. |
| 32 | S66–45682 | S66–45732 | 11 | July 19, 1966 | 16:22 | 405 | Clouds over eastern Pacific; stereo with 33. |
| 33 | S66–45683 | S66–45733 | 11 | July 19, 1966 | 16:23 | 405 | Clouds over eastern Pacific; stereo with 32. |
| 34 | S66–45684 | S66–45734 | 11 | July 19, 1966 | 16:23 | 404 | Clouds over eastern Pacific; stereo with 35. |
| 35 | S66–45685 | S66–45735 | 11 | July 19, 1966 | 16:24 | 404 | Clouds over eastern Pacific; stereo with 34. |
| 36 | S66–45686 | S66–45736 | 11 | July 19, 1966 | 16:36 | 342 | Mexico, Central America: Yucatan, Gulf of Mexico. |
| 37 | S66–45687 | S66–45737 | 11 | July 19, 1966 | 16:36 | 342 | Mexico, Central America: Yucatan, Gulf of Mexico. |
| *38* | *S66–45688* | *S66–45738* | *12* | *July 19, 1966* | *16:37* | *334* | *Mexico, Cuba, Florida: Yucatan Channel, Gulf of Mexico, Caribbean Sea.* |
| 39 | S66–45689 | S66–45739 | 12 | July 19, 1966 | 16:38 | 326 | Cuba, Florida: Straits of Florida, Gulf of Mexico. |
| 40 | S66–45690 | S66–45740 | 12 | July 19, 1966 | 16:38 | 324 | Cuba, Florida: Straits of Florida, Gulf of Mexico. |
| 41 | S66–45691 | S66–45741 | 12 | July 19, 1966 | 16:38 | 322 | Cuba: Gulf of Mexico, Caribbean Sea; Yucatan in background. |
| *42* | *S66–45692* | *S66–45742* | *12* | *July 19, 1966* | *16:39* | *315* | *Hurricane Celia; Cuba, Florida in background.* |
| 43 | S66–45693 | S66–45743 | 12 | July 19, 1966 | 16:39 | 313 | Hurricane Celia; Cuba, Florida in background. |
| 44 | S66–45694 | S66–45744 | 12 | July 19, 1966 | 16:55 | 193 | Morocco: Straits of Gibraltar, Spain, Portugal in background. |
| 45 | S66–45695 | S66–45745 | 12 | July 19, 1966 | 16:56 | 192 | Morocco: Straits of Gibraltar, Spain, Portugal in background. |
| 46 | S66–45696 | S66–45746 | 12 | July 19, 1966 | 16:56 | 191 | Morocco: Straits of Gibraltar, Spain, Portugal in background. |
| 47 | S66–45697 | S66–45747 | 12 | July 19, 1966 | 16:56 | 186 | Morocco, Algeria: Straits of Gibraltar, Spain, Portugal in background. |
| 48 | S66–45698 | S66–45748 | 12 | July 19, 1966 | 16:56 | 183 | Morocco, Algeria: Straits of Gibraltar, Spain in background. |
| 49 | S66–45699 | S66–45749 | 12 | July 19, 1966 | 16:57 | 181 | Morocco, Algeria: Straits of Gibraltar, Spain in background. |
| 50 | S66–45700 | S66–45750 | 12 | July 19, 1966 | 16:57 | 180 | Morocco, Algeria: Straits of Gibraltar, Spain in background. |

MAGAZINE 28

| Frame | NASA/MSC Color No. | NASA/MSC B&W No. | Revolution | Date | GMT | Alt, N. Mi. | Area description |
|---|---|---|---|---|---|---|---|
| 1 | ........ | ........ | ........ | ........ | ........ | ........ | Blank. |
| 2 | S66–46231 | S66–46288 | 12 | July 19, 1966 | 16:54 | 205 | Docked with Agena No. 5005; looking toward Spain, Portugal, Morocco, Straits of Gibraltar. |
| 3 | S66–46232 | S66–46289 | 12 | July 19, 1966 | 16:54 | 202 | Docked with Agena No. 5005; looking toward Spain, Portugal, Morocco, Straits of Gibraltar. |
| 4 | S66–46233 | S66–46290 | 12 | July 19, 1966 | 16:55 | 199 | Docked with Agena No. 5005; looking toward Spain, Portugal, Morocco, Straits of Gibraltar. |
| 5 | S66–46234 | S66–46291 | 12 | July 19, 1966 | 16:55 | 196 | Docked with Agena No. 5005, Agena No. 5003 in distance; Spain, Portugal, Morocco, Straits of Gibraltar. |
| 6 | S66–46235 | S66–46292 | 12 | July 19, 1966 | 16:56 | 193 | Docked with Agena No. 5005, Agena No. 5003 in distance; Spain, Portugal, Morocco, Straits of Gibraltar. |
| 7 | S66–46236 | S66–46293 | 12 | July 19, 1966 | 16:56 | 189 | Docked with Agena No. 5005, Agena No. 5003 in distance; Algeria, Mediterranean Sea. |
| 8 | S66–46237 | S66–46294 | 12 | July 19, 1966 | 16:57 | 186 | Docked with Agena No. 5005, Agena No. 5003 in distance; Algeria, Mediterranean Sea. |
| 9 | S66–46238 | S66–46295 | 12 | July 19, 1966 | 16:57 | 184 | Docked with Agena No. 5005; Algeria, Mediterranean Sea. |
| 10 | S66–46239 | S66–46296 | 12 | July 19, 1966 | 17:00 | 171 | Docked with Agena No. 5005, Agena No. 5003 in distance; Tunisia, Libya, Mediterranean Sea. |
| 11 | S66–46240 | S66–46297 | 12 | July 19, 1966 | 17:01 | 169 | Docked with Agena No. 5005; Libya, Mediterranean Sea. |
| 12 | S66–46241 | S66–46298 | 12 | July 19, 1966 | ........ | ........ | Docked with Agena No. 5005; Spacecraft window showing debris on glass. |
| 13 | S66–46242 | S66–46299 | 12 | July 19, 1966 | ........ | ........ | Docked with Agena No. 5005; spacecraft window showing debris on glass. |
| 14 | S66–46243 | S66–46300 | 12 | July 19, 1966 | ........ | ........ | Docked with Agena No. 5005; spacecraft window showing debris on glass. |
| 15 | S66–46244 | S66–46301 | 12 | July 19, 1966 | ........ | ........ | Docked with Agena No. 5005; spacecraft window showing debris on glass. |
| 16 | S66–46245 | S66–46302 | 12 | July 19, 1966 | ........ | ........ | Docked with Agena No. 5005; limb near terminator. |
| 17 | S66–46246 | S66–46303 | 12 | July 19, 1966 | ........ | ........ | Docked with Agena No. 5005; underexposed. |
| 18 | S66–46247 | S66–46304 | 12 | July 19, 1966 | ........ | ........ | Docked with Agena No. 5005; excellent view of Agena display panel and L-band antenna. |
| 19 | ........ | ........ | ........ | ........ | ........ | ........ | Blank. |
| 20 | ........ | ........ | ........ | ........ | ........ | ........ | Blank. |
| 21 | ........ | ........ | ........ | ........ | ........ | ........ | Blank. |
| 22 | ........ | ........ | ........ | ........ | ........ | ........ | Blank. |
| 23 | ........ | ........ | ........ | ........ | ........ | ........ | Blank. |
| 24 | ........ | ........ | ........ | ........ | ........ | ........ | Blank. |
| 25 | ........ | ........ | ........ | ........ | ........ | ........ | Blank. |
| 26 | ........ | ........ | ........ | ........ | ........ | ........ | Blank. |
| 27 | ........ | ........ | 12 | July 19, 1966 | 17:48 | ........ | Green lights on display panel of Agena No. 5005. |
| 28 | S66–46248 | S66–46305 | 12 | July 19, 1966 | 17:48 | ........ | Docked to Agena No. 5005; excellent view of Agena display panel and L-band antenna. |
| 29 | S66–46249 | S66–46306 | 12 | July 19, 1966 | 17:48 | ........ | Docked to Agena No. 5005; excellent view of Agena display panel, glow from Agena PPS. |
| 30 | S66–46250 | S66–46307 | 12 | July 19, 1966 | 17:49 | ........ | Docked to Agena No. 5005; excellent view of Agena display panel. |
| 31 | S66–46251 | S66–46308 | 12 | July 19, 1966 | 17:49 | ........ | Docked to Agena No. 5005; excellent view of Agena display panel. |
| 32 | S66–46252 | S66–46309 | 12 | July 19, 1966 | 17:49 | ........ | Docked to Agena No. 5005; excellent view of Agena display panel. |
| 33 | S66–46253 | S66–46310 | 12 | July 19, 1966 | 17:49 | ........ | Docked to Agena No. 5005; excellent view of Agena display panel. |

MAGAZINE 28 Continued

| Frame | NASA/MSC Color No. | NASA/MSC B&W No. | Revolution | Date | GMT | Alt, N. Mi. | Area description |
|---|---|---|---|---|---|---|---|
| 34 | S66–46254 | S66–46311 | 12 | July 19, 1966 | 17:49 | ........ | Docked to Agena No. 5005; excellent view of Agena display panel, particles of Agena fuel. |
| 35 | S66–46255 | S66–46312 | 12 | July 19, 1966 | 17:50 | ........ | Docked to Agena No. 5005; excellent view of Agena display panel, particles of Agena fuel. |
| 36 | S66–46256 | S66–46313 | 12 | July 19, 1966 | 17:50 | ........ | Docked to Agena No. 5005; excellent view of Agena display panel, particles of Agena fuel. |
| 37 | S66–46257 | S66–46314 | 12 | July 19, 1966 | 17:50 | ........ | Docked to Agena No. 5005; excellent view of Agena display panel, particles of Agena fuel. |
| 38 | S66–46258 | S66–46315 | 12 | July 19, 1966 | 17:50 | ........ | Docked to Agena No. 5005; excellent view of Agena display panel, particles of Agena fuel. |
| 39 | S66–46259 | S66–46316 | 12 | July 19, 1966 | 17:50 | ........ | Docked to Agena No. 5005; excellent view of Agena display panel, particles of Agena fuel. |
| 40 | S66–46260 | S66–46317 | 12 | July 19, 1966 | 17:50 | ........ | Docked to Agena No. 5005; excellent view of Agena display panel, particles of Agena fuel. |
| 41 | S66–46261 | S66–46318 | 12 | July 19, 1966 | 17:51 | ........ | Docked to Agena No. 5005; excellent view of Agena display panel, particles of Agena fuel. |
| 42 | S66–46262 | S66–46319 | 12 | July 19, 1966 | 17:51 | ........ | Docked to Agena No. 5005; excellent view of Agena display panel, particles of Agena fuel. |
| 43 | S66–46263 | S66–46320 | 12 | July 19, 1966 | 17:51 | ........ | Docked to Agena No. 5005; excellent view of Agena display panel, particles of Agena fuel. |
| 44 | S66–46264 | S66–46321 | 12 | July 19, 1966 | 17:51 | ........ | Docked to Agena No. 5005; underexposed. |
| 45 | S66–46265 | S66–46322 | 12 | July 19, 1966 | 17:52 | ........ | Docked to Agena No. 5005; underexposed. |
| 46 | S66–46266 | S66–46323 | 12 | July 19, 1966 | 18:00 | ........ | Inside Gemini X, Comdr. J. W. Young; underexposed. |
| 47 | S66–46267 | S66–46324 | 12 | July 19, 1966 | 18:01 | ........ | Inside Gemini X, Comdr. J. W. Young; underexposed. |
| 48 | S66–46268 | S66–46325 | 12 | July 19, 1966 | 18:01 | ........ | Inside Gemini X, Maj. M. Collins. |
| 49 | S66–46269 | S66–46326 | 12 | July 19, 1966 | 18:02 | ........ | Inside Gemini X, Maj. M. Collins. |
| 50 | S66–46270 | S66–46327 | 12 | July 19, 1966 | 18:02 | ........ | Inside Gemini X, Comdr. J. W. Young. |
| 51 | S66–46271 | S66–46328 | 12 | July 19, 1966 | 18:03 | ........ | Inside Gemini X, underexposed. |
| 52 | S66–46272 | S66–46329 | 12 | July 19, 1966 | 18:03 | ........ | Inside Gemini X, Maj. M. Collins. |
| 53 | S66–46273 | S66–46330 | 12 | July 19, 1966 | 18:03 | ........ | Skin of Gemini X, sharp focus. |
| 54 | S66–46274 | S66–46331 | 12 | July 19, 1966 | 18:04 | ........ | Skin of Gemini X, sharp focus. |
| 55 | S66–46275 | S66–46332 | 12 | July 19, 1966 | 18:04 | ........ | Skin of Gemini X, sharp focus. |
| 56 | S66–46276 | S66–46333 | ............ | .............. | ....... | ........ | Docked to Agena No. 5005; underexposed, out of focus. |
| 57 | S66–46277 | S66–46334 | ............ | .............. | ....... | ........ | Docked to Agena No. 5005; excellent view of Agena display panel. |
| 58 | S66–46278 | S66–46335 | 14 | July 19, 1966 | 20:20 | 168 | Docked to Agena No. 5005; clouds over water. |
| 59 | S66–46279 | S66–46336 | 14 | July 19, 1966 | 20:20 | 168 | Docked to Agena No. 5005; clouds over water. |
| 60 | S66–46280 | S66–46337 | 14 | July 19, 1966 | ....... | ........ | Blank. |
| 61 | S66–46281 | S66–46338 | 14 | July 19, 1966 | 20:06 | 159 | Docked to Agena No. 5005; west coast of Africa in background. |
| 62 | S66–46282 | S66–46339 | 14 | July 19, 1966 | 20:06 | 159 | Docked to Agena No. 5005; west coast of Africa in background. |
| 63 | S66–46283 | S66–46340 | 14 | July 19, 1966 | 20:07 | 159 | Docked to Agena No. 5005; west coast of Africa in background. |
| 64 | S66–46284 | S66–46341 | 14 | July 19, 1966 | 20:08 | 159 | Docked to Agena No. 5005; west coast of Africa in background. |
| 65 | S66–46285 | S66–46342 | 14 | July 19, 1966 | 20:09 | 159 | Docked to Agena No. 5005; Atlantic coast, Mauritania, Spanish Sahara, Algeria. |
| 66 | S66–46286 | S66–46343 | 14 | July 19, 1966 | 20:11 | 159 | Docked to Agena No. 5005; Atlantic coast, Mauritania, Spanish Sahara, Algeria. |
| 67 | S66–46287 | S66–46344 | 14 | July 19, 1966 | 20:11 | 159 | Docked to Agena No. 5005; Atlantic coast Mauritania, Spanish Sahara, Algeria. |
| 68 | S66–46288 | S66–46345 | 14 | July 19, 1966 | 20:12 | 159 | Docked to Agena No. 5005; Atlantic coast, Mauritania, Spanish Sahara, Algeria. |

## MAGAZINE 13

| Frame | NASA/MSC Color No. | NASA/MSC B&W No. | Revolution | Date | GMT | Alt, N. Mi. | Area description |
|---|---|---|---|---|---|---|---|
| 1 | S66–46017 | S66–46064 | ... | ... | ... | ... | Color patch, exposed in laboratory. |
| 2 | S66–46018 | S66–46065 | ... | ... | ... | ... | Color patch, exposed in laboratory. |
| 3 | S66–46019 | S66–46066 | ... | ... | ... | ... | Color patch, exposed in laboratory. |
| 4 | S66–46020 | S66–46067 | ... | ... | ... | ... | Color patch, exposed in laboratory. |
| 5 | S66–46021 | S66–46068 | ... | ... | ... | ... | Color patch, exposed in laboratory. |
| 6 | S66–46022 | S66–46069 | ... | ... | ... | ... | Color patch, exposed in laboratory. |
| 7 | S66–46023 | S66–46070 | 14 | July 19, 1966 | 21:49 | ... | Color patch, exposed during EVA, in its own shadow; f/8, 1/250 sec. |
| 8 | S66–46024 | S66–46071 | 14 | July 19, 1966 | 21:50 | ... | Color patch, exposed during EVA; f/8, 1/250 sec. |
| 9 | S66–46025 | S66–46072 | 14 | July 19, 1966 | 21:50 | ... | Color patch, exposed during EVA; f/8, 1/250 sec. |
| 10 | S66–46026 | S66–46073 | 14 | July 19, 1966 | 21:50 | ... | Color patch, exposed during EVA; f/8, 1/250 sec. |
| 11 | S66–46027 | S66–46074 | ... | July 19, 1966 | ... | ... | Out of focus. |
| 12 | S66–46028 | S66–46075 | ... | July 19, 1966 | ... | ... | Out of focus. |
| 13 | S66–46029 | S66–46076 | ... | July 19, 1966 | ... | ... | Ocean, clouds. |
| 14 | S66–46030 | S66–46077 | 18 | July 20, 1966 | 02:28 | 210 | Peru, Brazil: Amazon Basin, Ucayali River, Andes with Huascaran Volcano (22 205 ft) in background. |
| 15 | S66–46031 | S66–46078 | 18 | July 20, 1966 | 02:28 | 210 | Peru, Brazil: Amazon Basin, Ucayali River, Andes with Huascaran Volcano (22 205 ft) in background. |
| 16 | S66–46032 | S66–46079 | 18 | July 20, 1966 | 02:29 | 210 | Peru, Brazil: Amazon Basin, Ucayali River, Andes with Huascaran Volcano. (22 205 ft) in background. |
| 17 | S66–46033 | S66–46080 | 18 | July 20, 1966 | 02:29 | 210 | Peru, Brazil: Amazon Basin, Ucayali River, Andes with Huascaran Volcano. (22 205 ft) in background. |
| 18 | S66–46034 | S66–46081 | 25 | July 20, 1966 | 15:36 | 206 | Costa Rica, Nicaragua, Panama: Pacific Ocean foreground, Caribbean Sea background. |
| 19 | S66–46035 | S66–46082 | 25 | July 20, 1966 | 15:36 | 206 | Costa Rica, Nicaragua, Panana; Pacific Ocean foreground, Caribbean Sea background. |
| 20 | S66–46036 | S66–46083 | 25 | July 20, 1966 | 15:36 | 206 | Costa Rica, Nicaragua, Panama: Pacific Ocean foreground, Caribbean Sea background, stereo with No. 21. |
| 21 | S66–46037 | S66–46084 | 25 | July 20, 1966 | 15:36 | 206 | Costa Rica, Nicaragua, Panama: Pacific Ocean foreground, Caribbean Sea background, stereo with No. 20. |
| 22 | S66–46038 | S66–46085 | 26 | July 20, 1966 | 15:51 | 208 | Vortex clouds over ocean, Canary Island area. |
| 23 | S66–46039 | S66–46086 | 26 | July 20, 1966 | 15:52 | 208 | Vortex clouds over ocean, Canary Island area. |
| *24* | *S66–46040* | *S66–46087* | *26* | *July 20, 1966* | *15:52* | *208* | *Vortex clouds over ocean, Canary Island area.* |
| 25 | S66–46041 | S66–46088 | 26 | July 20, 1966 | 15:54 | 208 | Vortex clouds near Straits of Gibraltar; Spain, Portugal in background, Morocco on right. |
| 26 | S66–46042 | S66–46089 | 26 | July 20, 1966 | 15:54 | 208 | Vortex clouds near Straits of Gibraltar; Spain, Portugal in background, Morocco on right. |
| 27 | S66–46043 | S66–46090 | 26 | July 20, 1966 | 15:54 | 208 | Vortex clouds near Straits of Gibraltar; Spain, Portugal in background, Morocco on right. |
| *28* | *S66–46044* | *S66–46091* | *26* | *July 20, 1966* | *15:54* | *208* | *Vortex clouds near Straits of Gibraltar; Spain, Portugal in background, Morocco on right.* |
| 29 | S66–46045 | S66–46092 | 39 | July 21, 1966 | 12:55 | 199 | Brazil: Amazonas State; cloud-covered Amazon Basin. |
| 30 | S66–46046 | S66–46093 | 39 | July 21, 1966 | 12:55 | 199 | Brazil: Amazonas State; cloud-covered Amazon Basin. |
| *31* | *S66–46047* | *S66–46094* | *39* | *July 21, 1966* | *12:56* | *198* | *Brazil: Amazonas State; cloud-covered Amazon Basin.* |
| 32 | S66–46048 | S66–46095 | 39 | July 21, 1966 | 12:56 | 198 | Brazil: Amazonas State; cloud-covered Amazon Basin. |
| 33 | S66–46049 | S66–46096 | 39 | July 21, 1966 | 12:56 | 196 | Brazil, Guyana, Venezuela: Rio Branco, Serra Pacaraima. |

MAGAZINE 13 Continued

| Frame | NASA/MSC Color No. | NASA/MSC B&W No. | Revolution | Date | GMT | Alt, N. Mi. | Area description |
|---|---|---|---|---|---|---|---|
| *34* | *S66–46050* | *S66–46097* | *39* | *July 21, 1966* | *12:56* | *196* | *Brazil, Guyana, Venezuela: Rio Branco, Serra Pacaraima.* |
| *35* | *S66–46051* | *S66–46098* | *39* | *July 21, 1966* | *12:57* | *196* | *Brazil, Guyana, Venezuela: La Gran Sabana, Orinoco Basin.* |
| *36* | *S66–46052* | *S66–46099* | *39* | *July 21, 1966* | *12:57* | *196* | *Guyana, Venezuela: Orinoco, Essequibo Rivers, La Gran Sabana.* |
| 37 | S66–46053 | S66–46100 | 39 | July 21, 1966 | 12:57 | 196 | Guyana, Venezuela: Orinoco, Essequibo Rivers, La Gran Sabana. |
| *38* | *S66–46054* | *S66–46101* | *39* | *July 21, 1966* | *12:57* | *196* | *Surinam, Guyana, Venezuela: Orinoco, Essequibo Rivers.* |
| 39 | S66–46055 | S66–46102 | 39 | July 21, 1966 | 12:58 | 195 | Surinam, Guyana: Paramaribo; Atlantic coast. |
| *40* | *S66–46056* | *S66–46103* | *39* | *July 21, 1966* | *12:58* | *194* | *Surinam, Guyana: Paramaribo; Atlantic coast.* |
| 41 | S66–46057 | S66–46104 | 39 | July 21, 1966 | 12:58 | 194 | Surinam, Guyana, French Guiana: Paramaribo, Georgetown; Atlantic coast. |
| 42 | S66–46058 | S66–46105 | 39 | July 21, 1966 | 12:58 | 193 | Surinam, Guyana, French Guiana: Paramaribo, Atlantic coast. |
| 43 | S66–46059 | S66–46106 | 39 | July 21, 1966 | 12:58 | 193 | Surinam, Guyana, French Guiana: Atlantic coast. |
| 44 | S66–46060 | S66–46107 | 39 | July 21, 1966 | 13:07 | 178 | Spanish Sahara, Mauritania: Port Etienne; Cap Blanc, Dhar Adrar. |
| 45 | S66–46061 | S66–46108 | 39 | July 21, 1966 | 13:07 | 178 | Spanish Sahara, Mauritania: Villa Cisneros; Erg Iguidi, Tindouf Basin. |
| 46 | S66–46062 | S66–46109 | 39 | July 21, 1966 | 13:09 | 174 | Spanish Sahara, Mauritania, Morocco, Algeria: Erg Iguidi, Tindouf Basin. |
| *47* | *S66–46063* | *S66–46110* | *39* | *July 21, 1966* | *13:11* | *171* | *Spanish Sahara, Mauritania, Morocco, Algeria: Erg Iguidi, Tindouf Basin, Hamada du Dra, Anti-Atlas Mountains.* |

MAGAZINE 14

| Frame | NASA/MSC. Color No. | NASA/MSC. B&W No. | Revolution | Date | GMT | Alt, N. Mi. | Area description |
|---|---|---|---|---|---|---|---|
| 1 | .......... | .......... | .......... | .......... | ...... | ...... | Blank. |
| 2 | .......... | .......... | .......... | .......... | ...... | ...... | Blank. |
| 3 | .......... | .......... | .......... | .......... | ...... | ...... | L-band antenna of Agena No. 5005; underexposed. |
| 4 | .......... | .......... | .......... | .......... | ...... | ...... | Blank. |
| 5 | .......... | .......... | .......... | .......... | ...... | ...... | Blank. |
| 6 | .......... | .......... | .......... | .......... | ...... | ...... | Blank. |
| 7 | S66–45751 | S66–45794 | .......... | .......... | ...... | ...... | Docked with Agena No. 5005; clouds, ocean; slightly overexposed. |
| 8 | S66–45752 | S66–45795 | .......... | .......... | ...... | ...... | Docked with Agena No. 5005; clouds, ocean; slightly overexposed. |
| 9 | S66–45753 | S66–45796 | .......... | .......... | ...... | ...... | Docked with Agena No. 5005; clouds, ocean; slightly overexposed. |
| 10 | S66–45754 | S66–45797 | .......... | .......... | ...... | ...... | Docked with Agena No. 5005; clouds, ocean; slightly overexposed. |
| 11 | S66–45755 | S66–45798 | .......... | .......... | ...... | ...... | Docked with Agena No. 5005; clouds, ocean; slightly overexposed. |
| 12 | S66–45756 | S66–45799 | .......... | .......... | ...... | ...... | Docked with Agena No. 5005; clouds, ocean; slightly overexposed. |
| 13 | S66–45757 | S66–45800 | .......... | .......... | ...... | ...... | Docked with Agena No. 5005, clear view of docking adapter. |
| 14 | S66–45758 | S66–45801 | .......... | .......... | ...... | ...... | Docked with Agena No. 5005, clear view of docking adapter. |
| 15 | S66–45759 | S66–45802 | .......... | .......... | ...... | ...... | Docked with Agena No. 5005, clear view of docking adapter. |
| 16 | S66–45760 | S66–45803 | 28 | July 20, 1966 | 20:20 | 207 | Clouds, overexposed. |

MAGAZINE 14 Continued

| Frame | NASA/MSC Color No. | NASA/MSC B&W No. | Revolution | Date | GMT | Alt, N. Mi. | Area description |
|---|---|---|---|---|---|---|---|
| 17 | S66–45761 | S66–45804 | 28 | July 20, 1966 | 20:24 | 208 | Mexico, Texas: Tamaulipas, gulf coast; overexposed. |
| *18* | *S66–45762* | *S66–45805* | *28* | *July 20, 1966* | *20:24* | *208* | *Mexico, Texas: Torreon; Coahuila Basin, Serrania del Burro, Rio Grande, gulf coast.* |
| 19 | S66–45763 | S66–45806 | 28 | July 20, 1966 | 20:25 | 208 | Mexico, Texas: Coahuila; Sierra Madre Oriental, Sierra de los Alamitos, Don Martin Reservoir. |
| *20* | *S66–45764* | *S66–45807* | *28* | *July 20, 1966* | *20:27* | *208* | *Mexico, Texas: Gulf coast from Corpus Christi Bay to Boca San Rafael.* |
| 21 | S66–45765 | S66–45808 | 28 | July 20, 1966 | 20:27 | 208 | Texas: Gulf coast, Matagordo Bay, mouth of Colorado River. |
| 22 | S66–45766 | S66–45809 | 28 | July 20, 1966 | 20:28 | 208 | Texas, Louisiana: Gulf coast from Freeport to Vermilion Bay. |
| 23 | S66–45767 | S66–45810 | 28 | July 20, 1966 | 20:28 | 209 | Clouds over Gulf of Mexico. |
| 24 | S66–45768 | S66–45811 | 31 | July 21, 1966 | 00:55 | ........ | Umbilical cord bag discarded; ocean, clouds. |
| 25 | S66–45769 | S66–45812 | 31 | July 21, 1966 | 00:55 | ........ | Umbilical cord bag discarded; ocean, clouds. |
| 26 | S66–45770 | S66–45813 | 31 | July 21, 1966 | 00:57 | 215 | Clouds over ocean, door open. |
| 27 | S66–45771 | S66–45814 | 31 | July 21, 1966 | 00:58 | ........ | Discarded debris, chest pack. |
| 28 | S66–45772 | S66–45815 | 31 | July 21, 1966 | 00:59 | ........ | Open hatch, out of focus. |
| 29 | S66–45773 | S66–45816 | 31 | July 21, 1966 | 00:59 | ........ | Open hatch, out of focus. |
| 30 | S66–45774 | S66–45817 | 31 | July 21, 1966 | 01:20 | 214 | Clouds, ocean; Agena No. 5005 in distance. |
| 31 | S66–45775 | S66–45818 | 31 | July 21, 1966 | 01:20 | 214 | Clouds, ocean. |
| 32 | S66–45776 | S66–45819 | 31 | July 21, 1966 | 01:20 | 214 | Clouds, ocean. |
| 33 | S66–45777 | S66–45820 | 31 | July 21, 1966 | 01:20 | 214 | Clouds, ocean. |
| 34 | S66–45778 | S66–45821 | 31 | July 21, 1966 | 01:21 | 214 | Clouds, ocean; Agena No. 5005 in distance. |
| 35 | S66–45779 | S66–45822 | 31 | July 21, 1966 | 01:21 | 214 | Clouds, ocean; Agena No. 5005 in distance. |
| 36 | S66–45780 | S66–45823 | 31 | July 21, 1966 | 01:21 | 214 | Clouds, ocean; Agena No. 5005 in distance. |
| 37 | S66–45781 | S66–45824 | 31 | July 21, 1966 | 01:21 | 214 | Docking bar against sky. |
| *38* | *S66–45782* | *S66–45825* | *32* | *July 21, 1966* | *02:14* | *200* | *Indonesia: Sumatra, Simeulue, Nias Islands.* |
| 39 | S66–45783 | S66–45826 | 32 | July 21, 1966 | 02:15 | 200 | Indonesia: Sumatra, Simeulue Islands. |
| 40 | S66–45784 | S66–45827 | 32 | July 21, 1966 | 02:15 | 200 | Indonesia: Sumatra, Nias, Batu Islands, Mentawai Archipelago. |
| *41* | *S66–45785* | *S66–45828* | *32* | *July 21, 1966* | *02:15* | *199* | *Indonesia: Sumatra (Padang), Mentawai Archipelago.* |
| 42 | S66–45786 | S66–45829 | 32 | July 21, 1966 | 02:15 | 199 | Indonesia: Nias Island, Mentawai Archipelago. |
| *43* | *S66–45787* | *S66–45830* | *32* | *July 21, 1966* | *02:16* | *198* | *Indonesia: Sumatra, Mentawai Archipelago.* |
| 44 | S66–45788 | S66–45831 | 32 | July 21, 1966 | 02:16 | 198 | Indonesia: Sumatra, Nias Island, Mentawai Archipelago. |
| 45 | S66–45789 | S66–45832 | 32 | July 21, 1966 | 02:16 | 197 | Indonesia: Sumatra (Padang), Mentawai Archipelago. |
| 46 | S66–45790 | S66–45833 | 32 | July 21, 1966 | 02:16 | 197 | Indonesia: Sumatra, Mentawai Archipelago. |
| *47* | *S66–45791* | *S66–45834* | *32* | *July 21, 1966* | *02:17* | *196* | *Indonesia, Malaysia: Sumatra, Malaya (Malacca): Strait of Malacca.* |
| 48 | S66–45792 | S66–45835 | 32 | July 21, 1966 | 02:18 | 195 | Malaysia: Kuala Lumpur; Strait of Malacca; southernmost Thailand beneath clouds in background. |
| 49 | S66–45793 | S66–45836 | 32 | July 21, 1966 | 02:18 | 193 | Anambas Islands, South China Sea. |

MAGAZINE 11

| Frame | NASA/MSC. Color No. | B&W No. | Revolution | Date | GMT | Alt, N. Mi. | Area description |
|---|---|---|---|---|---|---|---|
| 1 | ........... | ........... | ............ | .............. | ...... | ........ | Clouds-horizon-sky; overexposed. |
| 2 | S66–45837 | S66–45883 | 32 | July 21, 1966 | ...... | ........ | Spacecraft nose; underexposed. |
| 3 | S66–45838 | S66–45884 | 32 | July 21, 1966 | ...... | ........ | Spacecraft nose; underexposed. |
| 4 | S66–45839 | S66–45885 | 32 | July 21, 1966 | ...... | ........ | Clouds, ocean. |
| 5 | S66–45840 | S66–45886 | 32 | July 21, 1966 | ...... | ........ | Clouds, ocean. |
| *6* | *S66–45841* | *S66–45887* | *32* | *July 21, 1966* | *02:38* | *161* | *Clouds, ocean, west of Midway Island.* |
| 7 | S66–45842 | S66–45888 | 32 | July 21, 1966 | 02:39 | 161 | Midway Island, Kure Island. |
| 8 | S66–45843 | S66–45889 | 32 | July 21, 1966 | 02:39 | 161 | Midway Island, Kure Island. |
| *9* | *S66–45844* | *S66–45890* | *32* | *July 21, 1966* | *02:39* | *161* | *Pearl and Hermes Reef.* |
| 10 | S66–45845 | S66–45891 | 32 | July 21, 1966 | 02:39 | 161 | Pearl and Hermes Reef. |
| *11* | *S66–45846* | *S66–45892* | *33* | *July 21, 1966* | *03:44* | *202* | *Chagos Archipelago: Egmont Islands, Three Brothers; Indian Ocean, clouds.* |
| 12 | S66–45847 | S66–45893 | 33 | July 21, 1966 | 03:46 | 201 | Chagos Archipelago: Egmont Islands, Three Brothers; Diego Garcia; Indian Ocean, clouds. |
| *13* | *S66–45848* | *S66–45894* | *33* | *July 21, 1966* | *03:47* | *200* | *Chagos Archipelago: Egmont Islands, Three Brothers, Diego Garcia; Indian Ocean, clouds.* |
| 14 | S66–45849 | S66–45895 | 33 | July 21, 1966 | 03:47 | 200 | Chagos Archipelago: Diego Garcia, Blenheim Reef; Indian Ocean, clouds. |
| 15 | S66–45850 | S66–45896 | 33 | July 21, 1966 | 03:47 | 198 | Maldive Islands: Suvadiva and Addu Atolls; Indian Ocean, clouds. |
| *16* | *S66–45851* | *S66–45897* | *33* | *July 21, 1966* | *03:48* | *198* | *Maldive Islands: Suvadiva and Addu Atolls; Indian Ocean, clouds.* |
| 17 | S66–45852 | S66–45898 | 33 | July 21, 1966 | 03:48 | 196 | Maldive Islands: Nilandu, Kolamadulu, Haddummati, Suvadiva, Addu Atolls; Indian Ocean, clouds. |
| *18* | *S66–45853* | *S66–45899* | *33* | *July 21, 1966* | *03:49* | *196* | *Maldive Islands: Kolamadulu, Haddummati, Nilandu, Suvadiva, Addu Atolls; Indian Ocean, clouds.* |
| 19 | S66–45854 | S66–45900 | 33 | July 21, 1966 | 03:49 | 195 | Maldive Islands: Kolamadulu, Haddummati, Suvadiva, Addu Atolls; Indian Ocean, clouds. |
| 20 | S66–45855 | S66–45901 | 33 | July 21, 1966 | 03:49 | 195 | Maldive Islands: Kolamadulu, Haddummati, Suvadiva, Addu Atolls; Indian Ocean, clouds. |
| 21 | S66–45856 | S66–45902 | 33 | July 21, 1966 | 03:49 | 193 | Cloud streaks over Indian Ocean. |
| 22 | S66–45857 | S66–45903 | 33 | July 21, 1966 | 03:50 | 192 | Clouds streaks over Indian Ocean, Maldive Islands in background. |
| 23 | S66–45858 | S66–45904 | 33 | July 21, 1966 | 03:50 | 191 | Cloud streaks over Indian Ocean. |
| *24* | *S66–45859* | *S66–45905* | *33* | *July 21, 1966* | *03:51* | *190* | *Cloud streaks over Indian Ocean, Maldive Islands in background.* |
| *25* | *S66–45860* | *S66–45906* | *33* | *July 21, 1966* | *03:57* | *178* | *China, Taiwan: Formosa Strait.* |
| 26 | S66–45861 | S66–45907 | 33 | July 21, 1966 | 03:57 | 178 | China, Taiwan: Formosa Strait. |
| 27 | S66–45862 | S66–45908 | 33 | July 21, 1966 | 03:57 | 177 | China: Fukien, Chekiang, Kwangtung Provinces. |
| 28 | S66–45863 | S66–45909 | 33 | July 21, 1966 | 03:58 | 177 | China: Fukien, Kwangtung, Hunan, Kiangsi, Hupeh Provinces; lakes on Yangtze River. |
| 29 | S66–45864 | S66–45910 | 33 | July 21, 1966 | 03:58 | 177 | China, Taiwan: Fukien Province; Formosa Strait, Pescadores Islands. |
| 30 | S66–45865 | S66–45911 | 33 | July 21, 1966 | 03:58 | 176 | China: Fukien, Chekiang Provinces; Formosa Strait, Pescadores Islands. |
| *31* | *S66–45866* | *S66–45912* | *33* | *July 21, 1966* | *03:59* | *176* | *China (Fukien Province), Taiwan: Formosa Strait, Pescadores Islands.* |
| 32 | S66–45867 | S66–45913 | 33 | July 21, 1966 | 03:59 | 176 | China (Fukien Province), Taiwan: Formosa Strait, Pescadores Islands. |
| *33* | *S66–45868* | *S66–45914* | *33* | *July 21, 1966* | *04:00* | *176* | *Taiwan: Kaohsiung, south half of island.* |
| 34 | S66–45869 | S66–45915 | 33 | July 21, 1966 | 04:03 | 170 | Ryukya Islands: Sakishima Gunto group. |
| 35 | S66–45870 | S66–45916 | 33 | July 21, 1966 | 04:03 | 170 | Daito Islands: Kita Daito Jima. |
| *36* | *S66–45871* | *S66–45917* | *33* | *July 21, 1966* | *04:04* | *169* | *Daito Islands: Kita Daito Jima.* |
| 37 | S66–45872 | S66–45918 | 33 | July 21, 1966 | 04:04 | 168 | Ocean, clouds. |
| 38 | S66–45873 | S66–45919 | 33 | July 21, 1966 | 04:04 | 168 | Parece Vela (Douglas) Reef: ocean, clouds. |
| 39 | S66–45874 | S66–45920 | 33 | July 21, 1966 | 04:04 | 167 | Ocean, clouds, sea mount. |

MAGAZINE 11 Continued

| Frame | NASA/MSC. Color No. | NASA/MSC. B&W No. | Revolution | Date | GMT | Alt, N. Mi. | Area description |
|---|---|---|---|---|---|---|---|
| 40 | S66–45875 | S66–45921 | 33 | July 21, 1966 | 04:05 | 167 | Ocean, clouds. |
| 41 | S66–45876 | S66–45922 | 33 | July 21, 1966 | 04:05 | 166 | Ocean, clouds. |
| 42 | S66–45877 | S66–45923 | 34 | July 21, 1966 | 05:16 | 200 | East Africa coastline; Indian Ocean, cloud layers of several types. |
| *43* | *S66–45878* | *S66–45924* | *34* | *July 21, 1966* | *05:17* | *200* | *East Africa coastline; Indian Ocean, cloud layers of several types.* |
| 44 | S66–45879 | S66–45925 | 34 | July 21, 1966 | 05:17 | 199 | Indian Ocean, cloud layers of several types. |
| 45 | S66–45880 | S66–45926 | 34 | July 21, 1966 | 05:18 | 199 | Indian Ocean, cloud layers of several types. |
| 46 | S66–45881 | S66–45927 | 34 | July 21, 1966 | 05:18 | 198 | Indian Ocean, cloud layers of several types. |
| 47 | S66–45882 | S66–45928 | 34 | July 21, 1966 | 05:19 | 198 | Indian Ocean, cloud layers of several tpyes. |

MAGAZINE 12

| Frame | NASA/MSC. Color No. | NASA/MSC. B&W No. | Revolution | Date | GMT | Alt, N. Mi. | Area description |
|---|---|---|---|---|---|---|---|
| 1 | S66–45929 | S66–45973 | 34 | July 21, 1966 | 05:30 | 176 | China, North Vietnam, cloudy. |
| 2 | ........... | ........... | ........... | ........... | ...... | ....... | Blank. |
| 3 | S66–45930 | S66–45974 | 34 | July 21, 1966 | 05:30 | 176 | China, North Vietnam: Gulf of Tonkin, cloudy. |
| 4 | S66–45931 | S66–45975 | 34 | July 21, 1966 | 05:32 | 175 | China, North Vietnam: Gulf of Tonkin, cloudy. |
| 5 | S66–45932 | S66–45976 | 34 | July 21, 1966 | 05:32 | 174 | North Vietnam: Gulf of Tonkin, cloudy. |
| 6 | S66–45933 | S66–45977 | 34 | July 21, 1966 | 05:32 | 174 | China (Kwangsi Province), North Vietnam: Hanoi, Haiphong; Red River, Gulf of Tonkin. |
| 7 | S66–45934 | S66–45978 | 34 | July 21, 1966 | 05:33 | 173 | China (Kwangsi Province), North Vietnam: Red River. |
| 8 | S66–45935 | S66–45979 | 34 | July 21, 1966 | 05:33 | 173 | China (Kwangsi Province), North Vietnam: Hanoi, Haiphong; Red River, Gulf of Tonkin, South Vietnam on horizon. |
| 9 | S66–45936 | S66–45980 | 34 | July 21, 1966 | 05:33 | 172 | China (Kwangsi Province), North Vietnam: Gulf of Tonkin. |
| 10 | S66–45937 | S66–45981 | 34 | July 21, 1966 | 05:33 | 172 | China (Kwangsi Province), North Vietnam: Song Gam River. |
| 11 | S66–45938 | S66–45982 | 34 | July 21, 1966 | 05:34 | 172 | China (Kwangsi Province), North Vietnam: Song Gam River. |
| 12 | S66–45939 | S66–45983 | 34 | July 21, 1966 | 05:34 | 171 | China (Kwangsi Province), North Vietnam: Siang River. |
| 13 | S66–45940 | S66–45984 | 34 | July 21, 1966 | 05:34 | 171 | China (Kwangsi Province), North Vietnam, South Vietnam (background): Hanoi, Haiphong; Red River, Gulf of Tonkin. |
| 14 | S66–45941 | S66–45985 | 34 | July 21, 1966 | 05:35 | 170 | China (Kwangsi Province), North Vietnam: Siang River, Gulf of Tonkin. |
| 15 | S66–45942 | S66–45986 | 34 | July 21, 1966 | 05:35 | 169 | China: Kwangsi Province, Nan-ning; Yu River. |
| 16 | S66–45943 | S66–45987 | 34 | July 21, 1966 | 05:36 | 168 | China: Kwangtung, Kiangsi Provinces: South China Sea coast. |
| 17 | S66–45944 | S66–45988 | 34 | July 21, 1966 | 05:36 | 168 | China: Kwangtung, Kiangsi Provinces; South China Sea coast. |
| *18* | *S66–45945* | *S66–45989* | *34* | *July 21, 1966* | *05:36* | *167* | *China: Kwangtung, Kiangsi Provinces; South China Sea coast.* |
| 19 | S66–45946 | S66–45990 | 34 | July 21, 1966 | 05:36 | 167 | China: Kwangtung, Kiangsi Provinces; South China Sea coast. |
| 20 | S66–45947 | S66–45991 | 34 | July 21, 1966 | 05:36 | 167 | China: Kwangtung, Kiangsi, Fukien Provinces; South China Sea coast. |
| 21 | S66–45948 | S66–45992 | 34 | July 21, 1966 | 05:37 | 167 | China: Kwangtung, Kwangsi Provinces; Hsi River. |
| 22 | ........... | ........... | ........... | ........... | ...... | ....... | Blank. |
| 23 | S66–45949 | S66–45993 | 34 | July 21, 1966 | 05:37 | 167 | China: Kwangtung, Kiangsi, Fukien Provinces, South China Sea coast. |
| 24 | S66–45950 | S66–45994 | 34 | July 21, 1966 | 05:37 | 167 | China: Kwangtung, Kiangsi, Fukien Provinces; Quemoy, South China Sea coast. |

MAGAZINE 12 Continued

| Frame | NASA/MSC Color No. | NASA/MSC B&W No. | Revolution | Date | GMT | Alt, N. Mi. | Area description |
|---|---|---|---|---|---|---|---|
| 25 | S66-45951 | S66-45995 | 34 | July 21, 1966 | 05:37 | 167 | China: Kwangtung, Kiangsi, Fukien Provinces; Quemoy, South China Sea coast. |
| 26 | S66-45952 | S66-45996 | 34 | July 21, 1966 | 05:37 | 166 | China (Kwangtung, Fukien Provinces), Taiwan; Quemoy, Formosa Strait, Pescadores Islands. |
| 27 | S66-45953 | S66-45997 | 34 | July 21, 1966 | 05:37 | 166 | China: Fukien Province: Quemoy, South China Sea coast. |
| 28 | S66-45954 | S66-45998 | 34 | July 21, 1966 | 05:38 | 166 | Taiwan: Formosa Strait, Pescadores Islands, Pacific Ocean, clouds. |
| 29 | S66-45955 | S66-45999 | 34 | July 21, 1966 | 05:38 | 166 | Taiwan, China (Fukien Province): Formosa Strait, Quemoy, Pescadores Islands. |
| *30* | *S66-45956* | *S66-46000* | *34* | *July 21, 1966* | *05:38* | *165* | *Taiwan: Formosa Strait, Pescadores Islands, Pacific Ocean, clouds.* |
| 31 | S66-45957 | S66-46001 | 34 | July 21, 1966 | 05:38 | 165 | China: Fukien, Kiangsi, Chekiang Provinces; P'oyang and Tungt'ing Lakes on Yangtze River. |
| *32* | *S66-45958* | *S66-46002* | *34* | *July 21, 1966* | *05:38* | *165* | *China: Fukien, Kiangsi, Chekiang Provinces; P'oyang and Tungt'ing Lakes on Yangtze River.* |
| 33 | S66-45959 | S66-46003 | 34 | July 21, 1966 | 05:39 | 164 | Taiwan, China coast (Fukien Province): Formosa Strait. |
| 34 | ........... | ........... | ............ | ............. | ...... | ........ | Blank. |
| *35* | *S66-45960* | *S66-46004* | *34* | *July 21, 1966* | *05:39* | *164* | *China: Chekiang Province; mouth of Yangtze River, Hangchou Bay.* |
| 36 | S66-45961 | S66-46005 | 34 | July 21, 1966 | 05:39 | 164 | China: Chekiang Province; mouth of Yangtze River, Hangchou Bay. |
| 37 | S66-45962 | S66-46006 | 34 | July 21, 1966 | 05:39 | 164 | China: Chekiang, Kiangsu Provinces, Shanghai; Hangchou Bay. |
| 38 | S66-45963 | S66-46007 | ............ | July 21, 1966 | ...... | ........ | Double exposure. |
| 39 | S66-45964 | S66-46008 | ............ | July 21, 1966 | ...... | ........ | Ocean, clouds. |
| 40 | S66-45965 | S66-46009 | ............ | July 21, 1966 | ...... | ........ | Ocean, clouds. |
| 41 | S66-45966 | S66-46010 | ............ | July 21, 1966 | ...... | ........ | Ocean, clouds. |
| 42 | S66-45967 | S66-46011 | ............ | July 21, 1966 | ...... | ........ | Ocean, clouds. |
| 43 | ........... | ........... | ............ | ............. | ...... | ........ | Blank. |
| 44 | S66-45968 | S66-46012 | ............ | July 21, 1966 | ...... | ........ | Ocean, clouds near terminator. |
| 45 | S66-45969 | S66-46013 | ............ | July 21, 1966 | ...... | ........ | Ocean, clouds, near terminator. |
| 46 | S66-45970 | S66-46014 | ............ | July 21, 1966 | ...... | ........ | Ocean, clouds, near terminator. |
| 47 | S66-45971 | S66-46015 | ............ | July 21, 1966 | ...... | ........ | Ocean, clouds, near terminator. |
| 48 | S66-45972 | S66-46016 | 39 | July 21, 1966 | 12:52 | 204 | Peru, Brazil: Rio Ucayali, Cordillera Oriental; road to Pucallpas visible. |

## GEMINI XI

MAGAZINE 11

| Frame | NASA/MSC Color No. | NASA/MSC B&W No. | Revolution | Date | GMT | Alt, N. Mi. | Area description |
|---|---|---|---|---|---|---|---|
| 1 | S66-54888 | S66-54845 | 1 | Sept. 12, 1966 | 16:02 | ........ | Agena, docking end and side; range, 60 ft. |
| 2 | S66-54889 | S66-54846 | 1 | Sept. 12, 1966 | 16:02 | ........ | Agena, docking end; range, 60 ft. |
| 3 | S66-54890 | S66-54847 | 1 | Sept. 12, 1966 | 16:05 | ........ | Agena, side view; range, 25 ft. |
| 4 | S66-54891 | S66-54848 | 1 | Sept. 12, 1966 | 16:08 | ........ | Agena, side view; range, 35 ft. |
| 5 | S66-54892 | S66-54849 | 1 | Sept. 12, 1966 | 16:10 | ........ | Agena, side view; range, 75 ft. |
| 6 | S66-54893 | S66-54850 | 26 | Sept. 14, 1966 | 07:24 | 225 | United Arab Republic, Israel, Saudi Arabia, Jordon, Lebanon, Syria, Iraq: fire on Trans-Arabian pipeline. |
| 7 | S66-54894 | S66-54851 | 26 | Sept. 14, 1966 | ...... | ........ | Blank. |
| *8* | *S66-54895* | *S66-54852* | *26* | *Sept. 14 1966* | *07:26* | *249* | *United Arab Republic, Saudi Arabia: Lunayyir lava field, northern Red Sea.* |
| 9 | S66-54896 | S66-54853 | 26 | Sept. 14, 1966 | 07:28 | 290 | Saudi Arabia: Near Ar Riyad. |
| 10 | S66-54897 | S66-54854 | 26 | Sept. 14, 1966 | 07:29 | 298 | Saudi Arabia, Trucial States, Oman and Muscat: Empty Quarter, Iran, West Pakistan in background. |

MAGAZINE 11 Continued

| Frame | NASA/MSC Color No. | NASA/MSC B&W No. | Revolution | Date | GMT | Alt, N. Mi. | Area description |
|---|---|---|---|---|---|---|---|
| 11 | S66–54898 | S66–54855 | 26 | Sept. 14, 1966 | 07:29 | 306 | Arabian Sea: West Pakistan, India in background. |
| 12 | S66–54899 | S66–54856 | 26 | Sept. 14, 1966 | 07:29 | ........ | Image degraded because of window obscuration. |
| 13 | S66–54900 | S66–54857 | 26 | Sept. 14, 1966 | 07:33 | 365 | India: Gulf of Kutch, Gulf of Cambay. |
| 14 | S66–54901 | S66–54858 | 26 | Sept. 14, 1966 | 07:35 | 396 | India, Ceylon: Laccadive Islands, Arabian Sea. |
| 15 | S66–54902 | S66–54859 | 26 | Sept. 14, 1966 | 07:36 | 420 | India: Mysore, Pradesh, Madras and Kerala States. |
| 16 | S66–54903 | S66–54860 | 26 | Sept. 14, 1966 | 07:37 | 435 | India: central and northern portions; Tibet on horizon. |
| *17* | *S66–54904* | *S66–54861* | *26* | *Sept. 14, 1966* | *07:37* | *438* | *India, south from Hyderabad, part of Ceylon: Bay of Bengal.* |
| 18 | S66–54905 | S66–54862 | 26 | Sept. 14, 1966 | 07:37 | 440 | India, South from Hyderabad, part of Ceylon: Bay of Bengal. |
| 19 | S66–54906 | S66–54863 | 26 | Sept. 14, 1966 | 07:37 | 444 | India, southern and eastern portion, part of Ceylon: Bay of Bengal, Himalayas, Tibet on horizon. |
| 20 | S66–54907 | S66–54864 | 26 | Sept. 14, 1966 | 07:39 | 485 | Indian Ocean: Clouds. |
| 21 | S66–54908 | S66–54865 | 26 | Sept. 14, 1966 | 07:39 | 492 | Indian Ocean: Clouds. |
| 22 | S66–54909 | S66–54866 | 26 | Sept. 14, 1966 | 07:44 | 553 | Sumatra, Malaya: Clouds. |
| 23 | S66–54910 | S66–54867 | 26 | Sept. 14, 1966 | 07:44 | 563 | Sumatra, Malaya: Clouds. |
| 24 | S66–54911 | S66–54868 | 26 | Sept. 14, 1966 | 07:46 | 596 | Sumatra, Java, Borneo: Clouds. |
| 25 | S66–54912 | S66–54869 | 26 | Sept. 14, 1966 | 07:47 | 607 | Sumatra, Java, Borneo, Celebes: Clouds. |
| 26 | S66–54913 | S66–54870 | 26 | Sept. 14, 1966 | 07:47 | 612 | Sumatra, Java, Borneo: Clouds. |
| 27 | S66–54914 | S66–54871 | 26 | Sept. 14, 1966 | 07:48 | 620 | Sumatra, Java, Borneo, Celebes: clouds. |
| 28 | S66–54915 | S66–54872 | 26 | Sept. 14, 1966 | 07:48 | 628 | Java, Bali, Lombok. |
| 29 | S66–54916 | S66–54873 | 26 | Sept. 14, 1966 | 07:49 | 638 | Java, Bali, Lombok. |
| 30 | S66–54917 | S66–54874 | 26 | Sept. 14, 1966 | 07:49 | 648 | Java, Bali, Lombok, Sumbawa. |
| *31* | *S66–54918* | *S66–54875* | *26* | *Sept. 14, 1966* | *07:53* | *682* | *Western Australia: Eighty Mile Beach to Admiralty Gulf; Great Sandy Desert.* |
| 32 | S66–54919 | S66–54876 | 26 | Sept. 14, 1966 | 07:53 | 684 | Western Australia: Eighty Mile Beach to Joseph Bonaparte Gulf; Kimberley Plateau, Great Sandy Desert. |
| 33 | S66–54920 | S66–54877 | 26 | Sept. 14, 1966 | 07:53 | 686 | Western Australia: Eighty Mile Beach to Joseph Bonaparte Gulf; Kimberley Plateau, Great Sandy Desert. |
| 34 | S66–54921 | S66–54878 | 26 | Sept. 14, 1966 | 07:53 | 688 | Western Australia: Eighty Mile Beach to Joseph Bonaparte Gulf; Kimberley Plateau, Great Sandy Desert. |
| 35 | S66–54922 | S66–54879 | 26 | Sept. 14, 1966 | ....... | ........ | Blank. |
| 36 | S66–54923 | S66–54880 | 26 | Sept. 14, 1966 | 07:53 | 690 | Western Australia: Eighty Mile Beach to Joseph Bonaparte Gulf; Kimberley Plateau, Great Sandy Desert. |
| *37* | *S66–54924* | *S66–54881* | *26* | *Sept. 14, 1966* | *07:54* | *691* | *Western Australia: Eighty Mile Beach to Joseph Bonaparte Gulf; Kimberley Plateau, Great Sandy Desert.* |
| *38* | *S66–54925* | *S66–54882* | *26* | *Sept. 14, 1966* | *07:54* | *694* | *Western Australia, Northern Territory: King Sound to Gulf of Carpentaria.* |
| 39 | S66–54926 | S66–54883 | 26 | Sept. 14, 1966 | 07:54 | 697 | Timor Sea, Indonesian Islands, Timor to Java, Borneo and Celebes: Scott Reef, Bonaparte Archipelago; clouds. |
| 40 | S66–54927 | S66–54884 | 26 | Sept. 14, 1966 | 07:55 | 699 | Western Australia, Northern Territory: Roebuck Bay to Darwin; Kimberley Plateau. |
| 41 | S66–54928 | S66–54885 | 26 | Sept. 14, 1966 | 07:55 | 701 | Western Australia, Northern Territory: Roebuck Bay to Darwin; Kimberley Plateau. |
| 42 | S66–54929 | S66–54886 | 26 | Sept. 14, 1966 | 07:55 | 703 | Western Australia, Northern Territory: Roebuck Bay to Darwin; Kimberley Plateau. |
| 43 | S66–54930 | S66–54887 | 26 | Sept. 14, 1966 | 07:55 | 704 | Western Australia, Northern Territory: King Sound to Van Diemen Gulf; Kimberley Plateau. |

MAGAZINE 8

| Frame | NASA/MSC Color No. | NASA/MSC B&W No. | Revolution | Date | GMT | Alt, N. Mi. | Area description |
|---|---|---|---|---|---|---|---|
| 1 | S66–54652 | S66–54589 | 16 | Sept. 13, 1966 | 16:27 | ........ | Inside spacecraft, Lt. Comdr. Gordon's hand, helmet; hatch open preparing for used equipment jettison. |
| 2 | S66–54653 | S66–54590 | 16 | Sept. 13, 1966 | 16:27 | ........ | Inside spacecraft, hatch open; Lt. Comdr. Gordon prepares for used equipment jettison. |
| 3 | S66–54654 | S66–54591 | 16 | Sept. 13, 1966 | 16:27 | ........ | Inside spacecraft, hatch open; Lt. Comdr. Gordon prepares for used equipment jettison. |
| 4 | S66–54655 | S66–54592 | ............ | Sept. 13, 1966 | ....... | ........ | Blank. |
| 5 | S66–54656 | S66–54593 | 16 | Sept. 13, 1966 | 16:29 | ........ | Agena, nose of Gemini through open hatch. |
| 6 | S66–54657 | S66–54594 | 16 | Sept. 13, 1966 | 16:29 | ........ | Tether line, patch on Lt. Comdr. Gordon's shoulder, through open hatch. |
| 7 | S66–54658 | S66–54595 | ............ | Sept. 13, 1966 | ....... | ........ | Blank. |
| 8 | S66–54659 | S66–54596 | 18 | Sept. 13, 1966 | 18:25 | ........ | L-band antenna, overexposed. |
| 9 | S66–54660 | S66–54597 | 18 | Sept. 13, 1966 | 18:25 | ........ | L-band antenna, overexposed. |
| 10 | S66–54661 | S66–54598 | 18 | Sept. 13, 1966 | 18:25 | ........ | L-band antenna, overexposed. |
| 11 | S66–54662 | S66–54599 | 26 | Sept. 14, 1966 | 07:24 | 231 | United Arab Republic, Israel, Jordan: Nile Valley, Sinai Peninsula; image degraded because of window obscuration. |
| 12 | S66–54663 | S66–54600 | 26 | Sept. 14, 1966 | 07:25 | 237 | United Arab Republic, Saudi Arabia, Israel, Jordan: Nile Valley, Red Sea; image degraded because of window obscuration. |
| *13* | *S66–54664* | *S66–54601* | *26* | *Sept. 14, 1966* | *07:26* | *251* | *United Arab Republic, Saudi Arabia, Israel, Jordan: Foul Bay, Al Hijaz area.* |
| 14 | S66–54665 | S66–54602 | 26 | Sept. 14, 1966 | 07:28 | 288 | Saudi Arabia: Mecca, Medina; Nafud Desert, fire on Trans-Arabian pipeline. |
| 15 | S66–54666 | S66–54603 | 26 | Sept. 14, 1966 | 07:29 | 296 | Saudi Arabia, Qatar, Bahrain, Kuwait, Iraq, Iran: Empty Quarter; image degraded because of window obscuration. |
| 16 | S66–54667 | S66–54604 | 26 | Sept. 14, 1966 | 07:29 | 307 | Saudi Arabia, Trucial States, Muscat and Oman: Iran and West Pakistan in background; image degraded because of window obscuration. |
| 17 | S66–54668 | S66–54605 | 26 | Sept. 14, 1966 | 07:30 | 315 | Saudi Arabia, Muscat and Oman: Iran, West Pakistan in background. |
| *18* | *S66–54669* | *S66–54606* | *26* | *Sept. 14, 1966* | *07:30* | *318* | *Saudi Arabia, Muscat and Oman: Iran, West Pakistan, India in background.* |
| *19* | *S66–54670* | *S66–54607* | *26* | *Sept. 14, 1966* | *07:32* | *343* | *Muscat and Oman: Arabian Sea; Iran, West Pakistan, India in background.* |
| 20 | S66–54671 | S66–54608 | 26 | Sept. 14, 1966 | 07:33 | 370 | Arabian Sea, West Pakistan, India: Indus valley, Gulf of Kutch, Gulf of Cambay. |
| 21 | S66–54672 | S66–54609 | 26 | Sept. 14, 1966 | 07:34 | 387 | Arabian Sea, Laccadive Islands, India, Ceylon. |
| 22 | S66–54673 | S66–54610 | 26 | Sept. 14, 1966 | 07:35 | 405 | Arabian Sea, Laccadive Islands, India, Ceylon. |
| 23 | S66–54674 | S66–54611 | 26 | Sept. 14, 1966 | 07:36 | 417 | Arabian Sea, Laccadive Islands, India, Ceylon, Bay of Bengal. |
| 24 | S66–54675 | S66–54612 | 26 | Sept. 14, 1966 | 07:36 | 423 | India, Ceylon, Arabian Sea, Bay of Bengal. |
| 25 | S66–54676 | S66–54613 | 26 | Sept. 14, 1966 | 07:36 | 429 | India, Ceylon, Arabian Sea, Bay of Bengal. |
| *26* | *S66–54677* | *S66–54614* | *26* | *Sept. 14, 1966* | *07:37* | *441* | *India, Ceylon, Arabian Sea, Bay of Bengal.* |
| *27* | *S66–54678* | *S66–54615* | *26* | *Sept. 14, 1966* | *07:37* | *448* | *India, Ceylon, Bay of Bengal.* |
| 28 | S66–54679 | S66–54616 | 26 | Sept. 14, 1966 | 07:38 | 454 | India, Ceylon: Image degraded because of window obscuration. |
| 29 | S66–54680 | S66–54617 | 26 | Sept. 14, 1966 | 07:38 | 460 | India, Ceylon, Arabian Sea, Bay of Bengal: Image degraded because of window obscuration. |
| *30* | *S66–54681* | *S66–54618* | *26* | *Sept. 14, 1966* | *07:39* | *480* | *Ceylon, Indian Ocean, Sumatra: Southeast Asia on horizon.* |
| 31 | S66–54682 | S66–54619 | 26 | Sept. 14, 1966 | 07:40 | 489 | Southwest tip of Ceylon, Indian Ocean, Sumatra: Southeast Asia on horizon. |
| 32 | S66–54683 | S66–54620 | 26 | Sept. 14, 1966 | 07:41 | 502 | Indian Ocean, Sumatra. |
| 33 | S66–54684 | S66–54621 | 26 | Sept. 14, 1966 | 07:42 | 520 | Indian Ocean, Sumatra. |

MAGAZINE 8 Continued

| Frame | NASA/MSC Color No. | NASA/MSC B&W No. | Revolution | Date | GMT | Alt, N. Mi. | Area description |
|---|---|---|---|---|---|---|---|
| 34 | S66–54685 | S66–54622 | 26 | Sept. 14, 1966 | 07:43 | 537 | Sumatra, Java: Borneo on horizon. |
| *35* | *S66–54686* | *S66–54623* | *26* | *Sept. 14, 1966* | *07:44* | *553* | *Sumatra, Java: Borneo on horizon.* |
| 36 | S66–54687 | S66–54624 | 26 | Sept. 14, 1966 | 07:45 | 569 | Sumatra, Java, Borneo. |
| 37 | S66–54688 | S66–54625 | 26 | Sept. 14, 1966 | 07:46 | 585 | Sumatra, Java, Borneo. |
| 38 | S66–54689 | S66–54626 | 26 | Sept. 14, 1966 | 07:47 | 600 | Sumatra, Java, Borneo. |
| 39 | S66–54690 | S66–54627 | 26 | Sept. 14, 1966 | 07:48 | 614 | Sumatra, Java-to-Timor chain, Borneo, Celebes. |
| *40* | *S66–54691* | *S66–54628* | *26* | *Sept. 14, 1966* | *07:48* | *623* | *Sumatra, Java-to-Timor chain, Borneo, Celebes.* |
| 41 | S66–54692 | S66–54629 | 26 | Sept. 14, 1966 | 07:49 | 633 | Java-to-Timor chain, Borneo, Celebes, Sumatra, tip of Western Australia, Northern Territory. |
| 42 | S66–54693 | S66–54630 | 26 | Sept. 14, 1966 | 07:50 | 641 | Java-to-Timor chain, Borneo, Celebes, Sumatra, tip of Western Australia, Northern Territory. |
| 43 | S66–54694 | S66–54631 | 26 | Sept. 14, 1966 | 07:51 | 657 | Java-to-Timor chain, Borneo, Celebes, Sumatra, tip of Western Australia, Northern Territory. |
| 44 | S66–54695 | S66–54632 | 26 | Sept. 14, 1966 | 07:52 | 669 | Java-to-Timor chain, Borneo, Celebes, Western Australia, Northern Territory. |
| 45 | S66–54696 | S66–54633 | 26 | Sept. 14, 1966 | 07:52 | 674 | Java-to-Timor chain, Borneo, Celebes, Western Australia, Northern Territory. |
| 46 | S66–54697 | S66–54634 | 26 | Sept. 14, 1966 | 07:52 | 678 | Western Australia, Northern Territory: Eighty Mile Beach to Darwin; Celebes, Bali-to-Timor chain in background. |
| 47 | S66–54698 | S66–54635 | 26 | Sept. 14, 1966 | 07:53 | 681 | Western Australia, Northern Territory: Eighty Mile Beach to Darwin; Celebes, Bali-to-Timor chain in background. |
| 48 | S66–54699 | S66–54636 | 26 | Sept. 14, 1966 | 07:53 | 685 | Western Australia, Northern Territory: Eighty Mile Beach to Darwin; Celebes, Bali-to-Timor chain in background. |
| *49* | *S66–54700* | *S66–54637* | *26* | *Sept. 14, 1966* | *07:54* | *693* | *Western Australia, Northern Territory: Eighty Mile Beach to Darwin; Celebes, Sumba-to-Timor chain in background.* |
| 50 | S66–54701 | S66–54638 | 26 | Sept. 14, 1966 | 07:54 | 696 | Western Australia, Northern Territory, Eighty Mile Beach to Darwin; Celebes, Sumba-to-Timor chain in background. |
| 51 | S66–54702 | S66–54639 | 26 | Sept. 14, 1966 | 07:57 | 720 | Out of focus because of window obscuration. |
| 52 | S66–54703 | S66–54640 | 26 | Sept. 14, 1966 | 07:58 | 722 | Australia: western half, Perth to Darwin. |
| 53 | S66–54704 | S66–54641 | 26 | Sept. 14, 1966 | 07:58 | 724 | Australia: western half, Perth to Darwin. |
| 54 | S66–54705 | S66–54642 | 26 | Sept. 14, 1966 | 07:58 | 726 | Australia: northwest quarter, Broome to Gulf of Carpentaria. |
| 55 | S66–54706 | S66–54643 | 26 | Sept. 14, 1966 | 07:59 | 728 | Australia: western half, Perth to Gulf of Carpentaria. |
| 56 | S66–54707 | S66–54644 | 26 | Sept. 14, 1966 | 08:04 | 740 | Terminator at sunset, seen from east coast of Australia. |
| 57 | S66–54708 | S66–54645 | 26 | Sept. 14, 1966 | 08:04 | 740 | Terminator at sunset, seen from east coast of Australia. |
| 58 | S66–54709 | S66–54646 | 26 | Sept. 14, 1966 | 08:05 | 740 | Terminator at sunset, seen from east coast of Australia. |
| 59 | S66–54710 | S66–54647 | 26 | Sept. 14, 1966 | 08:05 | 741 | Terminator at sunset, seen from east coast of Australia. |
| 60 | S66–54711 | S66–54648 | 26 | Sept. 14, 1966 | 08:06 | 741 | Terminator at sunset, seen from east coast of Australia. |
| 61 | S66–54712 | S66–54649 | 26 | Sept. 14, 1966 | 08:06 | 741.5 | Terminator at sunset, seen from east coast of Australia; record high apogee. |
| 62 | S66–54713 | S66–54650 | 26 | Sept. 14, 1966 | 08:06 | 741 | Terminator at sunset, seen from east coast of Australia. |
| 63 | S66–54714 | S66–54651 | 26 | Sept. 14, 1966 | 08:07 | 741 | Terminator at sunset, seen from east coast of Australia. |

MAGAZINE 10

| Frame | NASA/MSC Color No. | NASA/MSC B&W No. | Revolution | Date | GMT | Alt, N. Mi. | Area description |
|---|---|---|---|---|---|---|---|
| *1* | *S66-54764* | *S66-54715* | *27* | *Sept. 14, 1966* | *09:02* | *186* | *Morocco, Ifni: Agadir; Cape Rhir, Atlas and Anti-Atlas Mountains.* |
| 2 | S66-54765 | S66-54716 | 27 | Sept. 14, 1966 | 09:02 | 190 | Morocco, Ifni, Algeria: Agadir, Cape Rhir, Atlas and Anti-Atlas Mountains. |
| 3 | S66-54766 | S66-54717 | 27 | Sept. 14, 1966 | 09:03 | 195 | Morocco, Algeria: Hamada du Dra, Erg Iguidi, Anti-Atlas Mountains. |
| 4 | S66-54767 | S66-54718 | 27 | Sept. 14, 1966 | 09:03 | 202 | Algeria: Erg Iguidi, Erg er Raoui, Oued Saoura. |
| 5 | S66-54768 | S66-54719 | 27 | Sept. 14, 1966 | 09:04 | 206 | Algeria: Erg Chech, Oued Saoura, Tademait Plateau. |
| 6 | S66-54769 | S66-54720 | 27 | Sept. 14, 1966 | 09:04 | 212 | Algeria: Ain Salah; Erg Chech, Tademait Plateau, Tidikelt region. |
| 7 | S66-54770 | S66-54721 | 27 | Sept. 14, 1966 | 09:05 | 219 | Algeria: Ain Salah; Tademait Plateau, Tidikelt region. |
| 8 | S66-54771 | S66-54722 | 27 | Sept. 14, 1966 | 09:05 | 223 | Algeria; Tidikelt region, Ajjer Plateau, Irrarene Dunes. |
| 9 | S66-54772 | S66-54723 | 27 | Sept. 14, 1966 | 09:05 | 231 | Algeria, Libya: Ajjer Plateau, Irrarere Dunes, Telu Basalt. |
| *10* | *S66-54773* | *S66-54724* | *27* | *Sept. 14, 1966* | *09:06* | *237* | *Algeria, Libya: Ghat; Ajjer Plateau, Mellet Plateau.* |
| 11 | S66-54774 | S66-54725 | 27 | Sept. 14, 1966 | 09:06 | 246 | Algeria, Libya: Ghat; Ajjer Plateau, Mellet Plateau, Marzuq Sand Plain. |
| 12 | S66-54775 | S66-54726 | 27 | Sept. 14, 1966 | 09:09 | 274 | Libya: Northern Tibesti Mountains, Rebiana Sand Sea, Jebel Tarhuni. |
| 13 | S66-54776 | S66-54727 | 27 | Sept. 14, 1966 | 09:11 | 302 | Libya, United Arab Republic, Sudan: Libyan Desert, Jebel Arkenu, Jebel Uweinat, Gilf Kebir Plateau. |
| 14 | S66-54777 | S66-54728 | 27 | Sept. 14, 1966 | 09:12 | 321 | United Arab Republic, Sudan: Dongola, Wadi Halfa; Great Bend of the Nile River, Nubian Desert. |
| 15 | S66-54778 | S66-54729 | 27 | Sept. 14, 1966 | 09:13 | 331 | United Arab Republic, Sudan: Dongola, Wadi Halfa, Merowe; Great Bend of the Nile River, Nubian Desert, Dungunab Bay on Red Sea. |
| *16* | *S66-54779* | *S66-54730* | *27* | *Sept. 14, 1966* | *09:13* | *347* | *Sudan, Ethiopia, Saudi Arabia: Atbara, Port Sudan, Kassala; Nile and Atbara Rivers, Red Sea.* |
| 17 | S66-54780 | S66-54731 | 27 | Sept. 14, 1966 | 09:14 | 355 | Sudan, Ethiopia, Saudi Arabia: Kassala, Asmara; Atbara River, Red Sea, Dahlak Archipelago, Farasan Islands. |
| 18 | S66-54781 | S66-54732 | 27 | Sept. 14, 1966 | 09:15 | 362 | Sudan, Ethiopia, Saudi Arabia, Yemen: Kassala, Asmara; Red Sea, Dahlak Archipelego, Farasan Islands. |
| 19 | S66-54782 | S66-54733 | 27 | Sept. 14, 1966 | 09:15 | 374 | Ethiopia, Saudi Arabia, Yemen: Asmara, Assab; Red Sea, Dahlak Archipelago, Farasan Islands. |
| *20* | *S66-54783* | *S66-54734* | *27* | *Sept. 14, 1966* | *09:16* | *392* | *Ethiopia, French Somaliland, Somali Republic, Yemen, South Arabia: Assab, Djibouti, Aden; Lake Abbe, Red Sea, Gulf of Aden, Mandab Gate.* |
| 21 | S66-54784 | S66-54735 | 27 | Sept. 14, 1966 | 09:17 | 403 | Ethiopia, French Somaliland, Somali Republic, Yemen, South Arabia: Djibouti, Berbera, Aden; Mandab Gate, Gulf of Aden. |
| 22 | S66-54785 | S66-54736 | 27 | Sept. 14, 1966 | 09:17 | 418 | Ethiopia, Somali Republic, South Arabia: Gulf of Aden, Ras Hafun, Indian Ocean. |
| 23 | S66-54786 | S66-54737 | 27 | Sept. 14, 1966 | 09:18 | 433 | Ethiopia, Somali Republic: Gulf of Aden, Ras Hafun, Indian Ocean. |
| 24 | S66-54787 | S66-54738 | 27 | Sept. 14, 1966 | 09:19 | 455 | Indian Ocean, clouds. |
| 25 | S66-54788 | S66-54739 | 27 | Sept. 14, 1966 | 09:20 | 470 | Indian Ocean, clouds. |
| 26 | S66-54789 | S66-54740 | 27 | Sept. 14, 1966 | 09:22 | 502 | Maldive Islands, Indian Ocean; clouds. |
| 27 | S66-54790 | S66-54741 | 27 | Sept. 14, 1966 | 09:22 | 510 | Maldive Islands, Indian Ocean; clouds. |
| 28 | S66-54791 | S66-54742 | 27 | Sept. 14, 1966 | 09:23 | 521 | Maldive Islands, Indian Ocean; clouds. |

MAGAZINE 10 Continued

| Frame | NASA/MSC Color No. | NASA/MSC B&W No. | Revolution | Date | GMT | Alt, N. Mi. | Area description |
|---|---|---|---|---|---|---|---|
| 29 | S66-54792 | S66-54743 | 27 | Sept. 14, 1966 | 09:23 | 530 | Maldive Islands, Indian Ocean, coast of India; clouds. |
| *30* | *S66-54793* | *S66-54744* | *27* | *Sept. 14, 1966* | *09:24* | *538* | *Maldive Islands, India, Ceylon, Indian Ocean; clouds.* |
| 31 | S66-54794 | S66-54745 | 27 | Sept. 14, 1966 | 09:24 | 547 | Maldive Islands, India, Ceylon, Indian Ocean; clouds. |
| 32 | S66-54795 | S66-54746 | 27 | Sept. 14, 1966 | 09:33 | 670 | Clouds over Indian Ocean. |
| 33 | S66-54796 | S66-54747 | 27 | Sept. 14, 1966 | 09:34 | 678 | Clouds over Indian Ocean. |
| 34 | S66-54797 | S66-54748 | 27 | Sept. 14, 1966 | 09:35 | 690 | Clouds over Indian Ocean. |
| 35 | S66-54798 | S66-54749 | 27 | Sept. 14, 1966 | 09:36 | 696 | Clouds over Indian Ocean. |
| 36 | S66-54799 | S66-54750 | 27 | Sept. 14, 1966 | 09:37 | 705 | Clouds over Indian Ocean; west coast of Australia on horizon. |
| 37 | S66-54800 | S66-54751 | 27 | Sept. 14, 1966 | 09:40 | 725 | Australia: west coast, North West Cape and Shark Bay; clouds over Indian Ocean. |
| 38 | S66-54801 | S66-54752 | 27 | Sept. 14, 1966 | 09:42 | 734 | Terminator in eastern Australia. |
| 39 | S66-54802 | S66-54753 | 31 | Sept. 14, 1966 | ....... | ........ | Agena tethered to Gemini; sky background. |
| 40 | S66-54803 | S66-54754 | 31 | Sept. 14, 1966 | ....... | ........ | Agena tethered to Gemini; sky background. |
| 41 | S66-54804 | S66-54755 | 31 | Sept. 14, 1966 | ....... | ........ | Agena tethered to Gemini; sky background. |
| 42 | S66-54805 | S66-54756 | 31 | Sept. 14, 1966 | ....... | ........ | Agena tethered to Gemini; sunlit cloud tops, background. |
| 43 | S66-54806 | S66-54757 | 31 | Sept. 14, 1966 | ....... | ........ | Agena tethered to Gemini, TDA down; Pacific Ocean off Mexico, clouds. |
| 44 | S66-54807 | S66-54758 | 31 | Sept. 14, 1966 | ....... | ........ | Agena tethered to Gemini, TDA down; Pacific Ocean off Mexcio, clouds. |
| 45 | S66-54808 | S66-54759 | 31 | Sept. 14, 1966 | ....... | ........ | Agena tethered to Gemini, TDA down; Pacific Ocean off Mexico, clouds. |
| 46 | S66-54809 | S66-54760 | 31 | Sept. 14, 1966 | ....... | ........ | Agena tethered to Gemini, TDA down; Pacific Ocean off Mexico, clouds. |
| 47 | S66-54810 | S66-54761 | 31 | Sept. 14, 1966 | 16:48 | 157 | Agena tethered to Gemini, over Mexico: Gulf of California, Baja California at La Paz, Sinaloa near Los Mochis. |
| 48 | S66-54811 | S66-54762 | 31 | Sept. 14, 1966 | 16:50 | 157 | Agena tethered to Gemini, over Mexico; Fresnillo, Zacatecas area. |
| 49 | S66-54812 | S66-54763 | 31 | Sept. 14, 1966 | 16:50 | 157 | Agena tethered to Gemini, over Mexico; Fresnillo, Zacatecas, Aguascalientes area. |

MAGAZINE 9

| Frame | NASA/MSC Color No. | NASA/MSC B&W No. | Revolution | Date | GMT | Alt, N. Mi. | Area description |
|---|---|---|---|---|---|---|---|
| 1 | ........... | ........... | ............ | .............. | ...... | ........ | Blank. |
| 2 | S66-54523 | S66-54457 | 27 | Sept. 14, 1966 | 09:03 | 201 | Algeria, Morocco, Mauritania: Erg Iguidi, Atlas Mountains; image degraded because of window obscuration. |
| 3 | S66-54524 | S66-54458 | 27 | Sept. 14, 1966 | 09:05 | 218 | Algeria: Tidikelt region, Tademait Plateau, Grand Erg Occidental; image degraded because of window obscuration. |
| *4* | *S66-54525* | *S66-54459* | *27* | *Sept. 14, 1966* | *09:06* | *236* | *Algeria, Libya, Niger, Chad: Ajjer Plateau, Marzuq Sand Plain, the Black Haruj; Gulf of Sirte in background.* |
| 5 | S66-54526 | S66-54460 | 27 | Sept. 14, 1966 | 09:06 | 239 | Libya, Niger, Chad: Ajjer Plateau, Marzuq Sand Plain, The Black Haruj, Gulf of Sirte in background. |
| 6 | S66-54527 | S66-54461 | 27 | Sept. 14, 1966 | 09:07 | 250 | Libya, Niger, Chad: Marzuq Sand Plain, The Black Haruj, Tibesti Mountains, Mediterranean coast in background. |
| 7 | S66-54528 | S66-54462 | 27 | Sept. 14, 1966 | 09:09 | 272 | Libya, Chad, United Arab Republic, Sudan: Northern Tibesti Mountains, sand seas and gravel plains of eastern Sahara. |

MAGAZINE 9 Continued

| Frame | NASA/MSC | | Revolution | Date | GMT | Alt, N. Mi. | Area description |
|---|---|---|---|---|---|---|---|
| | Color No. | B&W No. | | | | | |
| *8* | *S66-54529* | *S66-54463* | *27* | *Sept. 14, 1966* | *09:10* | *285* | *Libya, United Arab Republic, Sudan: sand seas and gravel plains of eastern Sahara.* |
| 9 | S66-54530 | S66-54464 | 27 | Sept. 14, 1966 | 09:11 | 307 | United Arab Republic, Sudan: Western Desert, Nile River, Red Sea; Saudi Arabia in background. |
| *10* | *S66-54531* | *S66-54465* | *27* | *Sept. 14, 1966* | *09:12* | *327* | *United Arab Republic, Sudan: Nile River, Nubian Desert, Red Sea; Saudi Arabia in background.* |
| 11 | S66-54532 | S66-54466 | 27 | Sept. 14, 1966 | 09:13 | 341 | Sudan, Ethiopia, French Somaliland, Somali Republic, Saudi Arabia, Yemen, South Arabia: Lake Tana, Red Sea, Gulf of Aden. |
| *12* | *S66-54533* | *S66-54467* | *27* | *Sept. 14, 1966* | *09:14* | *353* | *Sudan, Ethiopia, French Somaliland, Somali Republic, Saudi Arabia, Yemen, South Arabia: Lake Tana, Red Sea, Gulf of Aden.* |
| 13 | S66-54534 | S66-54468 | 27 | Sept. 14, 1966 | 09:14 | 357 | Sudan, Ethiopia, French Somaliland, Somali Republic, Saudi Arabia, Yemen, South Arabia: Lake Tana, Red Sea, Gulf of Aden. |
| 14 | S66-54535 | S66-54469 | 27 | Sept. 14, 1966 | 09:15 | 368 | Ethiopia, French Somaliland, Somali Republic, Saudi Arabia, Yemen, South Arabia: Red Sea, Gulf of Aden. |
| *15* | *S66-54536* | *S66-54470* | *27* | *Sept. 14, 1966* | *09:15* | *379* | *Ethiopia, French Somaliland, Somali Republic, Saudi Arabia, Yemen, South Arabia: Red Sea, Gulf of Aden.* |
| *16* | *S66-54537* | *S66-54471* | *27* | *Sept. 14, 1966* | *09:16* | *385* | *Ethiopia, French Somaliland, Somali Republic, Saudi Arabia, Yemen, South Arabia: Red Sea, Gulf of Aden.* |
| *17* | *S66-54538* | *S66-54472* | *27* | *Sept. 14, 1966* | *09:17* | *408* | *Ethiopia, Somali Republic, Saudi Arabia, South Arabia: Gulf of Aden, Arabian Sea, Indian Ocean.* |
| 18 | S66-54539 | S66-54473 | 27 | Sept. 14, 1966 | 09:18 | 421 | Ethiopia, Somali Republic, South Arabia: Gulf of Aden, Arabian Sea, Indian Ocean. |
| 19 | S66-54540 | S66-54474 | 27 | Sept. 14, 1966 | 09:21 | 473 | Arabian Sea, Indian Ocean, tip of India and Ceylon on horizon. |
| 20 | S66-54541 | S66-54475 | 27 | Sept. 14, 1966 | 09:22 | 487 | Indian Ocean, southern India, Ceylon, Maldive Islands. |
| 21 | S66-54542 | S66-54476 | 27 | Sept. 14, 1966 | 09:22 | 495 | Indian Ocean, southern India, Ceylon, Maldive Islands. |
| 22 | S66-54543 | S66-54477 | 27 | Sept. 14, 1966 | 09:23 | 504 | Indian Ocean, southern India, Ceylon, Maldive Islands. |
| *23* | *S66-54544* | *S66-54478* | *27* | *Sept. 14, 1966* | *09:23* | *512* | *Indian Ocean, southern India, Ceylon, Maldive Islands.* |
| 24 | S66-54545 | S66-54479 | 27 | Sept. 14, 1966 | 09:24 | 516 | Indian Ocean, Ceylon. |
| 25 | S66-54546 | S66-54480 | 27 | Sept. 14, 1966 | 09:35 | 681 | Indian Ocean, west of Australia. |
| 26 | S66-54547 | S66-54481 | 27 | Sept. 14, 1966 | 09:36 | 688 | Indian Ocean, west of Australia. |
| 27 | S66-54548 | S66-54482 | 27 | Sept. 14, 1966 | 09:37 | 693 | Indian Ocean, west of Australia. |
| 28 | S66-54549 | S66-54483 | 27 | Sept. 14, 1966 | 09:38 | 699 | Indian Ocean, western Australia on horizon. |
| 29 | S66-54550 | S66-54484 | 27 | Sept. 14, 1966 | 09:38 | 707 | Indian Ocean, western Australia; Northwest Cape on horizon. |
| 30 | S66-54551 | S66-54485 | 27 | Sept. 14, 1966 | 09:39 | 715 | Indian Ocean, western Australia; Northwest Cape on horizon. |
| 31 | S66-54552 | S66-54486 | 27 | Sept. 14, 1966 | 09:40 | 726 | Indian Ocean, Western Australia; Shark Bay in background. |
| 32 | S66-54553 | S66-54487 | 27 | Sept. 14, 1966 | 09:40 | 730 | Indian Ocean, Western Australia; Shark Bay in background. |
| 33 | S66-54554 | S66-54488 | 29 | Sept. 14, 1966 | 12:57 | ........ | Standup EVA, hatch open; L-band antenna, hatch door, 70-mm (Blue) Maurer, UV camera. |
| 34 | S66-54555 | S66-54489 | 29 | Sept. 14, 1966 | 13:02 | ........ | Standup EVA, hatch open; docked Agena clearly seen. |
| 35 | S66-54556 | S66-54490 | 29 | Sept. 14, 1966 | 13:38 | 156 | Clouds over Mexico at sunrise. |
| 36 | S66-54557 | S66-54491 | 29 | Sept. 14, 1966 | 13:38 | 156 | Clouds over Mexico at sunrise. |

MAGAZINE 9 Continued

| Frame | NASA/MSC Color No. | NASA/MSC B&W No. | Revolution | Date | GMT | Alt, N. Mi. | Area description |
|---|---|---|---|---|---|---|---|
| 37 | S66-54558 | S66-54492 | 29 | Sept. 14, 1966 | 13:38 | 156 | Texas, Mexico: Rio Grande, Big Bend area, Del Rio, Eagle Pass, gulf coast; near sunrise, dark. |
| 38 | S66-54559 | S66-54493 | 29 | Sept. 14, 1966 | 13:39 | 156 | Texas, Mexico: Del Rio to Corpus Christi, gulf coast to New Orleans; near sunrise, dark. |
| *39* | *S66-54560* | *S66-54494* | *29* | *Sept. 14, 1966* | *13:40* | *156* | *Texas, gulf coast: San Antonio Bay to Mobile, Galveston Bay, Houston; industrial smoke, contrails.* |
| 40 | S66-54561 | S66-54495 | 29 | Sept. 14, 1966 | 13:40 | 156 | Texas, Louisiana, gulf coast: Galveston to Mobile, Houston, Beaumont, Mississippi Delta. |
| 41 | S66-54562 | S66-54496 | 29 | Sept. 14, 1966 | 13:41 | 156 | Louisiana, Alabama: gulf coast, White Lake to Mobile, New Orleans, mouth of Mississippi. |
| 42 | S66-54563 | S66-54497 | 29 | Sept. 14, 1966 | 13:42 | 156 | Louisiana, Alabama, Florida: gulf coast, Grand Isle to Apalachicola, New Orleans, mouth of Mississippi. |
| 43 | S66-54564 | S66-54498 | 29 | Sept. 14, 1966 | 13:42 | 157 | Florida: Gulf coast and Atlantic coast, north of Tampa; image blurred. |
| 44 | S66-54565 | S66-54499 | 29 | Sept. 14, 1966 | 13:43 | 157 | Florida, Georgia: Gulf and Atlantic coasts, from Sarasota-Fort Pierce to north of Jacksonville; clouds, dark. |
| 45 | S66-54566 | S66-54500 | 29 | Sept. 14, 1966 | 13:43 | 157 | Florida, Georgia: Gulf and Atlantic coasts, from Sarasota-Fort Pierce to north of Jacksonville; clouds, dark. |
| 46 | S66-54567 | S66-54501 | 29 | Sept. 14, 1966 | 13:43 | 157 | Florida, Georgia: Gulf and Atlantic coasts from Tampa-Fort Pierce to north of Jacksonville; clouds, dark. |
| 47 | S66-54568 | S66-54502 | 29 | Sept. 14, 1966 | 13:43 | 157 | Florida: Tampa-Fort Pierce-Jacksonville; clouds, dark. |
| 48 | S66-54569 | S66-54503 | 29 | Sept. 14, 1966 | 13:44 | 157 | Florida: Cape Kennedy; very dark, last photo taken during standup EVA. |
| 49 | S66-54570 | S66-54504 | 32 | Sept. 14, 1966 | 18:12 | ........ | Agena tethered to Gemini XI; ocean, clouds, atolls. |
| *50* | *S66-54571* | *S66-54505* | *32* | *Sept. 14, 1966* | *18:12* | ........ | *Agena tethered to Gemini XI; ocean, clouds, atolls.* |
| 51 | S66-54572 | S66-54506 | 32 | Sept. 14, 1966 | 18:22 | ........ | Agena tethered to Gemini XI; black sky background. |
| 52 | S66-54573 | S66-54507 | 32 | Sept. 14, 1966 | 18:22 | ........ | Agena tethered to Gemini XI; black sky background. |
| 53 | S66-54574 | S66-54508 | 32 | Sept. 14, 1966 | 18:23 | ........ | Agena tethered to Gemini XI; black sky background. |
| 54 | S66-54575 | S66-54509 | 32 | Sept. 14, 1966 | 18:23 | ........ | Agena tethered to Gemini XI; black sky background. |
| 55 | S66-54576 | S66-54510 | 32 | Sept. 14, 1966 | 18:24 | ........ | Agena tethered to Gemini XI; black sky background. |
| 56 | S66-54577 | S66-54511 | 32 | Sept. 14, 1966 | 18:24 | ........ | Agena tethered to Gemini XI; black sky bakcground. |
| 57 | S66-54578 | S66-54512 | 32 | Sept. 14, 1966 | 18:25 | ........ | Agena tethered to Gemini XI; black sky background. |
| 58 | S66-54579 | S66-54513 | 33 | Sept. 14, 1966 | 19:52 | ........ | Agena (side view), tether line loose; range, 65 ft. |
| 59 | S66-54580 | S66-54514 | 33 | Sept. 14, 1966 | 19:53 | ........ | Agena (side view), tether line loose; range, 75 ft. |
| 60 | S66-54581 | S66-54515 | 34 | Sept. 14, 1966 | 21:12 | 156 | Typhoon Elsie, southeast of Japan. |
| 61 | S66-54582 | S66-54516 | 42 | Sept. 15, 1966 | 09:13 | ........ | Agena, sky background; range, 250 ft; rerendezvous sequence. |
| 62 | S66-54583 | S66-54517 | 42 | Sept. 15, 1966 | 09:14 | ........ | Agena, sky background; range, 300 ft; out of focus. |
| 63 | S66-54584 | S66-54518 | 42 | Sept. 15, 1966 | 09:17 | ........ | Agena, docking cone end, tether line loose; range, 90 ft; Lake Chad, Chari River in background. |
| 64 | S66-54585 | S66-54519 | 42 | Sept. 15, 1966 | 09:20 | ........ | Agena, side view, tether line loose; range, 80 ft; over East Africa. |

MAGAZINE 9 Continued

| Frame | NASA/MSC Color No. | NASA/MSC B&W No. | Revolution | Date | GMT | Alt, N. Mi. | Area description |
|---|---|---|---|---|---|---|---|
| 65 | S66–54586 | S66–54520 | 42 | Sept. 15, 1966 | 09:21 | ........ | Agena, side view, tether line loose; range, 90 ft; over East Africa. |
| 66 | S66–54587 | S66–54521 | 42 | Sept. 15, 1966 | 09:22 | ........ | Agena, side view, tether line loose; range, 95 ft; over East Africa. |
| 67 | S66–54588 | S66–54522 | 42 | Sept. 15, 1966 | 09:22 | ........ | Agena, side view, tether line loose; range, 100 ft; over East Africa. |

MAGAZINE 12

| Frame | NASA/MSC Color No. | NASA/MSC B&W No. | Revolution | Date | GMT | Alt, N. Mi. | Area description |
|---|---|---|---|---|---|---|---|
| 1 | S66–54829 | S66–54813 | 33 | Sept. 14, 1966 | 19:51 | ........ | Agena on tether line. |
| 2 | S66–54830 | S66–54814 | 33 | Sept. 14, 1966 | 19:53 | ........ | Agena at time of tether drop; range, 50 ft. |
| 3 | S66–54831 | S66–54815 | 34 | Sept. 14, 1966 | 20:14 | 165 | Peru: Fog-shrouded coastline from Punta Chala to Rio Ocona, western slope of Andes. |
| *4* | *S66–54832* | *S66–54816* | *34* | *Sept. 14, 1966* | *20:15* | *165* | *Peru: Arequipa; fog-shrouded coastline from Rio Atico to Rio Tambo; Laguna Salinas, Volcano Misti, Nevado Chachani.* |
| 5 | S66–54833 | S66–54817 | 34 | Sept. 14, 1966 | 20:15 | 165 | Peru: Arequipa; fog-shrouded coastline from Punta Chala to Rio Tambo; Laguna Salinas, Volcano Misti, Nevado Chachani. |
| 6 | S66–54834 | S66–54818 | 34 | Sept. 14, 1966 | 20:16 | 165 | Peru, Chile, Bolivia: La Paz beneath clouds; Lake Titicaca, Rio Desaquadero, Cordillera Real. |
| 7 | S66–54835 | S66–54819 | 34 | Sept. 14, 1966 | 20:17 | 165 | Bolivia: Sucre, Santa Cruz; Cordillera Oriental, Rio Grande, Rio Parapeti. |
| 8 | S66–54836 | S66–54820 | 34 | Sept. 14, 1966 | 20:17 | 165 | Bolivia, Paraguay: Gran Chaco, edge of Cordillera Oriental, Rio Grande, Rio Parapeti; hazy. |
| 9 | S66–54837 | S66–54821 | 35 | Sept. 14, 1966 | 22:48 | 155 | Typhoon Elsie, southeast of Japan; out of focus. |
| 10 | S66–54838 | S66–54822 | 35 | Sept. 14, 1966 | 22:48 | 155 | Typhoon Elsie, southeast of Japan; out of focus. |
| 11 | S66–54839 | S66–54823 | 37 | Sept. 15, 1966 | 01:44 | 156 | West Pakistan, India, China: Himalayas, Hindu Kush, Karakoram Range, Sinkiang Desert, Indus River. |
| *12* | *S66–54840* | *S66–54824* | *37* | *Sept. 15, 1966* | *01:49* | *156* | *East Pakistan, India, Bhutan, Sikkim: Himalayas, Mount Everest, Brahmaputra River, Tibetan Highlands, Ganges Plain in background.* |
| 13 | S66–54841 | S66–54825 | 40 | Sept. 15, 1966 | 06:45 | 162 | Western Australia: Eighty Mile Beach, Great Sandy Desert, Percival Lakes and Lake Disappointment, Fitzroy River. |
| 14 | S66–54842 | S66–54826 | ............ | ............... | ........ | ........ | Agena, side view, range, 70 ft. |
| 15 | S66–54843 | S66–54827 | ............ | ............... | ........ | ........ | Blank. |
| 16 | S66–54844 | S66–54828 | ............ | ............... | ........ | ........ | Agena, side view; range, 200 ft. |

## GEMINI XII

### MAGAZINE 8

| Frame | NASA/MSC Color No. | NASA/MSC B&W No. | Revolution | Date | GMT | Alt, N. Mi. | Area description |
|---|---|---|---|---|---|---|---|
| 1 | S66-63386 | S66-63236 | 1 | Nov. 11, 1966 | 22:19 | 124 | Mexico: Monterrey-Saltillo-Torreon area; Sierra Madre Oriental Gulf coastal plain. |
| 2 | S66-63387 | S66-63237 | 3 | Nov. 12, 1966 | ....... | ........ | Agena station keeping; range, 15 ft. |
| 3 | S66-63388 | S66-63238 | 3 | Nov. 12, 1966 | ....... | ........ | Agena station keeping; range, 15 ft. |
| 4 | S66-63389 | S66-63239 | 3 | Nov. 12, 1966 | ....... | ........ | Agena station keeping; range, 15 ft. |
| 5 | S66-63390 | S66-63240 | 3 | Nov. 12, 1966 | 00:55 | 156 | Agena station keeping; range, 50 ft; Borneo, Philippine Islands; Sulu Archipelago. |
| 6 | S66-63391 | S66-63241 | 3 | Nov. 12, 1966 | 00:55 | 156 | Agena station keeping; range, 50 ft; Borneo, Philippine Islands; Sulu Archipelago. |
| 7 | S66-63392 | S66-63242 | 3 | Nov. 12, 1966 | 00:55 | 156 | Agena station keeping; range, 50 ft; Borneo, Philippine Islands; Sulu Archipelago. |
| 8 | S66-63393 | S66-63243 | 3 | Nov. 12, 1966 | 00:55 | 156 | Agena station keeping; range, 50 ft; Borneo, Philippine Islands; Sulu Archipelago. |
| 9 | S66-63394 | S66-63244 | 3 | Nov. 12, 1966 | 00:55 | 156 | Agena station keeping; range, 50 ft; Borneo, Philippine Islands; Sulu Archipelago. |
| 10 | S66-63395 | S66-63245 | 3 | Nov. 12, 1966 | 00:56 | 156 | Agena station keeping; range, 50 ft; Borneo, Philippine Islands; Sulu Archipelago. |
| 11 | S66-63396 | S66-63246 | 3 | Nov. 12, 1966 | 00:56 | 156 | Agena station keeping; range, 50 ft; Borneo, Philippine Islands; Sulu Archipelago. |
| 12 | S66-63397 | S66-63247 | 3 | Nov. 12, 1966 | 01:06 | 159 | Docked to Agena. |
| 13 | S66-63398 | S66-63248 | 3 | Nov. 12, 1966 | 01:07 | 159 | Docked to Agena. |
| 14 | S66-63399 | S66-63249 | 3 | Nov. 12, 1966 | 01:07 | 159 | Docked to Agena. |
| 15 | S66-63400 | S66-63250 | 3 | Nov. 12, 1966 | 01:08 | 159 | Docked to Agena. |
| 16 | S66-63401 | S66-63251 | 3 | Nov. 12, 1966 | 01:10 | 159 | Docked to Agena. |
| 17 | S66-63402 | S66-63252 | 3 | Nov. 12, 1966 | 01:31 | ........ | Agena station keeping; range, 25 ft. |
| 18 | S66-63403 | S66-63253 | 3 | Nov. 12, 1966 | 01:32 | ........ | Agena station keeping; range, 25 ft. |
| 19 | S66-63404 | S66-63254 | 3 | Nov. 12, 1966 | 01:32 | ........ | Agena station keeping; range, 27 ft. |
| 20 | S66-63405 | S66-63255 | 3 | Nov. 12, 1966 | 01:33 | ........ | Agena station keeping; range, 34 ft. |
| 21 | S66-63406 | S66-63256 | 3 | Nov. 12, 1966 | 01:33 | ........ | Agena station keeping; range, 37 ft. |
| 22 | S66-63407 | S66-63257 | 3 | Nov. 12, 1966 | 01:33 | ........ | Agena station keeping; range, 42 ft. |
| 23 | S66-63408 | S66-63258 | 3 | Nov. 12, 1966 | 01:34 | ........ | Agena station keeping; range, 45 ft. |
| 24 | S66-63409 | S66-63259 | 3 | Nov. 12, 1966 | 01:34 | ........ | Agena station keeping; range, 50 ft. |
| 25 | S66-63410 | S66-63260 | 3 | Nov. 12, 1966 | 01:35 | ........ | Agena station keeping; range, 55 ft. |
| 26 | S66-63411 | S66-63261 | 3 | Nov. 12, 1966 | 01:35 | ........ | Agena station keeping; range, 60 ft. |
| 27 | S66-63412 | S66-63262 | 3 | Nov. 12, 1966 | 01:36 | ........ | Agena station keeping; range, 45 ft. |
| 28 | S66-63413 | S66-63263 | 3 | Nov. 12, 1966 | 01:36 | ........ | Agena station keeping; range, 45 ft. |
| 29 | S66-63414 | S66-63264 | 3 | Nov. 12, 1966 | 12:47 | ........ | Solar eclipse, partial. |
| 30 | S66-63415 | S66-63265 | 3 | Nov. 12, 1966 | 12:48 | ........ | Solar eclipse, total. |
| 31 | S66-63416 | S66-63266 | ............ | Nov. 12, 1966 | ....... | ........ | Blank. |
| 32 | S66-63417 | S66-63267 | 15 | Nov. 12, 1966 | 19:13 | 150 | Southern Florida, Bahama Islands, Cuba. |
| *33* | *S66-63418* | *S66-63268* | *15* | *Nov. 12, 1966* | *19:13* | *150* | *Southern Florida, Bahama Islands, Cuba.* |
| 34 | S66-63419 | S66-63269 | 15 | Nov. 12, 1966 | 19:13 | 150 | Southern Florida, Bahama Islands, Cuba. |
| 35 | S66-63420 | S66-63270 | 15 | Nov. 12, 1966 | 19:13 | 150 | Southern Florida, Bahama Islands, Cuba. |
| 36 | S66-63421 | S66-63271 | 15 | Nov. 12, 1966 | 19:14 | 150 | Southern Florida, Bahama Islands, Cuba. |
| 37 | S66-63422 | S66-63272 | 15 | Nov. 12, 1966 | 19:14 | 150 | Southern Florida, Bahama Islands, Cuba. |
| *38* | *S66-63423* | *S66-63273* | *15* | *Nov. 12, 1966* | *19:14* | *149* | *Southern Florida, Bahama Islands, Cuba.* |
| 39 | S66-63424 | S66-63274 | 15 | Nov. 12, 1966 | 19:14 | 149 | Southern Florida, Bahama Islands, Cuba. |
| 40 | S66-63425 | S66-63275 | 15 | Nov. 12, 1966 | 19:14 | 149 | Southern Florida, Bahama Islands, Cuba. |
| 41 | S66-63426 | S66-63276 | 15 | Nov. 12, 1966 | 20:43 | 150 | Texas, Mexico: Del Rio, Eagle Pass; Edwards Plateau, Big Bend, Rio Grande, Serrania del Burro, Sierra Madre Oriental. |
| 42 | S66-63427 | S66-63277 | 15 | Nov. 12, 1966 | 20:43 | 150 | Texas, Mexico: Del Rio, Eagle Pass; Laredo; Edwards Plateau, Big Bend, Rio Grande, Serrania del Burro, Sierra Madre Oriental. |

MAGAZINE 8 Continued

| Frame | NASA/MSC Color No. | NASA/MSC B&W No. | Revolution | Date | GMT | Alt, N. Mi. | Area description |
|---|---|---|---|---|---|---|---|
| *43* | *S66–63428* | *S66–63278* | *15* | *Nov. 12, 1966* | *20:44* | *149* | *Texas: San Antonio, Austin, Corpus Christi; Edwards Plateau, Balcones Escarpment, gulf coast, Matagorda Bay.* |
| 44 | S66–63429 | S66–63279 | 15 | Nov. 12, 1966 | 20:44 | 149 | Texas: Corpus Christi; gulf coast from Baffin Bay to Matagorda Bay, Interstate 10 at Columbus. |
| 45 | S66–63430 | S66–63280 | 15 | Nov. 12, 1966 | 20:44 | 149 | Texas: Gulf coast at Matagorda Bay, Interstate 10 at Columbus. |
| 46 | S66–63431 | S66–63281 | 15 | Nov. 12, 1966 | 20:47 | 146 | Florida: Tampa, St. Petersburg, Fort Myers, Palm Beach; Cape Kennedy, Lake Okeechobee. |
| 47 | S66–63432 | S66–63282 | 15 | Nov. 12, 1966 | 20:48 | 146 | Florida: Tampa, St. Petersburg, Fort Myers, Palm Beach, Miami; Keys, Lake Okeechobee, Everglades. |
| 48 | S66–63433 | S66–63283 | 15 | Nov. 12, 1966 | 20:48 | 146 | Florida: Cape Kennedy, Palm Beach, Orlando. |
| 49 | S66–63434 | S66–63284 | 15 | Nov. 12, 1966 | 20:48 | 146 | Florida: Cape Kennedy, Orlando. |
| 50 | S66–63435 | S66–63285 | 16 | Nov. 12, 1966 | 20:48 | 146 | Florida: Cape Kennedy; underexposed. |
| 51 | S66–63436 | S66–63286 | 16 | Nov. 12, 1966 | 20:48 | 146 | Bahama Islands; underexposed. |
| 52 | S66–63437 | S66–63287 | 16 | Nov. 12, 1966 | ....... | ........ | Blank. |
| 53 | S66–63438 | S66–63288 | 16 | Nov. 12, 1966 | 22:17 | 147 | Mexico: Guaymas; Baja California, Gulf of California. |
| 54 | S66–63439 | S66–63289 | 16 | Nov. 12, 1966 | 22:17 | 147 | Mexico: Guaymas; Baja California, Gulf of California. |
| 55 | S66–63440 | S66–63290 | 16 | Nov. 12, 1966 | 22:17 | 146 | Mexico: Guaymas; Baja California, Gulf of California. |
| 56 | S66–63441 | S66–63291 | 17 | Nov. 12, 1966 | 22:17 | 146 | Mexico: Guaymas; Baja California, Gulf of California. |
| 57 | S66–63442 | S66–63292 | 17 | Nov. 12, 1966 | ....... | ........ | Blank. |
| 58 | S66–63443 | S66–63293 | 17 | Nov. 12, 1966 | ....... | ........ | Cellular cloud formations. |
| 59 | S66–63444 | S66–63294 | 17 | Nov. 12, 1966 | 23:18 | 160 | Indonesia: Islands of Alor, Wetar, Timor, Babar, Jamdena; Bandar Sea. |
| 60 | S66–63445 | S66–63295 | 17 | Nov. 12, 1966 | 23:19 | 160 | Indonesia: Islands of Alor, Wetar, Timor, Babar, Jamdena; Bandar Sea. |
| 61 | S66–63446 | S66–63296 | 17 | Nov. 12, 1966 | 23:19 | 160 | Indonesia: Islands of Alor, Wetar, Timor, Babar, Jamdena; Bandar Sea. |
| 62 | S66–63447 | S66–63297 | 17 | Nov. 12, 1966 | 23:33 | 156 | Clouds over Pacific Ocean. |
| 63 | S66–63448 | S66–63298 | 17 | Nov. 12, 1966 | 23:34 | 156 | Clouds over Pacific Ocean. |
| 64 | S66–63449 | S66–63299 | 17 | Nov. 12, 1966 | 23:34 | 156 | Clouds over Pacific Ocean. |
| 65 | S66–63450 | S66–63300 | 17 | Nov. 12, 1966 | 23:35 | 156 | Clouds over Pacific Ocean. |
| 66 | S66–63451 | S66–63301 | 17 | Nov. 12, 1966 | ....... | ........ | Inside spacecraft; underexposed. |
| 67 | S66–63452 | S66–63302 | 17 | Nov. 12, 1966 | 23:35 | 155 | Clouds over Pacific Ocean. |
| 68 | S66–63453 | S66–63303 | 17 | Nov. 12, 1966 | 23:36 | 155 | Clouds over Pacific Ocean. |
| 69 | S66–63454 | S66–63304 | 17 | Nov. 12, 1966 | 23:36 | 155 | Clouds over Pacific Ocean. |
| 70 | S66–63455 | S66–63305 | 17 | Nov. 12, 1966 | 23:37 | 155 | Clouds over Pacific Ocean. |
| 71 | S66–63456 | S66–63306 | 17 | Nov. 12, 1966 | 23:37 | 155 | Clouds over Pacific Ocean. |
| 72 | S66–63457 | S66–63307 | 17 | Nov. 12, 1966 | ....... | ........ | Blank. |
| 73 | S66–63458 | S66–63308 | 17 | Nov. 12, 1966 | 23:38 | 153 | Clouds over Pacific Ocean. |
| 74 | S66–63459 | S66–63309 | 17 | Nov. 12, 1966 | ....... | ........ | Blank. |
| 75 | S66–63460 | S66–63310 | 17 | Nov. 12, 1966 | 23:39 | 153 | Clouds over Pacific Ocean. |
| 76 | S66–63461 | S66–63311 | 17 | Nov. 12, 1966 | 23:40 | 153 | Clouds over Pacific Ocean. |
| 77 | S66–63462 | S66–63312 | 17 | Nov. 12, 1966 | 23:40 | 152 | Clouds over Pacific Ocean. |
| 78 | S66–63463 | S66–63313 | 17 | Nov. 12, 1966 | 23:41 | 152 | Clouds over Pacific Ocean. |
| *79* | *S66–63464* | *S66–63314* | *17* | *Nov. 12, 1966* | *23:42* | *151* | *Clouds over Pacific Ocean.* |
| 80 | S66–63465 | S66–63315 | 17 | Nov. 12, 1966 | 23:43 | 150 | Clouds over Pacific Ocean. |
| 81 | S66–63466 | S66–63316 | 17 | Nov. 12, 1966 | 23:44 | 150 | Clouds over Pacific Ocean. |
| 82 | S66–63467 | S66–63317 | 25 | Nov. 13, 1966 | 11:31 | 158 | Mauritania, Mali: Dhar Adrar, Richat Structure, Aouker Basin, El Djouf Desert. |
| 83 | S66–63468 | S66–63318 | 25 | Nov. 13, 1966 | 11:31 | 158 | Mauritania, Mali: Dhar Adrar, Richat Structure, Aouker Basin, El Djouf Desert. |

MAGAZINE 8 Continued

| Frame | NASA/MSC Color No. | NASA/MSC B&W No. | Revolution | Date | GMT | Alt, N. Mi. | Area description |
|---|---|---|---|---|---|---|---|
| 138 | S66–63523 | S66–63373 | 31 | Nov. 13, 1966 | 22:18 | 146 | Agena on tether; Mexico: Durango-San Luis Potosí-Guadalajara area. |
| 139 | S66–63524 | S66–63374 | 31 | Nov. 13, 1966 | ...... | ........ | Docking bar; terminator, limb. |
| 140 | S66–63525 | S66–63375 | 31 | Nov. 13, 1966 | ...... | ........ | Docking bar; terminator, limb. |
| 141 | S66–63526 | S66–63376 | 31 | Nov. 13, 1966 | ...... | ........ | Agena on tether; limb, sunset. |
| 142 | S66–63527 | S66–63377 | 31 | Nov. 13, 1966 | ...... | ........ | Agena on tether; limb, sunset. |
| 143 | S66–63528 | S66–63378 | ............ | .............. | ...... | ........ | Blank. |
| 144 | S66–63529 | S66–63379 | 54 | Nov. 15, 1966 | 10:05 | 154 | United Arab Republic, Saudi Arabia, Sudan: Nile River, Red Sea, jetstream clouds. |
| *145* | *S66–63530* | *S66–63380* | *54* | *Nov. 15, 1966* | *10:06* | *153* | *United Arab Republic, Saudi Arabia, Sudan: Nile River, Red Sea, jetstream clouds.* |
| 146 | S66–63531 | S66–63381 | 54 | Nov. 15, 1966 | 10:06 | 153 | United Arab Republic, Saudi Arabia, Sudan: Nile River, Red Sea, jetstream clouds. |
| 147 | S66–63532 | S66–63382 | 54 | Nov. 15, 1966 | 10:06 | 153 | United Arab Republic, Saudi Arabia, Sudan: Nile River, Red Sea, jetstream clouds. |
| 148 | S66–63533 | S66–63383 | 54 | Nov. 15, 1966 | 10:06 | 153 | United Arab Republic, Saudi Arabia, Sudan: Nile River, Red Sea, jetstream clouds. |
| 149 | S66–63534 | S66–63384 | 54 | Nov. 15, 1966 | 10:06 | 153 | United Arab Republic, Saudi Arabia, Sudan: Nile River, Red Sea, jetstream clouds. |
| 150 | S66–63535 | S66–63385 | 54 | Nov. 15, 1966 | 10:06 | 153 | United Arab Republic, Saudi Arabia, Sudan: Nile River, Red Sea, jetstream clouds. |

MAGAZINE 10

| Frame | NASA/MSC Color No. | NASA/MSC B&W No. | Revolution | Date | GMT | Alt, N. Mi. | Area description |
|---|---|---|---|---|---|---|---|
| 1 | S66–62749 | S66–62701 | 3 | Nov. 12, 1966 | 00:47 | ........ | Agena; range, 50 ft. |
| 2 | S66–62750 | S66–62702 | 3 | Nov. 12, 1966 | 00:48 | ........ | Agena; range, 50 ft. |
| 3 | S66–62751 | S66–62703 | 3 | Nov. 12, 1966 | 00:48 | ........ | Agena; range, 50 ft. |
| 4 | S66–62752 | S66–62704 | 3 | Nov. 12, 1966 | 00:51 | ........ | Agena; range, 12 ft. |
| 5 | S66–62753 | S66–62705 | 3 | Nov. 12, 1966 | 00:52 | ........ | Agena; range, 12 ft. |
| 6 | S66–62754 | S66–62706 | 3 | Nov. 12, 1966 | 00:52 | ........ | Agena; range, 14 ft. |
| 7 | S66–62755 | S66–62707 | 3 | Nov. 12, 1966 | 00:55 | ........ | Agena; range, 50 ft; exellent side view, stereo. |
| 8 | S66–62756 | S66–62708 | 3 | Nov. 12, 1966 | 00:56 | ........ | Agena; range, 53 ft; excellent side view, stereo. |
| 9 | S66–62757 | S66–62709 | 3 | Nov. 12, 1966 | 00:56 | ........ | Agena; range, 55 ft; excellent side view, stereo. |
| 10 | S66–62758 | S66–62710 | ............ | .............. | ...... | ........ | Blank. |
| 11 | S66–62759 | S66–62711 | 28 | Nov. 13, 1966 | ...... | ........ | Major Aldrin, extravehicular acitivity. |
| 12 | S66–62760 | S66–62712 | 28 | Nov. 13, 1966 | ...... | ........ | Major Aldrin, extravehicular activity. |
| 13 | S66–62761 | S66–62713 | ............ | .............. | ...... | ........ | Blank. |
| 14 | S66–62762 | S66–62714 | 28 | Nov. 13, 1966 | ...... | ........ | Major Aldrin, extravehicular activity. |
| 15 | S66–62763 | S66–62715 | 28 | Nov. 13, 1966 | ...... | ........ | Major Aldrin, extravehicular acitvity. |
| 16 | S66–62764 | S66–62716 | 28 | Nov. 13, 1966 | ...... | ........ | Major Aldrin, extravehicular activity. |
| 17 | S66–62765 | S66–62717 | 28 | Nov. 13, 1966 | ...... | ........ | Major Aldrin, extravehicular activity. |
| 18 | S66–62766 | S66–62718 | 28 | Nov. 13, 1966 | ...... | ........ | Major Aldrin, extravehicular activity; Florida and Bahamas in background. |
| 19 | S66–62767 | S66–62719 | 28 | Nov. 13, 1966 | ...... | ........ | Major Aldrin, extravehicular activity. |
| 20 | S66–62768 | S66–62720 | 28 | Nov. 13, 1966 | ...... | ........ | Major Aldrin, extravehicular activity. |
| 21 | S66–62769 | S66–62721 | 28 | Nov. 13, 1966 | ...... | ........ | Major Aldrin, extravehicular activity. |
| 22 | S66–62770 | S66–62722 | ............ | .............. | ...... | ........ | Blank. |
| 23 | S66–62771 | S66–62723 | 28 | Nov. 13, 1966 | ...... | ........ | Major Aldrin, extravehicular activity. |
| 24 | S66–62772 | S66–62724 | 28 | Nov. 13, 1966 | ...... | ........ | Major Aldrin, extravehicular activity. |
| 25 | S66–62773 | S66–62725 | 28 | Nov. 13, 1966 | ...... | ........ | Major Aldrin, extravehicular activity. |
| 26 | S66–62774 | S66–62726 | 28 | Nov. 13, 1966 | ...... | ........ | Major Aldrin, extravehicular activity. |
| 27 | S66–62775 | S66–62727 | 28 | Nov. 13, 1966 | ...... | ........ | Major Aldrin, extravehicular activity. |
| 28 | S66–62776 | S66–62728 | 28 | Nov. 13, 1966 | ...... | ........ | Major Aldrin, extravehicular activity. |
| 29 | S66–62777 | S66–62729 | 28 | Nov. 13, 1966 | ...... | ........ | Major Aldrin, extravehicular activity. |
| 30 | S66–62778 | S66–62730 | 28 | Nov. 13, 1966 | ...... | ........ | Major Aldrin, extravehicular activity. |
| 31 | S66–62779 | S66–62731 | 28 | Nov. 13, 1966 | ...... | ........ | Major Aldrin, extravehicular activity. |

## MAGAZINE 10 Continued

| Frame | NASA/MSC | | Revolution | Date | GMT | Alt, N. Mi. | Area description |
|---|---|---|---|---|---|---|---|
| | Color No. | B&W No. | | | | | |
| 32 | S66–62780 | S66–62732 | ............ | Nov. 13, 1966 | ....... | ........ | Blank. |
| 33 | S66–62781 | S66–62733 | 28 | Nov. 13, 1966 | ....... | ........ | Major Aldrin, extravehicular activity. |
| 34 | S66–62782 | S66–62734 | 28 | Nov. 13, 1966 | ....... | ........ | Major Aldrin, extravehicular activity; best view of series. |
| 35 | S66–62783 | S66–62735 | 28 | Nov. 13, 1966 | ....... | ........ | Major Aldrin, extravehicular activity. |
| 36 | S66–62784 | S66–62736 | 28 | Nov. 13, 1966 | ....... | ........ | Major Aldrin, extravehicular activity. |
| 37 | S66–62785 | S66–62737 | 30 | Nov. 13, 1966 | ....... | ........ | Agena on tether; clouds, ocean. |
| 38 | S66–62786 | S66–62738 | 30 | Nov. 13, 1966 | ....... | ........ | Agena on tether; clouds, ocean. |
| 39 | S66–62787 | S66–62739 | 30 | Nov. 13, 1966 | ....... | ........ | Agena on tether; clouds, ocean. |
| 40 | S66–62788 | S66–62740 | 30 | Nov. 13, 1966 | ....... | ........ | Agena on tether; clouds, ocean. |
| 41 | S66–62789 | S66–62741 | 30 | Nov. 13, 1966 | ....... | ........ | Agena on tether; clouds, ocean. |
| 42 | S66–62790 | S66–62742 | 30 | Nov. 13, 1966 | ....... | ........ | Agena on tether; clouds, ocean. |
| 43 | S66–62791 | S66–62743 | 30 | Nov. 13, 1966 | ....... | ........ | Agena on tether; clouds, ocean. |
| 44 | S66–62792 | S66–62744 | 30 | Nov. 13, 1966 | ....... | ........ | Agena on tether; clouds, ocean. |
| 45 | S66–62793 | S66–62745 | 30 | Nov. 13, 1966 | 20:40 | 153 | California, Arizona, New Mexico, Nevada, Utah, Colorado: Grand Canyon, Colorado River, Death Valley, Lake Mead. |
| 46 | S66–62794 | S66–62746 | 30 | Nov. 13, 1966 | 20:40 | 152 | Arizona, New Mexico, Mexico: Tucson, Phoenix; Sonoran Desert, Mogollon Rim, Painted Desert. |
| 47 | S66–62795 | S66–62747 | 30 | Nov. 13, 1966 | 20:41 | 152 | Arizona, New Mexico, Mexico: Chihuahuan Desert, Rio Grande, Sierra Madre Occidental, Painted Desert. |
| 48 | S66–62796 | S66–62748 | 30 | Nov. 13, 1966 | 20:41 | 152 | Arizona, New Mexico, Texas, Mexico: Chihuahuan Desert, Rio Grande, White Sands, Painted Desert, Rocky Mountains. |

## MAGAZINE 11

| Frame | NASA/MSC | | Revolution | Date | GMT | Alt, N. Mi. | Area description |
|---|---|---|---|---|---|---|---|
| | Color No. | B&W No. | | | | | |
| 1 | S66–62940 | S66–63088 | 32 | Nov. 13, 1966 | ....... | ........ | Agena on tether; clouds over Pacific Ocean. |
| 2 | S66–62941 | S66–63089 | 32 | Nov. 13, 1966 | ....... | ........ | Agena on tether; clouds over Pacific Ocean. |
| 3 | S66–62942 | S66–63090 | 32 | Nov. 13, 1966 | ....... | ........ | Agena on tether; clouds over Pacific Ocean. |
| 4 | S66–62943 | S66–63091 | 32 | Nov. 13, 1966 | ....... | ........ | Agena on tether; clouds over Pacific Ocean. |
| 5 | S66–62944 | S66–63092 | 32 | Nov. 13, 1966 | ....... | ........ | Agena on tether; clouds over Pacific Ocean. |
| 6 | S66–62945 | S66–63093 | 32 | Nov. 13, 1966 | ....... | ........ | Agena on tether; clouds over Pacific Ocean. |
| 7 | S66–62946 | S66–63094 | 32 | Nov. 13, 1966 | ....... | ........ | Agena on tether; clouds over Pacific Ocean. |
| 8 | S66–62947 | S66–63095 | 32 | Nov. 13, 1966 | ....... | ........ | Agena on tether; clouds over Pacific Ocean. |
| 9 | S66–62948 | S66–63096 | 32 | Nov. 13, 1966 | ....... | ........ | Agena on tether; clouds over Pacific Ocean. |
| 10 | S66–62949 | S66–63097 | 32 | Nov. 13, 1966 | ....... | ........ | Agena on tether; clouds over Pacific Ocean. |
| 11 | S66–62950 | S66–63098 | 32 | Nov. 13, 1966 | ....... | ........ | Agena on tether; clouds over Pacific Ocean. |
| *12* | *S66–62951* | *S66–63099* | *32* | *Nov. 13, 1966* | ....... | ........ | *Agena on tether; clouds over Pacific Ocean.* |
| 13 | S66–62952 | S66–63100 | 32 | Nov. 13, 1966 | ....... | ........ | Agena on tether; clouds over Pacific Ocean. |
| 14 | S66–62953 | S66–63101 | 32 | Nov. 13, 1966 | ....... | ........ | Agena on tether; clouds over Pacific Ocean. |
| 15 | S66–62954 | S66–63102 | 32 | Nov. 13, 1966 | 23:51 | 144 | Agena on tether; Mexico: Baja California Sur. |
| 16 | S66–62955 | S66–63103 | 32 | Nov. 13, 1966 | 23:53 | 142 | Agena on tether; Mexico: Pacific coast at Manzanillo; note long cloud shadows. |
| 17 | S66–62956 | S66–63104 | 32 | Nov. 13, 1966 | 23:53 | 142 | Agena on tether; Mexico: Pacific coast at Manzanillo; note long cloud shadows. |
| 18 | S66–62957 | S66–63105 | 32 | Nov. 13, 1966 | 23:53 | 142 | Agena on tether; Mexico: Pacific coast at Manzanillo; note long cloud shadows. |
| 19 | S66–62958 | S66–63106 | 32 | Nov. 13, 1966 | 23:54 | ........ | Agena on tether, at sunset. |
| 20 | S66–62959 | S66–63107 | 32 | Nov. 13, 1966 | 23:55 | ........ | Earth limb at sunset. |
| 21 | S66–62960 | S66–63108 | 32 | Nov. 13, 1966 | 23:55 | ........ | Earth limb at sunset. |
| 22 | S66–62961 | S66–63109 | 32 | Nov. 13, 1966 | 23:55 | ........ | Earth limb at sunset. |
| 23 | S66–62962 | S66–63110 | 32 | Nov. 13, 1966 | 23:56 | ........ | Earth limb at sunset. |
| 24 | S66–62963 | S66–63111 | 32 | Nov. 13, 1966 | 23:56 | ........ | Earth limb at sunset. |

MAGAZINE 11 Continued

| Frame | NASA/MSC Color No. | NASA/MSC B&W No. | Revolution | Date | GMT | Alt, N. Mi. | Area description |
|---|---|---|---|---|---|---|---|
| 25 | S66–62964 | S66–63112 | 32 | Nov. 13, 1966 | 23:56 | ........ | Earth limb at sunset. |
| 26 | S66–62965 | S66–63113 | 32 | Nov. 13, 1966 | 23:56 | ........ | Earth limb at sunset. |
| 27 | S66–62966 | S66–63114 | 32 | Nov. 13, 1966 | 23:56 | ........ | Earth limb at sunset. |
| 28 | S66–62967 | S66–63115 | 32 | Nov. 13, 1966 | 23:56 | ........ | Earth limb at sunset. |
| 29 | S66–62968 | S66–63116 | 32 | Nov. 13, 1966 | 23:57 | ........ | Earth limb at sunset. |
| 30 | S66–62969 | S66–63117 | 32 | Nov. 13, 1966 | 23:57 | ........ | Earth limb at sunset. |
| 31 | S66–62970 | S66–63118 | 32 | Nov. 13, 1966 | 23:57 | ........ | Earth limb at sunset. |
| 32 | S66–62971 | S66–63119 | 32 | Nov. 13, 1966 | 23:57 | ........ | Earth limb at sunset. |
| 33 | S66–62972 | S66–63120 | 32 | Nov. 13, 1966 | 23:58 | ........ | Earth limb at sunset. |
| 34 | S66–62973 | S66–63121 | 32 | Nov. 13, 1966 | 23:59 | ........ | Earth limb at sunset. |
| *35* | *S66–62974* | *S66–63122* | *34* | *Nov. 14, 1966* | *02:17* | *160* | *Southern end of Maldive Islands.* |
| 36 | S66–62975 | S66–63123 | 34 | Nov. 14, 1966 | 02:23 | 160 | Andaman Islands, Bay of Bengal. |
| *37* | *S66–62976* | *S66–63124* | *34* | *Nov. 14, 1966* | *02:24* | *160* | *Burma: Mouths of Irrawaddy and Salween Rivers.* |
| 38 | S66–62977 | S66–63125 | 34 | Nov. 14, 1966 | 02:24 | 160 | Burma: Mouths of Irrawaddy and Salween Rivers. |
| 39 | S66–62978 | S66–63126 | 34 | Nov. 14, 1966 | 02:24 | 160 | Burma: Mouths of Irrawaddy and Salween Rivers. |
| *40* | *S66–62979* | *S66–63127* | *34* | *Nov. 14, 1966* | *02:25* | *160* | *Burma: Mouths of Irrawaddy and Salween Rivers.* |
| 41 | S66–62980 | S66–63128 | ............ | Nov. 14, 1966 | ...... | ........ | Blank. |
| 42 | S66–62981 | S66–63129 | ............ | Nov. 14, 1966 | ...... | ........ | Major Aldrin inside spacecraft; underexposed. |
| 43 | S66–62982 | S66–63130 | ............ | Nov. 14, 1966 | ...... | ........ | Major Aldrin inside spacecraft; underexposed. |
| 44 | S66–62983 | S66–63131 | ............ | Nov. 14, 1966 | ...... | ........ | Major Aldrin inside spacecraft; underexposed. |
| 45 | S66–62984 | S66–63132 | ............ | Nov. 14, 1966 | ...... | ........ | Major Aldrin inside spacecraft; underexposed. |
| 46 | S66–62985 | S66–63133 | ............ | Nov. 14, 1966 | ...... | ........ | Blank. |
| 47 | S66–62986 | S66–63134 | 39 | Nov. 14, 1966 | 10:06 | 156 | United Arab Republic, Libya: Mediterranean coast from Bengazi to El Alamein, Libyan Plateau; slightly out of focus. |
| 48 | S66–62987 | S66–63135 | 39 | Nov. 14, 1966 | 10:06 | 156 | United Arab Republic: Mediterranean coast from Sidi Barrani to Nile Delta, El Faiyum and Qattara Depressions; slightly out of focus. |
| 49 | S66–62988 | S66–63136 | 39 | Nov. 14, 1966 | 10:13 | 152 | Iran, Saudi Arabia, Qatar, Bahrain: Persian Gulf, Zagros Mountains; slightly out of focus. |
| 50 | S66–62989 | S66–63137 | 39 | Nov. 14, 1966 | 10:13 | 151 | Iran, Trucial States: Persian Gulf, Qeshm Island, Zagros Mountains; slightly out of focus. |
| 51 | S66–62990 | S66–63138 | 39 | Nov. 14, 1966 | 10:14 | 151 | Iran: Gulf of Oman, Makran Ranges; slightly out of focus. |
| 52 | S66–62991 | S66–63139 | 39 | Nov. 14, 1966 | 10:14 | 151 | Iran, Pakistan, Afghanistan: Makran Ranges; slightly out of focus. |
| 53 | S66–62992 | S66–63140 | 39 | Nov. 14, 1966 | 10:15 | 150 | Pakistan; Makran and Kirthar Ranges, Arabian Sea coast; slightly out of focus. |
| 54 | S66–62993 | S66–63141 | 39 | Nov. 14, 1966 | 10:16 | 149 | Pakistan, India: Makran and Kirthar Ranges, Indus River, Thar Desert, Arabian Sea coast; slightly out of focus. |
| 55 | S66–62994 | S66–63142 | 39 | Nov. 14, 1966 | 10:17 | 149 | Pakistan, India: Thar Desert, Aravalli Range; slightly out of focus. |
| 56 | S66–62995 | S66–63143 | ............ | Nov. 14, 1966 | ...... | ........ | Light in spacecraft. |
| 57 | S66–62996 | S66–63144 | ............ | Nov. 14, 1966 | ...... | ........ | Blank. |
| 58 | S66–62997 | S66–63145 | ............ | Nov. 14, 1966 | ...... | ........ | Equipment jettison, ELSS, other gear. |
| 59 | S66–62998 | S66–63146 | ............ | Nov. 14, 1966 | ...... | ........ | Equipment jettison, ELSS, other gear. |
| 60 | S66–62999 | S66–63147 | ............ | Nov. 14, 1966 | ...... | ........ | Equipment jettison, ELSS, other gear. |
| 61 | S66–63000 | S66–63148 | ............ | Nov. 14, 1966 | ...... | ........ | Equipment jettison, ELSS, other gear. |
| 62 | S66–63001 | S66–63149 | ............ | Nov. 14, 1966 | ...... | ........ | Equipment jettison, ELSS, other gear. |
| 63 | S66–63002 | S66–63150 | ............ | Nov. 14, 1966 | ...... | ........ | Equipment jettison, ELSS, other gear. |
| 64 | S66–63003 | S66–63151 | ............ | Nov. 14, 1966 | ...... | ........ | Equipment jettison, ELSS, other gear. |
| 65 | S66–63004 | S66–63152 | ............ | Nov. 14, 1966 | ...... | ........ | Equipment jettison, ELSS, other gear. |
| 66 | S66–63006 | S66–63154 | ............ | Nov. 14, 1966 | ...... | ........ | Equipment jettison, ELSS, other gear. |
| 67 | S66–63007 | S66–63155 | ............ | Nov. 14, 1966 | ...... | ........ | Standup EVA, nose of spacecraft. |
| 68 | S66–63008 | S66–63156 | ............ | Nov. 14, 1966 | ...... | ........ | Standup EVA, rear view, adapter section. |
| 69 | S66–63009 | S66–63157 | ............ | Nov. 14, 1966 | ...... | ........ | Standup EVA, nose of spacecraft. |

MAGAZINE 11 Continued

| Frame | NASA/MSC Color No. | NASA/MSC B&W No. | Revolution | Date | GMT | Alt, N. Mi. | Area description |
|---|---|---|---|---|---|---|---|
| 70 | S66–63010 | S66–63158 | 44 | Nov. 14, 1966 | ....... | ........ | Standup EVA, nose of spacecraft. |
| 71 | S66–63011 | S66–63159 | 44 | Nov. 14, 1966 | ....... | ........ | Standup EVA, nose of spacecraft. |
| 72 | S66–63012 | S66–63160 | 44 | Nov. 14, 1966 | ....... | ........ | Standup EVA, nose of spacecraft. |
| *73* | *S66–63013* | *S66–63161* | *44* | *Nov. 14, 1966* | *17:37* | *150* | *Florida, Bahama Islands, north coast of Cuba.* |
| 74 | S66–63014 | S66–63162 | 44 | Nov. 14, 1966 | | | Out of focus. |
| *75* | *S66–63015* | *S66–63163* | *44* | *Nov. 14, 1966* | *19:04* | *154* | *Arizona, New Mexico, Mexico: Gulf of California, Baja California, Sonora, Chihuahua.* |
| 76 | S66–63016 | S66–63164 | 44 | Nov. 14, 1966 | 19:04 | 154 | Arizona, New Mexico, Mexico: Gulf of California, Baja California, Sonora, Chihuahua; contrail and shadow along coast. |
| 77 | S66–63017 | S66–63165 | 44 | Nov. 14, 1966 | 19:05 | 154 | Arizona, New Mexico, Mexico, Texas: Phoenix-El Paso-Presidio Panorama. |
| *78* | *S66–63018* | *S66–63166* | *44* | *Nov. 14, 1966* | *19:05* | *153* | *Arizona, New Mexico, Mexico, Texas: Phoenix-El Paso-Carlsbad Panorama.* |
| 79 | S66–63019 | S66–63167 | 44 | Nov. 14, 1966 | 19:06 | 153 | Mexico, Texas: Big Bend, Northern Sierra Madre Oriental, Glass Mountains, El Solitario, Marathon Uplift, Rio Grande. |
| 80 | S66–63020 | S66–63168 | 44 | Nov. 14, 1966 | 19:06 | 153 | Mexico, Texas: Big Bend, Northern Sierra Madre Oriental, Glass Mountains, El Solitario, Marathon Uplift, Rio Grande. |
| 81 | S66–63021 | S66–63169 | 44 | Nov. 14, 1966 | 19:07 | 153 | Texas, Louisiana, Oklahoma, Arkansas: San Antonio, Corpus Christi, Houston, Fort Worth-Dallas; Edwards Plateau, Gulf Coastal Plain. |
| 82 | S66–63022 | S66–63170 | 44 | Nov. 14, 1966 | 19:07 | 152 | Texas, Louisiana, Oklahoma, Arkansas: San Antonio, Corpus Christi, Houston, Fort Worth-Dallas; Edwards Plateau, Gulf Coastal Plain. |
| 83 | S66–63023 | S66–63171 | 44 | Nov. 14, 1966 | 19:07 | 152 | Texas, Louisiana, Oklahoma, Arkansas: San Antonio, Corpus Christi, Houston, Fort Worth-Dallas; Edwards Plateau, Gulf Coastal Plain. |
| *84* | *S66–63024* | *S66–63172* | *44* | *Nov. 14, 1966* | *19:07* | *152* | *Texas, Louisiana, Oklahoma, Arkansas: San Antonio, Corpus Christi, Houston, Fort Worth-Dallas; Edwards Plateau, Gulf Coastal Plain.* |
| *85* | *S66–63025* | *S66–63173* | *44* | *Nov. 14, 1966* | *19:08* | *152* | *Texas, Louisiana, Oklahoma, Arkansas: Austin, Waco, Shreveport, Beaumont, Houston; Edwards Plateau, Gulf Coastal Plain, Red River.* |
| 86 | S66–63026 | S66–63174 | 44 | Nov. 14, 1966 | 19:08 | 152 | Texas, Louisiana, Oklahoma, Arkansas: Austin, Waco, Shreveport, Beaumont, Houston; Edwards Plateau, Gulf Coastal Plain, Red River. |
| 87 | S66–63027 | S66–63175 | 44 | Nov. 14, 1966 | 19:08 | 152 | Texas, Louisiana, Arakansas: Houston, Beaumont; Gulf Coastal Plain from Matagorda Bay to Mississippi Delta; MSC area astrodome. |
| 88 | S66–63028 | S66–63176 | 44 | Nov. 14, 1966 | 19:08 | 152 | Texas, Louisiana, Arkansas: Houston, Beaumont; Gulf Coastal Plain from Matagorda Bay to Mississippi Delta; MSC area astrodome. |
| 89 | S66–63029 | S66–63177 | 44 | Nov. 14, 1966 | 19:08 | 152 | Texas, Louisiana, Arkansas: Houston, Beaumont; Gulf Coastal Plain from Matagorda Bay to Mississippi Delta; MSC area astrodome. |
| 90 | S66–63030 | S66–63178 | 44 | Nov. 14, 1966 | 19:08 | 152 | Texas, Louisiana, Arkansas: Houston, Beaumont; Gulf Coastal Plain from Matagorda Bay to Mississippi Delta; MSC area astrodome. |
| *91* | *S66–63031* | *S66–63179* | *44* | *Nov. 14, 1966* | *19:08* | *152* | *Texas, Louisiana, Arkansas: Houston, Beaumont; Gulf Coastal Plain from Matagorda Bay to Mississippi Delta; MSC area astrodome.* |
| 92 | S66–63032 | S66–63180 | 44 | Nov. 14, 1966 | 19:08 | 152 | Texas, Louisiana, Arkansas: Houston, Beaumont; Gulf Coastal Plain from Matagorda Bay to Mississippi Delta; MSC area astrodome. |

MAGAZINE 11 Continued

| Frame | NASA/MSC Color No. | NASA/MSC B&W No. | Revolution | Date | GMT | Alt, N. Mi. | Area description |
|---|---|---|---|---|---|---|---|
| 93 | S66–63033 | S66–63181 | 44 | Nov. 14, 1966 | 19:09 | 152 | Texas, Louisiana, Arkansas: Houston, Beaumont; Gulf Coastal Plain from Matagorda Bay to Mississippi Delta; MSC area astrodome. |
| *94* | *S66–63034* | *S66–63182* | *44* | *Nov. 14, 1966* | *19:09* | *152* | *Texas, Louisiana, Arkansas: Houston, Beaumont; Gulf Coastal Plain from Matagorda Bay to Mississippi Delta; MSC area astrodome.* |
| *95* | *S66–63035* | *S66–63183* | *44* | *Nov. 14, 1966* | *19:09* | *152* | *Texas, Louisiana: Houston, Beaumont; Gulf Coastal Plain from White Lake to Corpus Christi.* |
| 96 | S66–63036 | S66–63184 | 44 | Nov. 14, 1966 | 19:09 | 152 | Texas, Louisiana: Houston, Beaumont; Gulf Coastal Plain from Cameron to Brownsville. |
| 97 | S66–63037 | S66–63185 | 44 | Nov. 14, 1966 | 19:09 | 152 | Texas, Louisiana: Houston, Beaumont; Gulf Coastal Plain from Cameron to Brownsville. |
| *98* | *S66–63038* | *S66–63186* | *44* | *Nov. 14, 1966* | *19:09* | *151* | *Texas, Louisiana: Houston, Beaumont; Gulf Coastal Plain from Cameron to Brownsville.* |
| 99 | S66–63039 | S66–63187 | 44 | Nov. 14, 1966 | 19:10 | 151 | Texas, Louisiana: Houston, Beaumont; Gulf Coastal Plain from Cameron to Brownsville. |
| *100* | *S66–63040* | *S66–63188* | *44* | *Nov. 14, 1966* | *19:11* | *150* | *Florida: Orlando, Cape Kennedy.* |
| 101 | S66–63041 | S66–63189 | 44 | Nov. 14, 1966 | 19:12 | 150 | Florida: Orlando, Cape Kennedy. |
| 102 | S66–63042 | S66–63190 | 44 | Nov. 14, 1966 | 19:12 | 150 | Florida: Orlando, Cape Kennedy. |
| 103 | S66–63043 | S66–63191 | ............ | Nov. 14, 1966 | ...... | ........ | Blank. |
| *104* | *S66–63044* | *S66–63192* | *45* | *Nov. 14, 1966* | *20:40* | *152* | *Mexico: Baja California, from Angel de la Guarda to Santa Rosalia, cloud-covered mainland; Sun glint.* |
| 105 | S66–63045 | S66–63193 | 45 | Nov. 14, 1966 | 20:40 | 152 | Mexico: Baja California, from Angel de la Guarda to Santa Rosalia, cloud-covered mainland; Sun glint. |
| 106 | S66–63046 | S66–63194 | 45 | Nov. 14, 1966 | 20:40 | 151 | Mexico: Baja California, from Angel de la Guarda to Santa Rosalia, cloud-covered mainland; Sun glint. |
| 107 | S66–63047 | S66–63195 | 45 | Nov. 14, 1966 | 20:40 | 151 | Mexico: Baja California, from Angel de la Guarda to Santa Rosalia, cloud-covered mainland; Sun glint. |
| 108 | S66–63048 | S66–63196 | 45 | Nov. 14, 1966 | 20:40 | 151 | Mexico: Baja California, from Angel de la Guarda to Santa Rosalia, cloud-covered mainland; Sun glint. |
| 109 | S66–63049 | S66–63197 | 45 | Nov. 14, 1966 | 20:40 | 151 | Mexico: Baja California, from Angel de la Guarda to Santa Rosalia, cloud-covered mainland; Sun glint. |
| 110 | S66–63050 | S66–63198 | 45 | Nov. 14, 1966 | 20:40 | 151 | Mexico: Baja California, from Angel de la Guarda to Santa Rosalia, cloud-covered mainland; Sun glint. |
| 111 | S66–63051 | S66–63199 | 45 | Nov. 14, 1966 | 20:41 | 151 | Mexico: Baja California, from Angel de la Guarda to Santa Rosalia, cloud-covered mainland; Sun glint. |
| 112 | S66–63052 | S66–63200 | 45 | Nov. 14, 1966 | 20:41 | 151 | Mexico: Baja California, from Punta Eugenia to La Paz, cloud-covered mainland; Sun glint. |
| 113 | S66–63053 | S66–63201 | 45 | Nov. 14, 1966 | 20:41 | 151 | Mexico: Baja California, from Punta Eugenia to La Paz, cloud-covered mainland; Sun glint. |
| *114* | *S66–63054* | *S66–63202* | *45* | *Nov. 14, 1966* | *20:41* | *151* | *Mexico: Baja California, from Punta Eugenia to La Paz, cloud-covered mainland; Sun glint.* |
| *115* | *S66–63055* | *S66–63203* | *45* | *Nov. 14, 1966* | *20:41* | *151* | *Mexico, Texas: Chihuahua, Presidio; Sierra Madre Occidental, Big Bend, El Solitario, Rio Grande, Southern Basin and Range.* |
| 116 | S66–63056 | S66–63204 | 45 | Nov. 14, 1966 | 20:43 | 150 | Mexico, Texas: Valleys of Nueces and Frio Rivers, Rio Grande, Falcon Reservoir. |
| 117 | S66–63057 | S66–63205 | 45 | Nov. 14, 1966 | 20:43 | 150 | Mexico, Texas: Gulf coast, Laguna Madre-Corpus Christi-Matagorda Bay. |

MAGAZINE 11 Continued

| Frame | NASA/MSC Color No. | NASA/MSC B&W No. | Revolution | Date | GMT. | Alt, N. Mi. | Area description |
|---|---|---|---|---|---|---|---|
| 118 | S66-63058 | S66-63206 | 45 | Nov. 14, 1966 | 20:43 | 150 | Mexico, Texas: Gulf coast, Laguna Madre-Corpus Christi-Matagorda Bay. |
| 119 | S66-63059 | S66-63207 | 45 | Nov. 14, 1966 | 20:43 | 149 | Mexico, Texas: Gulf coast, Laguna Madre-Corpus Christi-Matagorda Bay. |
| *120* | *S66-63060* | *S66-63208* | *45* | *Nov. 14, 1966* | *20:43* | *149* | *Mexico, Texas: Gulf coast, Laguna Madre-Corpus Christi-Matagorda Bay.* |
| 121 | S66-63061 | S66-63209 | 45 | Nov. 14, 1966 | 20:43 | 149 | Texas, Louisiana, Oklahoma, Arkansas: gulf coast from Matagorda Bay to Mississippi Delta. |
| *122* | *S66-63062* | *S66-63210* | *45* | *Nov. 14, 1966* | *20:44* | *149* | *Texas, Louisiana, Oklahoma, Arkansas: gulf coast from Matagorda Bay to Mississippi Delta.* |
| *123* | *S66-63063* | *S66-63211* | *45* | *Nov. 14, 1966* | *20:46* | *147* | *Florida: Keys, Cay Sal Bank, Florida Straits.* |
| 124 | S66-63064 | S66-63212 | 45 | Nov. 14, 1966 | 20:46 | 147 | Cuba: La Habana, Piñar del Rio, Matanzas, Las Villas, Provinces. |
| 125 | S66-63065 | S66-63213 | 45 | Nov. 14, 1966 | 20:47 | 147 | Cuba: La Habana, Piñar del Rio, Matanzas, Las Villas Provinces. |
| 126 | S66-63066 | S66-63214 | 46 | Nov. 14, 1966 | 20:47 | 146 | Central Cuba; Bahama Bank. |
| 127 | S66-63067 | S66-63215 | 46 | Nov. 14, 1966 | 20:49 | 146 | Cuba: Oriente, Camaguey Provinces. |
| 128 | S66-63068 | S66-63216 | 46 | Nov. 14, 1966 | 20:49 | 146 | Cuba: Oriente, Camaguey Provinces; Jamaica. |
| 129 | S66-63069 | S66-63217 | 46 | Nov. 14, 1966 | 20:49 | 145 | Cuba: Oriente, Camaguey Provinces; Jamaica. |
| 130 | S66-63070 | S66-63218 | 46 | Nov. 14, 1966 | 20:49 | 145 | Bahama Islands: Great Inagua, Acklins, Mayaguana, The Caicos. |
| 131 | S66-63071 | S66-63219 | 46 | Nov. 14, 1966 | 20:50 | 145 | Bahama Islands: Great Inagua, Acklins, Mayaguana, The Caicos. |
| 132 | S66-63072 | S66-63220 | 46 | Nov. 14, 1966 | 20:50 | ........ | Bahama Islands: Great Inagua, Grand Turk, Mayaguana, The Caicos. |
| 133 | S66-63073 | S66-63221 | 46 | Nov. 14, 1966 | ....... | ........ | Limb, sunset. |
| 134 | S66-63074 | S66-63222 | 47 | Nov. 14, 1966 | ....... | ........ | Clouds over Pacific Ocean. |
| 135 | S66-63075 | S66-63223 | 47 | Nov. 14, 1966 | ....... | ........ | Clouds over Pacific Ocean. |
| *136* | *S66-63076* | *S66-63224* | *47* | *Nov. 14, 1966* | ....... | ........ | *Clouds over Pacific Ocean.* |
| *137* | *S66-63077* | *S66-63225* | *47* | *Nov. 14, 1966* | *23:34* | *154* | *Hawaiian Islands: Midway, Kure, Pearl and Hermes Reef.* |
| 138 | S66-63078 | S66-63226 | 47 | Nov. 14, 1966 | 23:34 | 154 | Hawaiian Islands: Midway, Kure, Pearl and Hermes Reef. |
| 139 | S66-63079 | S66-63227 | 47 | Nov. 14, 1966 | 23:35 | 154 | Hawaiian Islands: Pearl and Hermes Reef, Salmon Bank. |
| *140* | *S66-63080* | *S66-63228* | *47* | *Nov. 14, 1966* | *23:36* | *153* | *Hawaiian Islands: Pearl and Hermes Reef, Salmon Bank, Midway, Kure.* |
| *141* | *S66-63081* | *S66-63229* | *53* | *Nov. 15, 1966* | *08:32* | *154* | *United Arab Republic, Saudi Arabia, Sudan: Red Sea; jetstream clouds.* |
| *142* | *S66-63082* | *S66-63230* | *53* | *Nov. 15, 1966* | *08:36* | *153* | *Iran, Trucial States, Muscat and Oman: Qeshm Island, Gulf of Oman, Persian Gulf, Zagros Mountains, Makran Ranges.* |
| *143* | *S66-63083* | *S66-63231* | *55* | *Nov. 15, 1966* | *11:31* | *155* | *Mauritania, Spanish Sahara, Algeria: Erg Iguidi, Yetti Plains, south edge of Tindouf Basin.* |
| 144 | S66-63084 | S66-63232 | ............ | Nov. 15, 1966 | ....... | ........ | Blank. |
| 145 | S66-63085 | S66-63233 | 55 | Nov. 15, 1966 | ....... | ........ | Bénard cells over Pacific Ocean. |
| 146 | S66-63086 | S66-63234 | 55 | Nov. 15, 1966 | ....... | ........ | Bénard cells over Pacific Ocean. |
| 147 | S66-63087 | S66-63235 | 56 | Nov. 15, 1966 | 13:12 | 150 | Libya, Algeria: Hamada el Hamra, Tiririne Dunes, Grand Erg Oriental; note contrail and shadow. |

MAGAZINE 17

| Frame | NASA/MSC | | Revolution | Date | GMT | Alt, N. Mi. | Area description |
|---|---|---|---|---|---|---|---|
| | Color No. | B&W No. | | | | | |
| 1 | S66–62867 | S66–62797 | ... | ... | ... | ... | Blank. |
| 2 | S66–62868 | S66–62798 | 13 | Nov. 12, 1966 | ... | ... | Docked to Agena, hatch open. |
| 3 | S66–62869 | S66–62799 | 13 | Nov. 12, 1966 | ... | ... | Docked to Agena, hatch open. |
| 4 | S66–62870 | S66–62800 | 13 | Nov. 12, 1966 | ... | ... | Docked to Agena, hatch open. |
| 5 | S66–62871 | S66–62801 | 13 | Nov. 12, 1966 | ... | ... | Docked to Agena, hatch open. |
| 6 | S66–62872 | S66–62802 | 13 | Nov. 12, 1966 | ... | ... | Docked to Agena, hatch open. |
| 7 | S66–62873 | S66–62803 | 13 | Nov. 12, 1966 | ... | ... | Spacecraft skin, looking aft, hatch open; Maurer 16-mm movie camera. |
| 8 | S66–62874 | S66–62804 | 13 | Nov. 12, 1966 | ... | ... | Spacecraft skin, looking aft, hatch open; Maurer 16-mm movie camera. |
| 9 | S66–62875 | S66–62805 | 13 | Nov. 12, 1966 | ... | ... | Spacecraft skin, hatch open. |
| 10 | S66–62876 | S66–62806 | 13 | Nov. 12, 1966 | ... | ... | Docked to Agena, hatch open; clouds, ocean. |
| 11 | S66–62877 | S66–62807 | 13 | Nov. 12, 1966 | ... | ... | Docked to Agena, hatch open; clouds, ocean. |
| 12 | S66–62878 | S66–62808 | 13 | Nov. 12, 1966 | ... | ... | Docked to Agena, hatch open; clouds, ocean. |
| 13 | S66–62879 | S66–62809 | 13 | Nov. 12, 1966 | ... | ... | Docked to Agena, hatch open; clouds, ocean. |
| 14 | S66–62880 | S66–62810 | 13 | Nov. 12, 1966 | ... | ... | Docked to Agena, hatch open; Mexico: Baja California. |
| 15 | S66–62881 | S66–62811 | 13 | Nov. 12, 1966 | ... | ... | Docked to Agena, hatch open; Mexico: Baja California. |
| 16 | S66–62882 | S66–62812 | 13 | Nov. 12, 1966 | ... | ... | Docked to Agena, hatch open; Mexico: Baja California. |
| *17* | *S66–62883* | *S66–62813* | *13* | *Nov. 12, 1966* | *17:30* | *158* | *Docked to Agena, hatch open; Mexico: West coast from Culiacan to Manzanillo.* |
| 18 | S66–62884 | S66–62814 | 13 | Nov. 12, 1966 | 17:30 | 158 | Docked to Agena, hatch open; Mexico; West coast from Culiacan to Manzanillo. |
| 19 | S66–62885 | S66–62815 | 13 | Nov. 12, 1966 | 17:31 | 158 | Docked to Agena, hatch open; Mexico: West coast from Culiacan to Manzanillo. |
| 20 | S66–62886 | S66–62816 | 13 | Nov. 12, 1966 | 17:31 | 158 | Docked to Agena, hatch open; Mexico: West coast north of Manzanillo. |
| *21* | *S66–62887* | *S66–62817* | *13* | *Nov. 12, 1966* | *17:32* | *158* | *Docked to Agena, hatch open; Mexico: Mexico City, Puebla; Neo-Volcanic plateau, Lago de Chapala.* |
| 22 | S66–62888 | S66–62818 | 13 | Nov. 12, 1966 | 17:32 | 157 | Docked to Agena, hatch open; Mexico: Mexico City, Puebla; Neo-Volcanic plateau, Lago de Chapala. |
| *23* | *S66–62889* | *S66–62819* | *13* | *Nov. 12, 1966* | *17:32* | *157* | *Docked to Agena, hatch open; Mexico: Central and eastern Mexico, north of Leon, Coahuila Basin, Sierra Madre Occidental and Oriental.* |
| 24 | S66–62890 | S66–62820 | 13 | Nov. 12, 1966 | 17:32 | 157 | Docked to Agena, hatch open; Mexico: Mexico City, Pueblo; Neo-Volcanic plateau. |
| *25* | *S66–62891* | *S66–62821* | *13* | *Nov. 12, 1966* | *17:33* | *157* | *Docked to Agena, hatch open; Mexico: Isthmus of Tehuantepec, Yucatan Peninsula.* |
| 26 | S66–62892 | S66–62822 | 13 | Nov. 12, 1966 | 17:34 | 156 | Docked to Agena, hatch open; Mexico: Yucatan Peninsula, Yucatan Channel. |
| 27 | S66–62893 | S66–62823 | 13 | Nov. 12, 1966 | 17:34 | 156 | Docked to Agena, hatch open; Gulf of Mexico, U.S. gulf coast. |
| 28 | S66–62894 | S66–62824 | 13 | Nov. 12, 1966 | 17:35 | 156 | Docked to Agena, hatch open; Gulf of Mexico, U.S. gulf coast. |
| 29 | S66–62895 | S66–62825 | 13 | Nov. 12, 1966 | 17:35 | 156 | Docked to Agena, hatch open; Gulf of Mexico, U.S. gulf coast. |
| 30 | S66–62896 | S66–62826 | 13 | Nov. 12, 1966 | 17:35 | 155 | Docked to Agena, hatch open; Gulf of Mexico, U.S. gulf coast. |
| *31* | *S66–62897* | *S66–62827* | *13* | *Nov. 12, 1966* | *17:36* | *155* | *Docked to Agena, hatch open; Florida.* |
| 32 | S66–62898 | S66–62828 | 13 | Nov. 12, 1966 | 17:37 | 155 | Docked to Agena, hatch open; Florida. |
| 33 | S66–62899 | S66–62829 | 13 | Nov. 12, 1966 | 17:37 | 155 | Docked to Agena, hatch open; Florida. |
| *34* | *S66–62900* | *S66–62830* | *13* | *Nov. 12, 1966* | *17:37* | *155* | *Docked to Agena, hatch open; Florida, Bahama Islands.* |
| 35 | S66–62901 | S66–62831 | 13 | Nov. 12, 1966 | 17:37 | 155 | Docked to Agena, hatch open; Florida, Bahama Islands. |

MAGAZINE 17 Continued

| Frame | NASA/MSC Color No. | NASA/MSC B&W No. | Revolution | Date | GMT | Alt, N. Mi. | Area description |
|---|---|---|---|---|---|---|---|
| 36 | S66–62902 | S66–62832 | 13 | Nov. 12, 1966 | 17:37 | 155 | Docked to Agena, hatch open; Florida, Bahama Islands. |
| *37* | *S66–62903* | *S66–62833* | *13* | *Nov. 12, 1966* | *17:37* | *155* | *Docked to Agena, hatch open; Florida, Bahama Islands.* |
| 38 | S66–62904 | S66–62834 | 13 | Nov. 12, 1966 | 17:37 | 154 | Docked to Agena, hatch open; Florida, Bahama Islands. |
| *39* | *S66–62905* | *S66–62835* | *13* | *Nov. 12, 1966* | *17:37* | *154* | *Docked to Agena, hatch open; Florida, Bahama Islands.* |
| 40 | S66–62906 | S66–62836 | 14 | Nov. 12, 1966 | 17:38 | 154 | Docked to Agena, hatch open; Florida. |
| 41 | S66–62907 | S66–62837 | 14 | Nov. 12, 1966 | 17:38 | 154 | Docked to Agena, hatch open; Florida. |
| *42* | *S66–62908* | *S66–62838* | *14* | *Nov. 12, 1966* | *17:38* | *154* | *Docked to Agena, hatch open; Florida, Bahama Islands: Miami Keys.* |
| 43 | S66–62909 | S66–62839 | 14 | Nov. 12, 1966 | 17:38 | 154 | Docked to Agena, hatch open; Bahama Islands. |
| 44 | S66–62910 | S66–62840 | 14 | Nov. 12, 1966 | 17:38 | 154 | Docked to Agena, hatch open; Bahama Islands. |
| *45* | *S66–62911* | *S66–62841* | *14* | *Nov. 12, 1966* | ....... | ........ | *Docked to Agena, hatch open; clouds, ocean.* |
| 46 | S66–62912 | S66–62842 | 14 | Nov. 12, 1966 | ....... | ........ | Docked to Agena, hatch open; clouds, ocean. |
| *47* | *S66–62913* | *S66–62843* | *14* | *Nov. 12, 1966* | ....... | ........ | *Docked to Agena, hatch open; clouds, ocean.* |
| *48* | *S66–62914* | *S66–62844* | *14* | *Nov. 12, 1966* | ....... | ........ | *Docked to Agena, hatch open; clouds, ocean.* |
| 49 | S66–62915 | S66–62845 | 14 | Nov. 12, 1966 | ....... | ........ | Inside spacecraft, out of focus. |
| 50 | S66–62916 | S66–62846 | 14 | Nov. 12, 1966 | ....... | ........ | Inside spacecraft, out of focus. |
| 51 | S66–62917 | S66–62847 | 14 | Nov. 12, 1966 | ....... | ........ | Hatch open, looking aft; Maurer 16-mm movie camera. |
| 52 | S66–62918 | S66–62848 | 14 | Nov. 12, 1966 | ....... | ........ | Hatch open, looking aft; Maurer 16-mm movie camera. |
| 53 | S66–62919 | S66–62849 | 14 | Nov. 12, 1966 | ....... | ........ | Hatch open, looking aft; Maurer 16-mm movie camera. |
| 54 | S66–62920 | S66–62850 | 14 | Nov. 12, 1966 | ....... | ........ | Hatch open, looking aft; Maurer 16-mm movie camera. |
| 55 | S66–62921 | S66–62851 | 14 | Nov. 12, 1966 | ....... | ........ | Major Aldrin's helmet; out of focus. |
| 56 | S66–62922 | S66–62852 | 14 | Nov. 12, 1966 | ....... | ........ | Major Aldrin's helmet. |
| 57 | S66–62923 | S66–62853 | 14 | Nov. 12, 1966 | ....... | ........ | Major Aldrin's helmet. |
| 58 | S66–62924 | S66–62854 | 14 | Nov. 12, 1966 | ....... | ........ | Major Aldrin's helmet, open hatch. |
| 59 | S66–62925 | S66–62855 | 14 | Nov. 12, 1966 | ....... | ........ | Major Aldrin's helmet, open hatch. |
| 60 | S66–62926 | S66–62856 | 14 | Nov. 12, 1966 | ....... | ........ | Major Aldrin's helmet, open hatch; Blue Maurer camera. |
| 61 | S66–62927 | S66–62857 | 14 | Nov. 12, 1966 | ....... | ........ | Major Aldrin's helmet, open hatch; Blue Maurer camera. |
| 62 | S66–62928 | S66–62858 | 14 | Nov. 12, 1966 | 17:52 | 143 | Docked to Agena, hatch open; Spanish Sahara, Mauritania: Atlantic coast at Cap Blanc and Cap Barbas. |
| 63 | S66–62929 | S66–62859 | 14 | Nov. 12, 1966 | 17:52 | 143 | Docked to Agena, hatch open; Spanish Sahara, Mauritania: Atlantic coast at Cap Blanc and Cap Barbas. |
| 64 | S66–62930 | S66–62860 | 14 | Nov. 12, 1966 | 17:52 | 143 | Docked to Agena, hatch open; Spanish Sahara, Mauritania: Atlantic coast at Cap Blanc and Cap Barbas. |
| 65 | S66–62931 | S66–62861 | 14 | Nov. 12, 1966 | 17:52 | 142 | Docked to Agena, hatch open; Spanish Sahara, Mauritania: Atlantic coast at Cap Blanc and Cap Barbas. |
| 66 | S66–62932 | S66–62862 | 14 | Nov. 12, 1966 | 17:52 | 142 | Docked to Agena, hatch open; Spanish Sahara, Mauritania: Atlantic coast at Cap Blanc and Cap Barbas. |
| 67 | S66–62933 | S66–62863 | 14 | Nov. 12, 1966 | 19:07 | 155 | Docked to Agena, hatch open; Mexico: West coast north of Culiacan; Sierra Madre Oriental, Baja California. |
| 68 | S66–62934 | S66–62864 | 14 | Nov. 12, 1966 | 19:07 | 155 | Docked to Agena, hatch open; Mexico: West coast north of Mazatlan; Sierra Madre Oriental, Baja California. |

| Frame | NASA/MSC | | Revolution | Date | GMT | Alt, N. Mi. | Area description |
|---|---|---|---|---|---|---|---|
| | Color No. | B&W No. | | | | | |
| 69 | S66–62935 | S66–62865 | 14 | Nov. 12, 1966 | 19:07 | 154 | Docked to Agena, hatch open; Mexico: West coast north of Cabo Corrientes; Sierra Madre Oriental, Baja California. |
| 70 | S66–62936 | S66–62866 | 14 | Nov. 12, 1966 | 19:08 | 154 | Docked to Agena, hatch open; Mexico: West coast from Culiacan to head of Gulf of California, Sierra Madre Oriental, Baja California. |

# GLOSSARY

**airglow** Broadly defined as the nonthermal radiation emitted by the Earth's atmosphere with the exception of auroral emission (northern lights) and radiation of cataclysmic origin such as lightning and meteor trains. Airglow at night, also called nightglow, is always present and is readily observed by the naked eye on a clear night away from city lights. The peak of the night-glow layer occurs at approximately 90 kilometers, the emission being the result, for example, of excited molecular oxygen, atomic oxygen, and sodium.

**alluvium** A general term for all detrital deposits resulting from the operations of modern rivers; this includes the sediments laid down in river beds, flood plains, lakes, and estuaries.

**altocumulus** A cloud path or layer composed of laminae, rounded masses, or rolls which are sometimes partly diffused and may or may not merge. The cloud elements usually are smaller than stratocumulus and larger than cirrocumulus. They may occur at more than one level and are made up largely of small liquid water droplets.

**anticline** A fold or arch of rock strata, usually dipping in opposite directions away from an axis.

**anticyclone** A region of relatively high atmospheric pressure whose circulation is clockwise in the Northern Hemisphere and counterclockwise in the Southern Hemisphere. The region may be 3000 kilometers or more wide.

**island arc** Islands or mountains arranged in a great curve. A curved belt of islands, partly volcanic, in or near ocean basins, such as the Aleutian Islands.

**Archean** The term is generally applied to the oldest rocks of the Precambrian. However, usage is changing and the new term, *Early Precambrian,* is preferred. It means the same as *Archeozoic* also.

**atoll** A ringlike "coral or calcareous algae" island or islands encircling, or nearly encircling, a lagoon.

**basalt** A fine-grained, dark-colored, igneous rock containing about 50 percent $SiO_2$ and characteristic minerals.

**basin-and-swell structure** Geologic term for areas such as the central United States in which the dominant structures are very large domes, arches, and troughs with very shallow dips; characteristic of tectonically stable areas.

**bedrock** Any solid rock, in place, exposed at the surface of the Earth or overlain by unconsolidated material.

**Bénard cell** A form of cellular convection, studied in the laboratory by the French physicist, H. Bénard, in which the vertical circulation may be upward in the core of the cell and downward on the edges, or it may be reversed.

**carbonate** A compound containing the radical $CO_3$, used geologically as a short term for calcium or magnesium carbonate rocks such as limestone or dolomite.

**cay** A flat mound of sand built up on a reef flat slightly above high-tide level.

**Cenozoic** The latest of the four eras into which geologic time is divided, beginning about 70 million years ago. Also, the whole group of stratified rocks deposited during the Cenozoic era. The era includes Tertiary and Quaternary.

**cellular convection** An organized air motion in distinct convection cells, having either upward or downward motion in the central portions of the cell, and having the opposite either sinking or rising flow in the cell's outer regions. The phenomenon is similar to that often referred to as Bénard cells displayed in fluids on laboratory scale.

**cirrostratus** A whitish cloud veil of fibrous or smooth appearance occurring at altitudes of 6 to 18 kilometers, composed largely of ice crystals. It is frequently thin enough to be transparent.

**cirrus** White, delicate filaments, patches, or bands of cloud which have a fibrous appearance and often a silky sheen. The cloud is composed mainly of ice crystals and in the Tropics it is found at 6 to 18 kilometers in altitude.

**clastic** Consisting of fragments of rocks or of organic structures that have been moved from their places of origin.

**cloud street** A line or row of cumulus clouds usually alined nearly parallel to the wind direction.

**coesite** A high-pressure polymorph of $SiO_2$; first created artificially by L. Coes and later found in rock from Meteor Crater, Ariz., by E. Chao. It is believed to be indicative of meteoritic impact.

**cold front** A boundary zone between an advancing mass of cold air and a warmer air mass.

**color infrared film** A color film sensitive to infrared radiation as well as visible light; used chiefly to photograph vegetation. Colors are rendered differently from the colors seen by the eye; e.g., greens are reproduced as reds.

**continental drift** The supposed horizontal movement of entire continents for hundreds or thousands of miles over geologic time; indicated by similarities in geologic structure, lithology, and fossil affinities on opposite sides of oceans such as the South Atlantic. It is still a disputed concept.

**convection** Atmospheric motions that are predominantly vertical, resulting in the vertical transport and mixing of atmospheric properties, normally caused by heating from the land or water surface below (meteorological).

**convergence** An inflow of air on a horizontal plane. Near the Earth's surface the converging air may rise and produce convective clouds (meteorological). Situation whereby waters of different origins come together at a point or, more commonly, along a line known as a convergence line (oceanographic).

**coral** A calcareous skeleton of a coral or group of corals which are bottom-dwelling marine animals.

**Cretaceous period** The third and latest of the periods included in the Mesozoic era, beginning about 135 million years ago and lasting about 65 million years, also the system of strata deposited in the Cretaceous period.

**cuesta** Ridge with one steep and one gently sloping side.

**cumulonimbus cloud** A heavy and dense cloud of convective origin. It may develop to 10 or 20 kilometers in height. The top is nearly always flattened and often spreads out in an anvil or plume containing predominantly ice crystals; a thundercloud accompanied by lightning, thunder, rain, and sometimes hail.

**cumulus cloud** Individual detached cloud elements, generally dense and with sharp outlines, developing vertically in the form of rising mounds, domes, or towers. The cloud has a high density of small water droplets which frequently are supercooled.

**cumulus congestus cloud** A large cumulus cloud with sharp outlines and great vertical development. It may be producing rain, but not yet have reached the thunderstorm stage.

**current** Horizontal movement of a fluid.

**cyclone** An atmospheric circulation rotating counterclockwise in the Northern Hemisphere and clockwise in the Southern Hemisphere; a storm.

**dendritic drainage pattern** This phenomenon is characterized by treelike branching of streams in all directions, with the tributaries joining the main stream at all angles.

**Devonian** The fourth, in order of age, of the periods comprising the Paleozoic era, following the Silurian period, beginning about 400 million years ago and lasting about 50 million years. Also the system of strata deposited during that time. Sometimes called the "Age of Fishes."

**dike** A tabular body of rock (usually igneous) that cuts across the structure of adjacent rocks or cuts massive rocks. Most dikes result from intrusion of magma; some are formed by injection of sand or mud.

**dip** The maximum angle at which a stratum or any planar feature is inclined from the horizontal. The dip is at a right angle to the strike.

**divergence** A horizontal flow of water in different directions, from a common center or zone; often associated with upwelling.

**ebb tide, falling tide** The portion of the tide cycle between high water and the following low water.

**eddy** A circulation drawing its energy from a flow of much larger scale and brought about by flow irregularities (meteorological). A circular movement of water usually formed where currents pass obstructions, where two adjacent currents flow counter to each other, or along the edge of a permanent current (oceanographic).

**embayment** An embayment is similar to a basin of sedimentation and may be one flank of a larger subsiding feature. Used in a structural sense to designate a reentrant of sedimentary rocks into a crystalline massif.

**ephemeral stream** A stream or portion of a stream which flows only in direct response to precipitation. It receives little or no water from springs and no long-continued supply from melting snow or other sources. Its channel is at all times above the water table.

**epoch** Geologic time unit corresponding to a series; a subdivision of a period.

**equatorial counter current** An oceanic current flowing eastward in a narrow band in an equatorial region; usually imbedded in an equatorial current that is flowing westward.

**era** A large division of geologic time of the highest order, comprising one or more periods. The eras now generally recognized are the Archeozoic, Proterozoic, Paleozoic, Mesozoic, and Cenozoic. In some cases, Early Precambrian is substituted for Archeozoic and Late Precambrian for Proterozoic.

**erosion** The group of processes whereby earthy or rock material is loosened or dissolved and removed from any part of the Earth's surface. It includes the processes of weathering, solution, corrosion, and transportation. The mechanical wear and transportation are affected by running water, moving ice, or winds, which use rock fragments to pound or grind other rocks to powder or sand.

**escarpment** A cliff or relatively steep slope separating level or gently sloping tracts.

**estuary** Drainage channel adjacent to the sea in which the tide ebbs and flows. Some estuaries are the lower courses of rivers or smaller streams, others are no more than drainage ways that lead sea water into and out of coastal swamps.

**fault** A fracture or fracture zone along which there has been displacement of the two sides relative to one another parallel to the fracture. The displacement may be a few inches or many miles.

**fold** A bend in strata or any planar structures.

**friction layer** The layer of atmosphere from the surface to about 0.5 to 2 kilometers that is influenced by frictional and diurnal phenomena.

**gabbro** Loosely used for any coarse-grained dark igneous rock, chemically similar to basalt, and considered the plutonic (formed by solidification of molten magma deep within the Earth) equivalent of basalt.

**geosyncline** A large, generally linear trough that subsided deeply throughout a long period of geologic time and in which a thick secession of stratified sediments and possibly extrusive volcanic rocks has commonly accumulated. The strata of many geosynclines have been folded into mountains. Many types have been differentiated and named.

**glaciation** Alteration of the Earth's solid surface through erosion and deposition by glacial ice.

**glitter pattern** The specular reflectance of the Sun's rays off the ocean's surface.

**gneiss** A coarse-grained rock in which bands rich in granular minerals alternate with bands in which schistose minerals predominate.

**graben** Large blocks of the crust that have been downdropped along fractures.

**graben faulting** A block, generally long compared to its width, that has been downthrown along faults relative to the rocks on either side.

**gradient** The rate of decrease of one quantity with respect to another.

**granite** Light-colored, coarse to medium-grained, plutonic rock containing alkali feldspars, quartz, and accessory minerals such as mica; of igneous or metamorphic origin.

**granodiorite** An intrusive igneous rock, similar to granite but with a higher plagioclase content.

**greenstone** An old field term applied to altered basic igneous rocks which owe their color to the presence of chlorite, hornblende, and epidote.

**Greenwich mean time** The local mean time of the Greenwich (prime) meridian. Now called Universal Time (astronomical); sometimes, Zulu or Z-time (U.S. Navy).

**ground elapsed time (GET)** Time elapsed from launch of spacecraft.

**homocline** A general name for any block of bedded rocks all dipping in the same direction.

**igneous rock** Rocks formed by solidification from a molten or partially molten state. One of three principal classes into which all rocks are divided. The others are sedimentary and metamorphic.

**intrusive (igneous) rock** One formed by consolidation of magma beneath the surface of the Earth, as opposed to extrusive rock formed from erupted magma (lava).

**island wake** A wake resulting from the division of an ocean current by an island producing an elongated area of upwelling on the lee side.

**jebel** Arabic for mountain.

**jetstream** Relatively strong winds concentrated within a narrow stream in the atmosphere. It may be thousands of kilometers long, hundreds of kilometers wide, and some kilometers in depth. A subtropical jetstream is found, at some longitudes, between 20° and 30° latitude.

**Jurassic** The middle of the three geological periods comprising the Mesozoic era. Also the system of strata deposited during that period, beginning about 180 million years ago and lasting about 45 million years.

**laccolith** A concordant, intrusive body that has domed up the overlying rocks and has a floor that is generally horizontal, but may be convex downward.

**lagoon** A body of shallow water, particularly one possessing a restricted connection with the sea. A water body within an atoll or behind barrier reefs or islands.

**lignite** A brownish-black coal in which the alteration of vegetal material has proceeded further than in peat but not so far as subbituminous coal.

**limb** Geologically, one of the two parts of an anticline or syncline on either side of the axis. Astronomically, the edge of a celestial object as viewed.

**limestone** A general term for that class of sedimentary rocks which contain at least 80 percent of the carbonates of calcium or magnesium.

**lineament** A structurally controlled topographic line, generally of regional extent.

**lithographic texture** A term used to denote grain size in calcareous sedimentary rocks. The grain size corresponds to that of clay, or less than 1/256 millimeter.

**low-pressure system** An area of minimum atmospheric pressure associated with cyclonic circulation.

**marl** Usually defined as a calcareous clay, or an intimate mixture of clay and particles of calcite or dolomite, usually fragments of shells.

**massif** A body of plutonic igneous or metamorphic rock, at least 10 to 20 miles in diameter, occurring as a structurally resistant mass in an uplifted area that may have been a mountain core.

**mesoscale** Small-scale weather patterns that may occur over distances of perhaps 15 to 1500 kilometers.

**Mesozoic** One of the eras of geologic time. It comprises the Triassic, Jurassic, and Cretaceous periods beginning about 225 million years ago and lasting 255 million years. Also the group of strata formed during the era.

**metamorphic** Rocks which have formed in the solid state in response to pronounced changes of temperature, pressure, and chemical environments, usually at depth.

**metasediments** Metamorphosed sedimentary rocks.

**microgranite** A fine-grained granite, usually a marginal phase of a granite intrusion.

**micrometeoroid** A very small solid body, generally less than a millimeter in diameter, moving in interplanetary space.

**minaret** A towerlike rock form.

**Miocene** The fourth of the five epochs into which the Tertiary period is divided. Also the series of strata deposited during that epoch.

**monsoons** Seasonal winds caused primarily by the much greater annual variation of temperature over large land areas compared with neighboring ocean surfaces. An excess of pressure occurs over land in winter and a deficit in summer. Monsoons are strongest on the southern and eastern sides of Asia.

**mosaic** A composite picture formed by assembling overlapping vertical aerial photographs taken from different camera positions.

**Neogene** The later of the two periods into which the Cenozoic era is divided in the classification adopted by the International Geological Congress and used by many European geologists. Also the system of strata deposited during that period.

**Neo-Volcanic** Of or pertaining to volcanic rocks or volcanic phenomena formed or taking place during the Cenozoic era.

**orogeny** The process of forming mountains, particularly by folding and thrusting.

**orographic cloud** A cloud, the existence, form, and extent of which are determined by the upslope flow of air over hills or mountains.

**outcrop** Bedrock exposed at the surface of the Earth.

**Paleogene** The earlier of the two periods comprised in the Cenozoic era, and used by many European gologists. Not in wide use in the United States.

**Paleozoic** One of the eras of geologic time, between the Late Precambrian and Mesozoic eras, that comprises the Cambrian, Ordovician, Silurian, Devonian, Mississippian, Pennsylvanian, and Permian systems. Also the group of rocks deposited during this era.

**pegmatite** Igneous rocks of coarse grain that are usually found as dikes associated with a large mass of igneous rock of finer grain size. The name usually refers to granite pegmatites. Some pegmatites contain rare minerals.

**pelagic** Pertaining to communities of marine organisms which live free from direct dependence on bottom or shore; the two types are free-swimming (nektonic) and floating forms (planktonic).

**Permian** Last period of the Paleozoic era. Also the system of rocks formed during the period.

**pillow lavas** Lavas that exhibit a peculiar structure consisting of an agglomeration of rounded masses that resemble pillows. The pillow structure is generally believed to be the result of subaqueous deposition.

**Pleistocene** The earlier of the two epochs comprised in the Quaternary period. Also called Glacial epoch and formally called ice age. Also the series of sediments deposited during that period.

**Pliocene** The latest of epochs comprised in the Tertiary period in the classification generally used. Also the series of strata deposited during the epoch.

**Precambrian** An era of geologic time. All rocks formed before Cambrian time. The oldest and longest period of geologic time.

**Quaternary** The younger of the two geologic periods in the Cenozoic era. It is subdivided into Pleistocene and Recent epochs or series. It comprises all geologic time and deposits from the end of the Tertiary until and including the present.

**radiosonde** A balloon-borne instrument for simultaneous measurement and transmission of meteorological data.

**reef** A chain or range of rock or coral, elevated above the surrounding bottom of the sea, generally submerged and dangerous to surface navigation.

**reverse faults** A fault along which the hanging wall has been raised relative to the foot wall. A normal fault is just the opposite.

**rheid** A body of rock showing flow structure; also used for masses of rock which have flowed over geologic time while below the melting point.

**rhyolite** An extrusive igneous rock chemically equivalent to granite.

**rift** A topographic depression formed along major faults.

**rift valley** A large valley produced by subsidence along two parallel faults. (See *graben.*)

**ring dike** An arcuate, rarely circular, dike with steep dip. Larger ring dikes may be many miles long, hundreds or thousands of feet thick; the radius or arc is generally from 1 to 10 miles; although some dikes may form a nearly complete circle or ellipse, more commonly they encompass one-third to three-fourths of the circle or ellipse.

**rip tide** A seaward flowing current brought about when waves elevate the water level along a coast. These currents are confined to the surf zone and are usually no longer than a few tens of meters. They are not associated with diurnal tides.

**salt plug/salt dome** A structure resulting from the upward movement of a salt mass, and with which oil and gas fields are frequently associated. In the gulf coast area of the United States, the salt is in the form of a roughly circular plug of relatively narrow diameter but often several thousand feet in depth.

**sandstone** A cemented or otherwise compacted detrital sediment, usually composed predominantly of quartz grains; some varieties are composed partly of other minerals such as feldspar.

**savanna** A tropical or subtropical region of grassland and other drought-resistant vegetation. This type of growth occurs in warm regions having a long, dry season alternating with a rainy season.

**scarp** An escarpment, cliff, or steep slope of some extent along the margin of a plateau, mesa, terrace, or bench.

**schist** A medium or coarse-grained metamorphic rock, with subparallel orientation of the micaceous minerals which dominate its composition.

**sea breeze** A local coastal wind that blows from sea to land caused by the temperature difference when the sea surface is colder than the adjacent land.

**sea-surface structure** Features of the sea surface created by wind (waves), currents, differences in density of adjacent waters, and the shape of the ocean basin. Only the surface expressions of the features and their horizontal extent are visible from space.

**sedimentary rocks** Rocks formed by the accumulation of sediment. The sediment may consist of rock fragments or particles of various sizes (conglomerate, sandstone, shale); of the remains or products of animals or plants (certain limestones and coal); of the product of chemical action or evaporation (salt, gypsum, etc.); or of mixtures of these materials. A characteristic feature of sedimentary deposits is a layered structure known as bedding or stratification.

**shale** A laminated sediment in which the constituent particles are predominantly of the clay grade.

**shield** A continental block of the Earth's crust that has been relatively stable over a long period of time and has undergone only gentle warping (basin and swell structure) in contrast to the strong folding of bordering geosynclinal belts. Mostly composed of Precambrian rocks.

**sill** An intrusive body of igneous rock of approximately uniform thickness, relatively thin compared with its lateral extent, usually emplaced parallel to the bedding or schistosity of the intruded rocks.

**sinkhole** A funnelshaped depression in the land surface, generally in a limestone region, communicating with a subterranean passage developed by solution.

**stability** A condition in the atmosphere in which vertical motions are absent or definitely restricted.

**steppe** An area of grass-covered and generally treeless plains with a semiarid climate. They occupy large portions of eastern Europe and Asia.

**stratocumulus cloud** A patch, layer, or sheet of cloud composed of numerous elements which appear as rounded masses or rolls. They are nonfibrous and may or may not merge. They are composed of small water droplets and occur at altitudes up to 2 kilometers.

**stratum** A section of a formation that consists throughout of approximately the same kind of rock material. A single sedimentary bed or layer (plural, strata).

**stratus cloud** A cloud layer having a uniform base and top with widely dispersed water droplets. It occurs between the surface and 2 kilometers in the Tropics.

**stream piracy** The diversion of the upper part of a stream by the headward erosion of another stream.

**strike** The course or bearing of the outcrop of an inclined bed or structure on a level surface; the direction or bearing of a horizontal line in the plane of an inclined stratum, joint, fault, cleavage plane, or other structural plane; it is perpendicular to the direction of the dip.

**structure** The sum total of the structural features of an area. Petrology: one of the larger features of a rock mass, like bedding, jointing, cleavage; also the sum total of such features.

**subsidence** A descending motion in the atmosphere, usually over a rather broad area (meteorological). Gradual depression of an area, as in a geosyncline (geological).

**Sun glitter** A pattern of sunlight being reflected from water; also called Sun glint.

**syenite** An intrusive igneous rock consisting principally of alkalic feldspar and usually one or more mafic (dark) minerals.

**syncline** A fold in rocks in which the strata dip inward from both sides toward the axis. The opposite of *anticline.*

**tableland** A flat or undulating elevated area, a plateau or mesa.

**tectonic** Pertaining to the rock structure and external forms resulting from the deformation of the Earth's crust. As applied to earthquakes, it is used to describe shocks not caused by volcanic action or by collapse of caverns or landslides.

**terminator** The line separating the illuminated and dark portions of a celestial body which shines by reflected sunlight, as the Moon or the Earth.

**Tertiary** The earlier of the two geologic periods comprised in the Cenozoic era. Also the system of stratum deposited during that period.

**Tethys geosyncline** Elongated east-west geosyncline that separated Europe and Africa and extended across southern Asia in pre-Tertiary time.

**trachyte** An extrusive rock composed essentially of alkalic feldspar and minor biotite, hornblende, or pyroxene.

**trade winds** The wind system which occupies the lowest few kilometers in the atmosphere of most of the Tropics. It blows with consistency of direction from the subtropical highs toward the equatorial trough. The winds are predominantly northeasterly in the Northern Hemisphere and southerly in the Southern Hemisphere.

**trellis drainage** A drainage system in which the main streams are generally parallel, with smaller tributaries flowing at right angles to them.

**troposphere** That portion of the Earth's atmosphere from the surface to the tropopause which is the lower 10 to 20 kilometers of the atmosphere. Here the temperature normally decreases with height.

**tuff** A rock formed of compacted volcanic fragments, which are generally smaller than 4 millimeters in diameter.

**typhoon** A severe tropical storm in the western Pacific Ocean.

**uplift** Elevation of any extensive part of the Earth's surface relative to some other part; opposite to *subsidence.*

**upper-level trough** An elongated area of relatively low atmospheric pressure existing in the upper air.

**upwelling** The process by which water rises from a lower to a higher depth, usually as a result of divergence and offshore currents.

**von Kármán eddy** Vortices especially visible in cloud formations, resulting from frictional drag of air over and/or around raised obstacles such as islands. Named after Theodor von Kármán, the aerodynamicist.

**vortex** A whirl or eddy.

**vortex street** Two parallel rows of alternately placed, counterrotating vortices along the wake of an obstacle in a fluid or air; also called a von Kármán vortex street.

**wadi** A ravine or watercourse, dry except in the rainy season.

**watershed** The area contained within a drainage divide above a specified point on a stream. Also called drainage area, drainage basin, or catchment area.

**wind shear** The local variation of the wind vector in a horizontal or vertical direction.

**wave diffraction** The bending of waves around obstacles or over a shoal sea floor.

**wave length** The distance between corresponding points of two successive periodic waves in the direction of propagation, for which the oscillation has the same phase.

**wrench fault** A nearly vertical strike-slip fault.

**zodiacal light** A faint, diffuse light, triangular or cone shaped, seen on either side of the Sun along the zodiac or ecliptic plane. It is seen in middle northern latitudes in the spring after sunset in the western sky, or in the fall before sunrise (dawn) in the eastern sky (astronomical).

# BIBLIOGRAPHY


## Books

Earth Photographs from Gemini III, IV, and V. NASA SP-129, U.S. Government Printing Office, Washington, D.C., 1967.

Gemini Conference Summary, NASA SP-138, includes "Science Experiments Summary," by Jocelyn R. Gill and Willis B. Foster, Feb. 1-2, 1967, pp. 291-305; and "Space Photography," by Richard W. Underwood, pp. 231-290.

## Maps

GROSVENOR, M. B., ed.: National Geographic Atlas of the World. National Geographic Society, Washington, D.C., 1963.

BARTHOLEMEW, J., ed.: The Times Atlas of the World. Vol. I, "The World," Australia and East Asia, Houghton Mifflin Co., Boston, 1958.

Vol. II, "Southwest Asia and Russia," Houghton Mifflin Co., Boston, 1959.

Vol. IV, "Southern Europe and Africa," Houghton Mifflin Co., Boston, 1956.

Vol. V, "The Americas," Houghton Mifflin Co., Boston, 1957.

TIEDEMANN, H. A.: Gemini Synoptic Terrain Photography (S005). Indexes with Maps Showing Coverage (Gemini), including North and South America, Africa, Near East, India, Australia, Asia, Pacific. Maps through Gemini XII completed.

## Articles

### *Terrain*

LOWMAN, PAUL D., JR.: Terrain Photography on Gemini Missions. Geological Soc. of America Annual Meeting (1966), GSA Special Paper (in press).

LOWMAN, PAUL D., JR.: "The Earth from Orbit." *National Geographic,* Nov. 1966, pp. 645-670. Photos from Gemini IV from Southwestern United States, Florida, Morocco, Richat Structure, and some photos from Gemini V.

LOWMAN, PAUL D., JR.: "Photography from Space-Geologic Applications." Annals from the New York Academy of Sciences, vol. 140, pp. 99-106, Dec. 16, 1966.

### *Weather*

NAGLER, K. M.; AND SOULES, S. D.: "The Gemini Weather Photography Experiment." Presented at the XVIIth International Astronautical Congress, Madrid, Spain, October 1966. (Published in Proceedings of Congress. Twelve Gemini photos are used to illustrate meteorological features shown to advantage by selective color photography of Gemini.)

NAGLER, K. M.; AND SOULES, S. D.: "Experiment S006, Synoptic Weather Photography." Interim Report, Manned Space Flight Experiments, Gemini XII, Nov. 11-15, 1966 (MSC-TA-R-67-3), pp. 75-82. "Jetstream" cirrus clouds, eddies in the lee of Guadalupe Island, Mexico, Sun glint, smoke from forest fires, and windblown dust.

KUETTNER, J. P.; AND SOULES, S. D.: "Organized Convection as Seen from Space." Bull. Am. Meterol. Soc., vol. 47, Nov. 5, 1966, pp. 364-370. Using views from Gemini IV, V, and VII, and from ESSA I meteorological satellite as illustrations, the authors discuss the tendency for cumulus clouds to be alined in rows or streets.

### *Other*

OLIVER, V. J.: "Some Applications of Space Observations to Meteorology, Oceanography and Hydrology," 10 pp. Reprint of talk presented at the Fourth Annual Meeting and Technical Display of the American Institute of Aeronautics and Astronautics, Anaheim, Calif., Oct. 23-27, 1967. Use of some Gemini photos to illustrate how space photographs can delineate turbid water, the shallow water bottom configuration, and rain-soaked versus dry ground.

RANDERSON, DARRYL: "A Study of Air Pollution Sources as Viewed by Earth Satellites." Reprint of presentation at 60th Annual Meeting, Air Pollution Control Association, Cleveland, June 11-16, 1967. Illustrated by Gemini views of smoke from forest fires and haze and smoke from industrial sources.

GETTYS, R. F.: "Extraction of Color Photos Exposed From the Gemini Orbital Flights IV, V, and VII." U.S. Naval Oceanographic Office, A67-10322, Suitland, Md. *In*: Symposium on Remote Sensing of Environment, Univ. of Mich., Ann Arbor, Apr. 12-14, 1966, proceedings.

JONES, J. R.: Hydrologic Evaluation of Gemini Photographs of Fringes of Sahara, Africa. NASA Technical Letter 68.

MACCALLOR, J. A.: Photo-Mosaic Map of Peru From Gemini Photography (in preparation). NASA Technical Letter 87.

MCNAUGHTON, DUNCAN, A.; AND HUCKABA, WILLIAM A.: "Space Photo Points Way to Oil." Oil Gas J., vol. 64, no. 24, June 1966.

## Films

"Studying the Weather From Space." Educational television film produced by KCET, Los Angeles, R&D review series. Gemini views used to illustrate meteorological phenomena.

"First Photos From Space." Educational television film produced by KCET, Los Angeles, R&D review series, no. 37. Gemini views illustrate geography and geology of regions covered by orbital flight.


☆ U.S. GOVERNMENT PRINTING OFFICE: 1969 O—312-405